ELECTRICITY SUPPLY

THE BRITISH EXPERIMENT

The intentions were good

DAVID PORTER

ELECTRICITY SUPPLY

THE BRITISH EXPERIMENT

The intentions were good

DAVID PORTER

MEREO
Cirencester

Mereo Books

1A The Wool Market Dyer Street Cirencester Gloucestershire GL7 2PR
An imprint of Memoirs Publishing www.mereobooks.com

Electricity supply. The British experiment: 978-1-86151-385-4

First published in Great Britain in 2014
by Mereo Books, an imprint of Memoirs Publishing

The address for Memoirs Publishing Group Limited can be found at
www.memoirspublishing.com

The Memoirs Publishing Group Ltd Reg. No. 7834348

The Memoirs Publishing Group supports both The Forest Stewardship Council® (FSC®) and
the PEFC® leading international forest-certification organisations. Our books carrying both the
FSC label and the PEFC® and are printed on FSC®-certified paper. FSC® is the only
forest-certification scheme supported by the leading environmental organisations including
Greenpeace. Our paper procurement policy can be found at
www.memoirspublishing.com/environment

Typeset in 12/18pt Plantin
by Wiltshire Associates Publisher Services Ltd. Printed and bound in Great Britain by
Printondemand-Worldwide, Peterborough PE2 6XD

PREFACE

✑

In the developed world, most of us take electricity for granted. Few of us understand it. We cannot see it, nor, except in modest amounts, can we store it. But those who provide electricity are responsible for making sure that it is available when we want it – for heating, cooling and lighting and for powering everything from our phone chargers, computers, websites and vacuum cleaners to industry, hospitals, commerce and trains.

Public electricity supply in the UK began as a local function, under private ownership, or in the hands of municipalities. When demand for it grew, production and distribution was extended nationally and it became a responsibility of the state. Some companies produced their own electricity and sold their surplus to the state industry, but despite legislation in 1983 requiring the industry to buy privately-produced power and give independent producers access to its network, the industry did nothing to encourage its competitors. State monopolies tend not to like privately-owned interlopers – even small ones.

In 1987, the frustrated privateers decided to form an association to fight for a better deal. With a public and private sector background and some public relations experience – but no knowledge of electricity – I was invited to help. We caught a wave. The state industry was privatised and opportunities were opened up. But there was still a great deal for the association to fight for (or against), so it put down roots and it grew.

It soon dawned on politicians that although the state no longer owned the industry, it could still dictate how it should be run. Their policies sometimes conflicted with each other – par for the course in politics, but a headache to those who have to satisfy customers and investors. They also changed their minds from time to time about which policies were more important – unsettling for companies that need a stable framework against which to invest huge sums for the long term. The industry's customers – the people who should have been the driving force behind everything it did – grew to hate it, especially when it looked profitable, or it put its prices up; and even more so when those things coincided. The politicians argued about energy policy and many wanted it to be driven by the climate change agenda; a financial crisis shocked the world; rising prices caused a political storm; the industry's leading figures were vilified and unintended consequences of policy caused uncertainty. Policy-makers wobbled. Investors hesitated and some turned their backs on the UK electricity supply industry. There were even warnings of power shortages – surely the very last thing that customers expected.

This is how it looked from my desk.

This book is dedicated to my wife, Judith. She has encouraged me throughout my working life, not least in the 25 years when I was involved with the AIEP, AEP and Energy UK; picking me up when I was down and sharing the pleasure when things went well. The job meant that we usually had to spend a large part of the week miles apart, but Judith felt part of it. She was.

ACKNOWLEDGEMENTS

There would have been nothing for me to write about without the professionalism and years of commitment of the many people who worked for the Association of Independent Electricity Producers, the Association of Electricity Producers and Energy UK. I cannot list them all, but I thank every one of them. I really must record my thanks, however, to the two people who worked most closely with me in that time, as my Personal Assistant – Sam Inns from 1993 to 2007 and Su-Yen Foong from 2007 to 2012. They not only gave me the loyalty, support and understanding I needed, they knew how to look after the Association's members – our customers.

For more than 20 years, I enjoyed the support, encouragement and friendship of the President of the Association, Michael Spicer - later Sir Michael Spicer and finally Lord Spicer. I should have liked to have been able to record that it was his involvement in the Association that took him from being a plain 'Mr', via a knighthood, to the rank of peer. It was, of course, his great contribution to political life. But over that long period of time, his wisdom and carefully considered advice were invaluable to me. My most grateful thanks go not only to Michael but also to his wife Ann, upon whose life Michael's role with the AIEP-AEP impinged from time to time. It was a great privilege to work closely with Michael for so long.

My thanks also go to the following people who chaired the Executive Committee or Board of AIEP-AEP: George Rufford 1987-1989; Dr D C Pike 1989-1991; Neil Bryson 1991-1994; Dr Philip Jackson 1994-1996; Dr Graham Thomas 1996-1998; Richard Rigg 1998-2000; Dr Keith Miller 2000-2002; Mike Bowden 2002-2005; Dr Tony Cocker 2005-2007; Dr Steve Riley 2007-2009 and Martin Lawrence 2009-2012. They each brought personal style and commitment to the governance of the Association and gave me their support.

A special mention must go to Martin Alder, who was Vice Chairman of the Board for so many years and a distinguished and committed Chairman of its Renewable Energy Committee for even longer. Our views of the world of electricity may not always have been the same, but we worked together well and in our occasional visits to Loftus Road, we were able together to cheer (sometimes) and groan (frequently), even though he is a Liverpool fan.

When I started to write this book, I needed help to remind me why, when and how certain things happened. For their assistance, I should like to thank Neil Bryson, Gwyn Dolben, Depak Lal, David Lewis, Andy Limbrick, David Love, John Macadam, Margaret McKinlay, Keith Miller, Paul Mott, Nicola Pitts, George Rufford, Philip Russell, Jeremy Sainsbury and Lord Spicer.

NB: The views expressed in this book are my own and should not be associated with any person acknowledged here, nor with any person or organisation mentioned in the book. I also take responsibility for any errors that you may come across.

David Porter
December 2014

CONTENTS

INTRODUCTION

As I began writing this, the UK's electricity and gas supply industry seemed to be in everyone's bad books. Rising prices were seldom out of the news and an outgoing energy regulator, a learned engineering institution and even National Grid had warned of the risk of future power shortages. Surveys suggested that the public disliked energy companies even more than they disliked banks. In the midst of the debate about prices and security, those people who believe that by cutting its energy-related carbon emissions the UK can prevent the world's climates from changing, were also unhappy – critical of the lack of progress on reducing emissions. On the website of *The Guardian*, online responses to reports about higher energy prices revealed a predictable interest in renationalisation of the electricity industry and incidentally, one or two somewhat illiberal views about what should be done to the bosses of the biggest energy companies. Letters to the Head of Business at the *Daily Telegraph* blamed the energy companies for messing things up and called for the return of the engineering-led Central Electricity Generating Board (CEGB), but I suspect that this was more to do with their dissatisfaction with the companies than with any understanding of the part played by successive governments in causing many of the difficulties. On the other hand, comments on the website of that newspaper exposed its readers' huge frustration with the Coalition Government's role in all of this; contempt for the policies of the previous Labour government and on the part of many contributors, the belief that voting for the UK Independence Party would fix everything. Unlikely, but the instinct of those readers was at least partially right – we have to look beyond Westminster for the cause of some of the problems.

This book examines those controversial issues, and it does so from the point of view of someone who, for many years, headed a trade association which represented a wide range of energy interests – from small family businesses to huge international companies. But the book is also about the small part – a very enjoyable part – that I played in the liberalisation of the electricity supply industry in Britain and later, in the liberalised world; the growth of the association that now represents the industry, from its early life in a cottage in Cornwall to a London HQ close to the political corridors of power. It is also about some of the remarkable people that helped to make it all possible and importantly, the way public policy towards the industry changed after the industry was liberalised. Politicians, few of whom knew anything of engineering and not many about the world of finance and investment, found it irresistible to make demands of the industry – always with good intentions, of course.

The changes in public policy in the 25 years during which I was involved were huge. They seem to have brought us to a point where we pursued neither the post-war ideals of public ownership, nor the Thatcher government's belief that electricity supply should be competitive and driven by customers. Not only that, I suspect that bookmakers would not offer very compelling odds for any particular energy policy having a long shelf-life. The past may not always be the best guide to the future, but it is best not ignored. A glance in the rear-view mirror shows that policy has followed a winding road – definitely not the most economical route, and one which some industry players and investors might blame for inducing a certain amount of travel sickness. Threats of legislation to freeze prices or impose windfall taxes – the latter threat arising three or four times – did nothing to make investors feel any better, and they offered little real benefit to hard-pressed customers.

In the second decade of the century, the policies for electricity seemed to follow something akin to a political 'third way'. This way was certainly not state ownership, although it was subject to a huge amount of state control. It relied on private capital, but the owners enjoyed nothing like the freedom that was envisaged when the state industry was sold off in 1990-1991. The state industry's 'consumers' may have been elevated to the status of the privatised industry's 'customers', but somehow the industry had become dangerously alienated from them. Often that was a result of corporate clumsiness – companies, big ones especially, are apt to do silly things at times – but it was at least as much to do with the unintended consequences of government decisions.

In June 1982, the Secretary of State for Energy, Nigel Lawson MP, gave a speech to the International Association of Energy Economists in Cambridge in which he rejected the idea that government should own or control energy production and consumption and the notion of a 'natural monopoly' and argued that it should set a framework for the market to operate and minimise distortions in that market. In May of the following year, the Energy Act 1983 became law in the UK. But this was a small and no more than tentative step in the direction of Lawson's thinking and in June 1983, he was moved from the Department of Energy to become Chancellor of the Exchequer – the role for which he would become much better known and would play a big part in British political history. Peter Walker succeeded Lawson at the Department of Energy and found himself immersed in the government's strategy to handle the miners' strike of 1984-85. Not that it was very likely that Peter Walker would have had much enthusiasm for Lawson's agenda anyway, for he was inclined towards intervention, rather than liberalisation. Instead, it fell to his successor, Cecil Parkinson, and Parkinson's Energy Minister, Michael Spicer, to develop the thinking. So their Electricity Act 1989 was a far bigger and more confident step than the Energy Act of 1983. It led to the break-up and sale of the state-owned electricity monopoly and the emergence of private ownership and competitive markets. The government did not detach itself completely from the industry, but it handed many functions to an independent regulator and seemed to loosen considerably the political grip.

But nothing is for ever. Before long, the government's hands were not only where we might expect to find them – on the big decisions shaping the framework of the industry – but in detailed matters of customer choice (customers were deemed to have too much choice) and how domestic bills are presented (they were thought to be too complicated). The independent regulation of the industry, which other countries had soon come to admire, changed too. Ofgem (previously 'OFFER' and 'OFGAS') was essentially a creature of Parliament, but was meant to reach decisions independently. Nevertheless, it was asked more and more to become an instrument for implementing new policy and worse than that, to grapple with the conflicts in energy policy which had been created by the politicians. So not only did it regulate, but it also administered some of the schemes that successive governments required the industry to adopt. This was a far cry from the thinking that led to the freeing-up of the industry. In fact the first regulator, the 'Director General of Electricity Supply', Professor Stephen Littlechild, expected the success of a competitive market to reduce the regulator's role almost to that of regulating only the monopoly elements of the business. There was clearly no prospect of that happening. In fact, there was more regulation than ever, and it seemed that there was no aspect of the way that the industry was run that could not be improved upon with ideas from politicians or the huge number of people at Ofgem. Not only was there said to be far too much choice in tariffs, but many argued that there was too little choice as far as the number of suppliers is concerned – although, at the time of writing, a *Which?* Report listed as many as 15 of them. I make that 14 more than we were able to choose from when the industry was a state-owned bureaucracy.

In the late 1980s and early 1990s, there were many arguments against electricity privatisation and they were voiced strongly, even though often they had little substance. One argument that might well have concerned the politicians, however, was the claim that a privately-owned electricity industry would not be able or willing to make big investments in power stations and networks. For most of the post-privatisation era, this concern had been shown to be completely unfounded. National Grid's investment in the transmission network, for example, exceeded the achievements of the state-owned industry and in the electricity-producing sector, there was certainly no shortage of investment in gas-fired power stations in the 1990s. In fact, there was so much of it that the market eventually became over-provided, prices crashed and some companies – substantial ones – went bust.

In 2012-2013, however, with European air quality regulations closing many of our older power stations and the UK determined to go farther than the EU to reduce carbon emissions, there were deep concerns about the level of generating capacity which would be available to meet future peak demand in Britain. The companies that wanted to invest in their industry – and when they did, they were usually very good at it, of course – were facing uncertainty and much greater risk than one might expect. This was an astonishing state of affairs for an industry whose commodity is something upon which the whole of modern life depends and which, notwithstanding their distaste for the providers, its customers want very badly.

The issue was not confined to the UK. In 2012, as Chairman of its Energy Policy and Generation Committee, I was asked by the pan-European trade body Eurelectric, to chair a task force on investment in the industry across Europe. The composition of the task force extended beyond the electricity industry, to include one or two financiers, consultants and academics. We presented its findings to a large audience in Brussels on 6 December 2012. The report[1] revealed huge scepticism among electricity industry leaders about the feasibility of the investment that politicians thought could be achieved and it pointed very clearly to the political and regulatory risks that the industry faced. The report said, among other things:

'Investment decisions in the European electricity industry are more difficult than they should be. Today's business case for investments is influenced more by political and regulatory decisions than by customer demand. If political and regulatory risks are high, investment may be deferred or investors may look for a bigger return. This ultimately risks making electricity more expensive for customers.'

The European Commission, which seemed to think that it provided the industry with more than enough clarity to bring forward investment, did not like the report very much.

That report from Eurelectric received little coverage in the UK, but worries about investment were beginning to make a few headlines. On 19 February 2013, the outgoing Chief Executive of Ofgem, Alistair Buchanan, warned that in the British electricity market, the 'capacity margin' – the difference between peak demand and the generating capacity available to serve it – was going to shrink:

'Within three years we will see the reserve margin of generation fall from below 14% to below 5%. That is uncomfortably tight.'

In March 2013, I was invited by an international bank in London

---

[1] Powering Investments: Challenges for the liberalised electricity sector. Eurelectric. December 2012.

to discuss the Eurelectric report and to meet a number of investors. Sitting across the table from me, four managers of investment funds, each with billions of pounds at his disposal, declared that it was impossible to recommend investment in the industry.

Some three months later, on 27 June 2013, the interim Chief Executive of Ofgem, Andrew Wright, announced that, depending on demand, the generation capacity margin in 2015-2016 would be between 2% and 5% and that the probability of a supply disruption had increased.

Then, in October 2013, the Royal Academy of Engineering published *GB electricity capacity margin*, which stated '… the government should be mindful of the possibility of capacity shortages during the next five years.'[2]

The worst should not come to the worst. In fact, National Grid's efforts to strike deals with industrial customers who were prepared to reduce demand when things were tight should help; albeit there may well be press reports complaining about businesses not being able to manufacture their products when they are being paid not to use electricity. But faced with a forthcoming shortage of power station capacity, energy companies seemed very cautious about investing in their own industry and we should look carefully at why it has come about.

For the avoidance of doubt, this is not a textbook. And, although it starts at what was, for me, the beginning, and some of the dates in the story are important, nor is it a diary. Unlike the well-known politicians, when I was at work I did not record meticulously each day's events and my thoughts on them. My diaries contained no

[2] GB Electricity Capacity Margin Royal Academy of Engineering, October 2013. ISBN: 978-1-909327-02-3

more than the briefest details of my appointments. I was pleased to discover, however, that I still had most of those diaries – at least, as far back as 1992 – and many of the entries triggered memories which, although they were not always in high definition, did help to get some things more clearly in order. The book, however, is not written entirely in chronological order and I hope that this will not matter to the reader.

For those who do want to read serious text books on the last 25 years of the electricity industry in Britain, I recommend in particular, 'Energy, the State and the Market: British Energy Policy since 1979' by Dieter Helm[3] and 'The British Electric Industry 1990-2010: The Rise and Demise of Competition' by Alex Henney[4] . As for political books with relevant energy content, I recommend 'Right at the Centre: an autobiography', by Cecil Parkinson[5] and 'The Spicer Diaries', by Michael Spicer.[6]

I have asked myself once or twice why I went to the trouble of writing this book. Part of the answer is that it would give me the satisfaction that I had done something useful after retiring from full-time work – I can still achieve something. Vanity, yes, but there are two other reasons and they are no less important.

First, is to record how a tiny trade association grew to become influential and recognised nationally, having spent its early years in a six-foot-square office in a terraced cottage on a Cornish hillside. It is what modern managers and presenters like to call 'a journey'. I can say, however, that although we usually knew where the next stop was, the final destination was far from clear. I can also say that I wrote most of that history with a smile on my face, because, although it was often very tough, I enjoyed those times immensely.

[3] Energy, the State and the Market: British Energy Policy since 1979. Dieter Helm. Oxford University Press. ISBN 0-19-926203-9.
[4] The British Electric Industry 1990-2010: The Rise and Demise of Competition. Alex Henney. EEE Limited.
[5] Right at the Centre: an autobiography. Cecil Parkinson. Weidenfeld and Nicholson. ISBN 0-297-81262-9.
[6] The Spicer Diaries. Michael Spicer. Biteback Publishing. ISBN 9 781849 542388.

But the way that the Association grew in credibility and influence over the years was down to staff, advisers and members, who deserve to have their huge contribution acknowledged.

The second reason is to express some frustration with the way the industry has been treated by policy-makers. After freeing it up to ensure that investment and operational decisions were driven by the need to satisfy customers, governments gave themselves a huge amount of control over the industry, even though the state no longer owned it.

No less disconcerting is how they exercised that control. The emphasis of energy policy changed with surprising frequency and the policy-makers' good intentions often had unintended consequences. The industry, of course, invests vast sums for the long term, for which it relies on stable politics and clarity of purpose. Unfortunately, those who call the shots look towards a different horizon – one which is no farther away than the next general election. This helped to make the electricity supply industry riskier than it used to be. It increased costs, made investors hesitant and sometimes drove money into other sectors and other parts of the world. But perhaps belatedly, politicians seemed to recognise that no one was obliged to invest in the UK's energy market and potential investors might have needed some encouragement. Whether they recognised their responsibility for creating so much of the uncertainty that they were trying to reduce is not clear, but some of them began to talk about the need to give confidence to investors. So, unlike the Labour government's reform in 2001, the Coalition Government's electricity market reform programme, which began in 2010, was not a measure to increase competition and push down prices. The Coalition still claimed to want that (and vociferously in opposition, so did the Labour Party leadership), but at the very time when customers became hypersensitive about energy bills, it gave priority to the 'low carbon' agenda and – Ministers began to argue – security of supply.

The Coalition's 'Electricity Market Reform' (EMR) was intended to give investors confidence to invest in building huge amounts of 'low carbon' electricity production, which the previous market, based on the 'cheapest fuel and technology first', did not do to the extent that the policy-makers wanted – even with carbon emissions being priced into the economics of power generation. In the course of drafting legislation and in response to alarm in the press, the Coalition did decide to strengthen the justification for its reform by claiming that in years to come, electricity prices would be lower than they otherwise would have been – even quoting figures. Those figures were, in fact, surprisingly precise, so in my kindest moments, I felt able to conclude that the government had been employing people who were much better at forecasting than their predecessors ever were. But this political afterthought about 'savings' from EMR was not very convincing, nor was it of any comfort to those customers whose problem with paying their bills was very real and more immediate.

However successful the Association of Electricity Producers may have been in the course of all this and in its modern form – as Energy UK – still is, over the years, it found itself too often on the back foot, fighting battles from a defensive position. It won many of those battles, but whilst it was fighting, the industry and its representative bodies, including the one that I led, often failed to notice that they were losing the war.

A good working relationship between government[7] and the electricity supply industry is vital. It does not have to be cosy, but each side should have respect for the other, otherwise home truths may not be heard, or, may not even be told and bad decisions will be made. There was always a relationship between government and that industry and it seems to be quite close today, although many politicians are happy to take a swipe at the energy companies when there are headlines to be grabbed.

At AEP, from time to time, I or my senior staff would get a call from a civil servant on the lines of 'We are thinking of suggesting something like... What do you think the effect of that would be?' The discussion was conducted in confidence. The response was given in good faith and it was trusted. That is good trade association work. But it was about only one sector of the industry – power generation. And, it was usually about detail, typically short-term and definitely not the 'big picture'.

But under a never-ending torrent of consultations from government and regulators, we gave too little attention to the big picture, and the big picture was changing.

In the early years after privatisation, I was a regular visitor to the corridors of Westminster and Whitehall and on reflection, my colleagues and I should have been there far more often. But government was meant to be playing less of a part in the affairs of the industry. So my visits were either just to keep in touch, perhaps

---

[7] It is not just in Westminster, of course, that there is a problem. Policies are made in Brussels that can have a big impact on customers in the UK and the other 27 states of the EU, but those that make the policies are not the ones that have to explain the financial consequences for the paying customer

with Christopher Wilcock CB at the Department of Energy, who had played a big part in the privatisation and re-structuring, or to argue that government should *not* do something that it had been considering. Then it dawned on me that a) most policy-makers feel much more comfortable if they are doing things, or at least are seen to be doing them and b) nearly everyone else wearing a visitor's badge in the power house of SW1 was there for reasons that were exactly the opposite to mine. They wanted the government to intervene and as often as not, to spend other people's money on their cause. The efforts of a great number of lobbyists, each promoting a worthy but sectoral interest, were insidious. Over time, the market, in which, to some extent, government had intervened from day one, would become progressively less free, rather than more.

In the build-up to electricity privatisation, many critics pointed out that although they would be more efficient, privately-owned companies would find it more expensive than the state industry to raise capital. That was certainly the case, but it is ironic that, under private ownership, it was the state that added so much to the industry's risks and was responsible for increasing the cost of its investments. The customers pay for that, just as they do for the various legal obligations that governments impose on their electricity suppliers.

There was another change which was no less damaging. Soon after privatisation, the industry found itself in the news far more often than anyone had envisaged. The publicity was invariably unhelpful. In the years immediately after privatisation, it was about bosses' pay and share options, the lack of competition in power generation and complaints from large industrial customers about electricity prices. Weaning them off the deals they had had with the state electricity industry was difficult, not least because some operated in international markets, where their competitors enjoyed support from governments far less concerned with the notion of competition. Just occasionally, not only the pay but the private lives of senior figures in the industry also made the headlines. So any PhD student who is researching the reputational issues that afflict the modern industry will find much to interest them after the year 2000, but will discover that the roots of those issues go back to the 1990s, and there were plenty of sensational headlines in that decade too. The mistrust is very deep-rooted indeed and it is in the interests of all parties that this should be corrected. The industry is fully aware of the problem and is working hard on it. But the climb back to respectability will be slow. There can be no quick fix. Perhaps the only things that will happen quickly in that process will be the inevitable setbacks.

CHAPTER ONE

COMMUNICATING FOR OTHERS

'Two alligator steaks and make it snappy' was a line I used in my PR company's press release for a hotel and restaurant client in Cornwall in the late 1980s. If this were an email, rather than a book, you would be seeing after the last sentence a red-faced emoticon signifying my embarrassment. After abandoning a successful, but eventually frustrating, career in local government in favour of greater independence, I had created and run, with my wife, a guidebook-rated restaurant in a fishing village a couple of miles from that particular client's business, and I wondered why on earth the client wanted to be cooking and promoting alligator. I made a raised-eyebrow enquiry, but it was not for me to advise them on their menu. Rather, I had to help make the best of their intentions. That's life for those who earn their living trying to communicate for others.

Thankfully, the work was not always like that and it was certainly varied. I promoted a business that made and sold top-quality ice cream at a time when most people were satisfied with an industrial version; handled publicity for a range of health products; helped to promote a database which was still being marketed years later; prepared catalogues of hard-to-find music;

promoted holiday cottages; publicised top-quality hi-fi, lovingly built by Heybrook in Plymouth – these things and many more were hugely satisfying to work on. Even more so because I worked from a tiny office in our mid-terrace cottage on a beautiful hillside at Herodsfoot in south-east Cornwall. It was a miner's cottage where in the 19th century, 'hot bedding' had been the order of the day[8], but in the second half of the 1980s it bristled with new technology. Not only desk-top publishing, but email – Telecom Gold. Compared with today's offerings, it was fiendishly complicated to use. It was also somewhat limited in its usefulness, in that there did not seem to be that many other people with access to it, nor even with much interest in it. Worse still, most of those that were interested were rather obsessive about it and like many other computer users at the time were happy to be seen as members of a cult. Limited though it was, this was nevertheless a far cry from the previous era where, if we wanted a telephone, we were expected to be grateful for being allowed to go on a waiting list. It was an equally far cry from the electronic communications we take for granted today.

In fact, it was a good friend in that early email community – someone I had known for many years and who did have the vision to see where technology was going – whose recommendation led me to a client that would enable me to play a small part in a vitally important industry – one that was about to experience a seismic change.

My great friend and occasional business colleague, Barry Cooper, advised the energy consultant David Andrews to come and see me. Also working on a hillside, but in Welsh border country, Barry was a far-seeing engineer and distinguished transport planner, a crystal-clear thinker and a pioneer in the adoption of IT and remote working. David Andrews had a contract with the Cornwall

---

[8] When the mines were busy, the miners worked around the clock on shifts. Not to be confused with the reason for the bed being warm in the house on Church Hill, where other comforts were said to have been provided.

Energy Project and wanted publicity material. I was engaged to provide it. I remember little of the task, except that the study was about renewable energy and that having picked over the client's draft, I suggested that the frequently-used word 'renewables' should appear in inverted commas. It was 1987 and the word was hardly common parlance. The client, with different assumptions about the public's level of understanding, or, perhaps greater vision, did not agree with me though.

Midway through the work, in May 1987, David Andrews came to see me to check progress. He was on his way to Truro, having been in London.

'I have just been to an interesting meeting. We are going to start a campaign for independent electricity producers. They are being screwed by the CEGB and we are going to set up an association to fight for their interests. Would you be interested in doing some work for them?'

'An association for what? I thought electricity came from the state industry.'

'Most of it does, but there are small private producers that are not getting a fair deal. Some of them are using renewable energy, the others are using CHP. There's a wind turbine near Falmouth. Have you seen that?'

'I shall go and look, but some of them are using what?'

'CHP. Combined heat and power – an engine runs a generator to make electricity and they capture the heat from the engine to provide hot water and heating in nearby buildings. It's efficient.'

'What's this association called?'

'We haven't got a name for it yet, but it's going to be exciting.'

'Who did you say the association was for?'

'Independent electricity producers.'

'Then, shouldn't it be called the "Association of Independent Electricity Producers"?'

'I suppose it should.'

It all sounded interesting, but there was more to come.

'There's going to be a meeting of the likely members, in London, in September. You ought to come. You don't have to do anything. Just sit there in the audience, listen and take notes. It'll be perfect. You'll find out who they all are and what it's all about.'

I enthused about the idea, but not about having to go to London. My work was there, in Cornwall. Wasn't I one of those people in the vanguard of change? No office block. No factory. My 'commute' was down the stairs to a tiny, south-facing office, where I had a view over the valley of the West Looe River.

But he pressed the point and finally I agreed to go to his meeting in London. After all, apart from making a long train journey, all I had to do was listen and take some notes.

The meeting, in September 1987, was at the Connaught Rooms, in Covent Garden. I think there were perhaps 30 or more people present, 'theatre-style' with three or four people at the top table, on a platform. Most, perhaps all, of those present were men. Most were in suits. As it was in London, I also wore a suit. In fact, I wore my only suit. Purchased in Plymouth not long before (I had needed a suit for some work I did for the Merseyside Tourism Board), it was light grey, with mohair in it. Worn with a blue Jermyn Street shirt and a red silk tie, it was admittedly rather flashy.

As David Andrews had promised, the meeting was interesting. It appeared that there had been legislation to encourage private production of electricity in competition with the Central Electricity Generating Board (CEGB). It had been well-intentioned, but it was not working. There was also a problem with rates levied on privately-owned power facilities – much higher than the privateers thought that they should be. Per unit of capacity, they were higher than the rates applied to the CEGB's power stations.

Having left the public sector, disenchanted, some nine years earlier (and having got rid of my suits), I liked the sound of this little battle.

I listened with great interest and took copious notes. Then I heard someone on the platform say 'We have taken on someone to help us with our publicity. He's called, er... David Porter. I think he is here today and he is going to come up and tell us what he is going to do.'

What?

Unprepared, but trying not to look too surprised, I went to the platform and said a few words. On reflection, I must have sounded rather like a politician. But it didn't matter. The collective will to do something was tangible and they were on a high. They applauded. Perhaps that mohair suit had not looked too flashy after all.

At the end of the meeting, the chairman suggested that those present should contribute something to get the Association started. The sum proposed was £30 for each organisation represented. A trilby hat was passed round. I later learned that the collection had raised £470.47. One does not have to be a star of *Countdown* to work out that this was not an exact multiple of £30. More likely, it was evidence that many had come completely unprepared to start funding the organisation and that others were ready to donate at least their small change. Nine months later, however, the 'Income' in the Association's first set of annual accounts showed not only the proceeds of that collection, but membership subscriptions of £15,125 – enough to get the Association of Independent Electricity Producers up and running.

CHAPTER TWO

UP AND RUNNING

The new Association was soon functioning. An Executive Committee was set up, chaired by George Rufford, who, until his retirement had been Deputy Chairman of Eastern Electricity Board at Ipswich. George was not fully retired - he lectured on energy part-time at South Bank Polytechnic and did some consultancy. It was not his academic credentials, however, which made him an ideal chairman of this new lobby group. It was the experience of a successful career of 40 years in the electricity industry, allied to a strongly-held belief in competition and deep-seated scepticism about some of the practices of the industry to which he had dedicated his working life. George would ask discomforting questions such as why the industry was running and cross-subsidising retail outlets (yes, the 'Electricity Board' used to sell cookers, refrigerators, washing machines and other electrical appliances). He was also a thorn in the side of the Electricity Council, opposing his colleagues' support of the report of the Plowden Committee[9], which had called for the creation of a single public corporation for the electricity supply industry. That report spent rather a long time in the ministerial 'pending' tray, but in July 1980, to George's delight, the Secretary of State for Energy, David

---

[9] The Structure of the Electricity Supply Industry in England and Wales Cmnd 6388.

Howell MP, announced that he had decided not to accept its main proposal, namely to turn the industry into one corporation. Genial, lean, silver-haired, and usually with a twinkle in his eye, George had a hard cutting edge, honed from years of battling with bureaucracy. He was very clear, however, that the Association would not be fundamentalist in its approach to the state industry and – though some might have wished otherwise – nor would it adopt a stance which was hostile to nuclear power.

Among the members of the first Executive Committee were Fergus Wiggin, Managing Director of the Combined Heat and Power operation of Slough Estates; Cdr George Chapman RN, Honorary Secretary of the National Association of Water Power Users (NAWPU); Dr D C Pike of Green Land Reclamation, which served a gravel company which was developing a landfill gas business; Andrew Garrad of the wind energy consultancy Garrad Hassan; Chris Foster of C R Foster and Partners, a family-owned hydro-power business in the west of Scotland and John Kimber, a representative of Hawker Siddeley Power Engineering; the latter occasionally hosting meetings in an unlikely setting for this bunch of guerrillas – the company's prestigious board room in Duke Street, St James's, London SW1. To a man, these were strong characters, who were not only up for a fight, but would shape the way that the Association worked for years to come. In the case of 'Spike' Pike, the lasting nature of the Association was to prove somewhat ironic as, having seen other trade bodies develop then lose their way, he had expressed initially the perfectly sensible view that the organisation should form, fight, win its battle and promptly disband. Before too long, other strong personalities joined, including Martin Alder of Wessex Water, whose company had small-scale power generation running on sewage gas (Martin would later become an independent developer of wind energy), Ralph Sargent of Ahlstrom Pyropower and Lesley Potts of Hydro Energy

Developments in Dumfriesshire. Richard Cooper, from the commercial side of British Coal, also became involved and sometimes provided meeting facilities at Hobart House, the company's London HQ.

This colourful and formidable team would not have come together without the initiative of the consultancy Orchard Partners, where electrical and mechanical engineering work was led by William Orchard, whose father had founded the practice, and expertly managed by consultants John Macadam and Stephen Andrews. Some of the practice's clients were members of the Combined Heat and Power Association, but had become disenchanted with the performance of that organisation, arguing that the presence in its membership of representatives of the state electricity industry was a constraint on its effectiveness. They also recognised that the range of electricity-generating interests that were unhappy with their ability to trade went well beyond the users of CHP.

The meeting room at the front of the offices of Orchard Partners, in Southampton Row, London WC2 was the home for the initial meetings of the new association. Austere, gloomy and decidedly less salubrious than the Hawker Siddeley premises, it suffered from the noise of passing buses which occasionally drowned out discussion, but it was not too far from 'French Frank's' from whence came the sandwiches for lunch. The services of the above-mentioned John Macadam and Stephen Andrews were provided to the Association – as Treasurer[10] and Director respectively. They brought immense professional expertise and invaluable understanding of the industry and later would become highly respected and influential in their own consultancy.

I was made Business Manager, with a range of responsibilities including recruitment and publicity, the latter, at least initially, hand

[10] It was John's role as an adviser that was more important of course and before long the role of Treasurer went to Robert Armour, a solicitor at Wright Johnston & McKenzie in Edinburgh, who had small hydropower generators as clients. Robert was to become an important industry figure at British Energy and later at EDF Energy. He also chaired the European Committee of the Association of Electricity Producers for several years.

in hand with David Andrews. At this time, most of the AIEP's affairs were dealt with on trust. There was neither the time nor the appetite for written contracts, although I was invited by John Macadam, at the behest of the Executive Committee, to submit a proposal for arrangements under which I would be paid for a day or two's work per week. I wrote suggesting a fee of £100 per day – not a huge sum for a self-employed consultant, even in 1987. John Macadam called me to say that my proposal was perfectly reasonable. There was, however, a problem. The newly-formed AIEP did not have the funds to pay me what I had asked and he wondered whether I would accept a rate of £50 per day, with a £50 bonus for each new member I recruited to the Association. I was content with that and it was already beginning to look as though it would be fun.

But what was to be the Association's address? Initially, it was 'care of' Orchard Partners in Southampton Row, but using my phone number in Cornwall. This did not convey the sense of organisation that we needed. I had formed a company – South West One Ltd – for my various publicity and PR activities, registered at our home on the hillside in Herodsfoot. Quite soon, the Association's address became the South West One address, carefully avoiding any reference to the name of the cottage from which it operated.

Remote and tiny though it was, the office was packed with the leading-edge technology of the day. We had a desktop publishing (DTP) system, based on a Zenith 20MB hard-drive 640k RAM computer and a 300 dpi laser printer, the latter piece of equipment alone having cost me £4,400. I had been to a DTP exhibition and had visited the nearest Apple dealer 140 miles away in Poole. The technology was quite breathtaking in its capabilities and it seemed obvious to me that I should buy Apple Macintosh kit. Discussion with Barry Cooper, however, led me down a different route. Barry explained that the Apple machines were very different[11] from the industry-standard IBM PC and I was uneasy about spending a lot of money on equipment that was not 'mainstream'. I went down the IBM route and with the help of Andrew Reed of PMS Developments, nearly 200 miles away in Hereford, had to face up to learning how to use Ventura Publisher, a huge American program that would handle vast amounts of data, incorporate graphics and facilitate professional-looking page design. As a novice, I found this challenging. Even Andrew Reed was challenged, at times, but his experience helped him find the way round every obstacle that appeared and his cigars kept him calm through the entire process. The marks the cigar stubs caused in my office rubbish bin are still there today.

I was a wordsmith and not a graphic designer, but I knew that the DTP system would give me a little bit of design capability that far exceeded anything that I had taught myself to do with a pencil, a Rotring pen or Letraset. This proved helpful when I decided that the AIEP needed a letterhead. An hour or two playing around on-screen with the graphics and a 'logo' appeared – three rectangular pillars, each filled with a different density of tone. All in black and white, of course - colour was still a long way off. A few years later, I recall being asked about the meaning of the AIEP logo and felt obliged to confess that it had been the result of some doodling on the computer screen. The member who asked the question found my answer hard to cope with. He came from a big company, where branding was a serious business, involving months of drafting, evaluating and testing – and big cheques for specialist consultancies. He couldn't take it in. I should have used my imagination and spun him a yarn that he would have found re-assuring. Especially as, within a few years, several 'big corporate' people, like him, would be found sharing the same table as those who had come down from the hills in 1987 to form the band of rebels.

[11] They had a different operating system and software.

Having been reluctant to go to London for that meeting in September 1987, I now found myself a regular user of the 6.30 am train from Liskeard to Paddington – the 'Golden Hind.' From time to time, though, prospective members of the Association would ask to come and visit me. I was a bit smug about operating from a cottage on a Cornish hillside, but I knew that very few of the people from conventional businesses would understand it, so, because my diary was so 'crowded', they were dissuaded from making a trip to Cornwall that they may well have been looking forward to. They must have been amazed to discover how rarely I was at the office in Cornwall and how often I was (or could be) in London.

The principle of remote working was occasionally discussed in serious newspaper articles at the time, but it was still seen as futuristic and very few people gave it any credibility. But when Brian Beddoes, a good friend from our restaurant days, invited me to be the guest speaker at the dinner of the Looe Valley Rotary Club one Monday evening, 'I work from home' was the subject of my talk. Of course, there were other people in Britain who did that, but at the time, a good many of them seemed to be knitting woolly jumpers – a way of working not far removed from that of the cottage industries of the 18th century.

Remarkably quickly, the newly-formed Association found itself lobbying head-on about the ineffectiveness of the 1983 Energy Act. The prospect of the state electricity industry being privatised by the Thatcher government was occasionally in the news, but it was by no means certain that it would go ahead. Plenty of commentators thought it too difficult, inadvisable, or both. Doubts were fostered by an unhappy precedent which haunted the Conservative government. The privatisation of the state-owned gas industry in 1986 had succeeded, but only as far as the industry's management and trade unions had allowed it to. It had been privatised as an integrated monopoly with the expectation that on the world stage, it would be a 'national champion'. His diaries show that, on 22 June 1987, the Energy Minister, Michael Spicer MP, wrote that privatisation as a monopoly in the way that gas had been privatised had to be resisted, saying 'If I don't get my way on this I shall leave the government.'[12] The state electricity industry would almost certainly resist privatisation and if confronted with it, could be expected to take much the same stance as that taken by the gas industry. But as yet, there were no formal proposals; certainly no White Paper.

Shortly after the gathering at the Connaught Rooms in September 1987, the Association found itself in the corridors of power. At the Department of Energy's offices at Thames House South in Westminster an AIEP team met Secretary of State for Energy Cecil Parkinson MP and Energy Minister Michael Spicer MP accompanied by their senior officials, Bill McIntyre and Willy Rickett. Willy's input to the huge changes that lay ahead would prove to be crucial. Later, his career would take him to other departments of government only to return him years later to a more modern incarnation of the Department as Director General of Energy[13]. I noticed across the table Michael Spicer taking a keen interest in the up-to-date list of members that we had supplied to the Department. There were probably 60 names on that laser-printed sheet of A4 'Conqueror' paper.

Later experience of Ministerial meetings would show what an unusual one this had been. The welcome was warm. Nothing was particularly difficult. Nothing was refused, although tightening up the Energy Act looked pretty unlikely, because privatisation of the state industry was on the government's agenda. It was clear that the Department wanted our support for this. In principle, they had it,

---

[12] The Spicer Diaries. Lord Spicer. 2012. Biteback Publishing. ISBN 9781849542388.

[13] This would prove to be very different from the Department of Energy in 1987. The Department's role was to become a great deal more complicated.

but only if it put the state industry and the independents on a level playing field. On paper, it would do that, but politics being the 'art of the possible' there were many reasons why that level playing field would be hard to deliver. The state industry was a tangle of vested interests and public sector employment issues – among them coal mines, pensions, the railways that transported the coal and even the role of the body at the top of the pyramid, the Electricity Council, which employed 1,200 people. The private sector stood to be affected, too. How would the suppliers of the CEGB's equipment react? Corporatist Britain may have been learning the lessons of competition, but many big companies still enjoyed a rather cosy relationship with the power industry.

On the way out of the meeting at Thames House South, Cecil Parkinson put his hand on my shoulder and said to the departing band of lobbyists something he had told us in the meeting - 'Don't worry. The cavalry is coming.' This phrase, associated with the rescue in the final scenes of many a Hollywood western, became embedded in AIEP thinking. So much so that years later, when we became more established, I was going to propose it as the Association's motto – but in Latin. Discussion with Andy Limbrick left me doubting the wisdom of that. It translated, but only just and although there had been Roman horse soldiers, they played only a minor part in the success of the conquering armies, where military thinking was focused almost entirely on infantry.

In the late 1980s, it was important for the independent electricity producers that the arrival of the cavalry should prove to be helpful. There was always a risk that those rebels could be trampled on, rather than rescued. So, the demand for a level playing field had to be high on the list or the independents could have been victims of a quick and dirty privatisation that served only the interests of the state monopoly and HM Treasury. We certainly felt that we were entitled to a fair deal, not least because we had had to put up with the state industry's interpretation of the Energy Act and had heard that, under wraps in the Department of Energy, there was impartial evidence that the independents were not being treated fairly. On the grapevine had come the news that the Department had commissioned work on this issue from Price Waterhouse and that the report confirmed that the state industry was indeed paying the independents less than they were entitled to. The state industry paid independents only the marginal price for electricity, taking no account of the cost of their investment in generating plant – the latter was, of course, included in the CEGB's charges to its clients in the rest of the state industry. No doubt the legality of this approach would have been considered by the CEGB, but it was never tested. Nor, as far as I can tell, was the Price Waterhouse report ever released. I imagine that, in similar circumstances today, the Freedom of Information Act would be brought into play.

The AIEP's Executive Committee was keen that the Association should have a newsletter – partly to keep members informed and partly to get our messages out to the wider world. One such message, of course, was that independent electricity producers actually did exist and that they were poised to play a bigger part in the industry. David Andrews and I took the initiative on this and my company became the publisher[14]. I had publishing software and he had contacts in the industry – including Trevor Loveday, then of *Electrical Review,* who is a respected energy journalist to this day – and ideas for stories, some of which came from his clients in the CHP business. I used Ventura Publisher to create 'Independent Power News'. The first issues were somewhat crude, as I was learning on the job. Later, they began to look quite professional and with the help of Tony Savage at Looe Printing

[14] David would later withdraw from Independent Power News.

Company and on one or two occasions, the out-sourcing of the packing and labelling to some neighbours in the village, Independent Power News was published, bi-monthly. Anyone who has ever had to write, format, edit and create the printer's artwork for a professional-looking newsletter of 12 A4 pages and often more, will know that it does not simply 'happen'. Nor does securing advertising simply happen. It is all very time-consuming and it demands immense effort. Among other things, I discovered how one can suffer a repetitive strain injury in the shoulder from using a computer mouse for too many hours. But despite some welcome, one-off, help from AIEP with the postage bill, the journal was losing money – my money. With even more commitment, it would probably have succeeded, but it became obvious that, unless I dedicated my time solely to Independent Power News, making it bigger and better supported with advertising, the financing of it would never stack up. After a couple of years, I had to cease production. Thankfully, by that time, the AIEP could get itself into the news anyway.

I was also working closely with Stephen Andrews (no relation to David Andrews), the then part-time Director of AIEP. This included doing a day's 'media training' together, at a studio run by an ex-BBC journalist, in Berkshire. But we were also invited to talk to BBC 'Panorama' about a programme that they were planning to do on the electricity privatisation. This was a huge opportunity to put some pressure on the government and try to make sure that the privatisation terms were fair to our constituency. In La Rotisserie in Shepherd's Bush, Stephen and I met a BBC reporter to give her some thoughts on the programme, which would include her interviewing the Secretary of State for Energy, Cecil Parkinson MP. The BBC journalist was a young and inexperienced Nisha Stein (she became Nisha Pillai), who would later become better known – not least for being the BBC newsreader who had to deal live with the news and pictures from New York on 11 September 2001[15]. Nisha did a good job with the Panorama programme. Needless to say, Stephen and I thought that we did, too. In local government and in my own business, I had had plenty of contact with local newspapers and broadcasters, but this was to be the first of a huge number of encounters with the national news organisations.

[15] With a few members, the AEP staff and I watched Nisha Pillai on the screen of Su-Yen Foong's computer, after a meeting at Waterloo Place on 11 September 2001. Coincidentally, at the end of that meeting, I had said jokingly that it looked difficult to win an argument that we were having with the government and we might need some help from someone like that chap … what was he called? … 'Bin Liner' or something like that. A minute or two later we found ourselves looking at news pictures of the attack on the World Trade Centre.

CHAPTER THREE

DIVING INTO
THE POOL

At the Annual General Meeting of the AIEP in September 1989, George Rufford's term as Chairman ended, after two years in which he had shaped the privateers' raw enthusiasm into a focused and business-like organisation. His successor, who had great respect for George, was completely different from him. D C Pike, known to his friends as Spike, had not worked in the electricity industry, coming instead from the sand and gravel business and bringing experience of its trade body, the Sand and Gravel Association, where he had been at different times a member and a senior official. His company, Green Land Reclamation, was a subsidiary of the family-owned gravel company, Summerleaze, based in Maidenhead. The Managing Director of Summerleaze, Peter Prior, like Spike, was a strong character, who, when he believed in an idea, would put his money where his mouth was and his dedication to the idea of turning landfill gas from a problem to an opportunity was deserving of success.

Although George Rufford may have been sceptical about the behaviour of the industry in which he had had spent his entire career, Spike Pike's scepticism extended well beyond the electricity supply industry to big organisations where cosiness and laziness had set in and even to trade associations, which he considered were apt to lose focus and find themselves serving the interests not of their subscribers, but of the staff that ran them. Neither was he a fan of political correctness. This association, however, would be influenced not merely by what its chairman didn't like, but rather more by his insistence that it should be lean and focused, use good English, be courteous in its relationships and run its affairs in a disciplined way. Across the table, Spike could occasionally be disconcertingly direct, but he had great reserves of charm and would always express appreciation where it was due and discuss how things could have been done better when results had been less than perfect.

He also had a sense of humour which was slightly to the dry side of arid. One day, as the Executive Committee was assembling for its meeting, Stephen Andrews and I arrived, each wearing a brand new suit. The two suits were different, but they had one thing in common. They were styled in the most up-to-date fashion. That is, rather than being fitted, each jacket hung loosely from the shoulders; less structured and slightly longer than a conventional one. Spike, whose own suits were made by a traditional tailor in Reading, noticed this immediately. He said to me 'I am intrigued. What do you have to say to your tailor when you want him to make a jacket that doesn't fit?'

Apart from his regular early morning calls to my office from his car phone and the advice and encouragement that he gave me, I remember Spike's term as Chairman for several reasons. One is that his thoughts on what should happen when he left office were vitally important. I refer to those later. The others were a lobbying victory on the rating[16] of independent power stations, the reorganisation of the Association's management and crucially, its involvement in the new 'Electricity Pool of England and Wales'.

Even before the AIEP was formed, the valuation for business

[16] In the context of local authority taxation.

rates of independent power stations had become a controversial issue, with the case for the independents being led by the already well-established British Wind Energy Association. The *cause célèbre* was a wind turbine at Ilfracombe in north Devon. Valuations for business rates were set by the government's Valuation Office and were based on the notional rent that might be expected for the particular property - not easy at the best of times and definitely open to question when the property is one that is unlikely to be rented. Where the electricity industry was concerned, there had been efforts to avoid complication. The CEGB had a blanket valuation for its portfolio of power stations. On the rare occasion when new, privately-owned power production was commissioned, however, it was valued according to its capacity. This bore no resemblance to the valuation of the CEGB's fleet. The blanket valuation of the CEGB's stations, when divided by the Board's total capacity in megawatts of electricity, gave a valuation which was highly favourable compared with that of an individual plant such as the little one at Ilfracombe. The wind power industry argued that the Ilfracombe turbine was being asked to pay rates at anything up to 40 times the level of the CEGB, and AIEP backed them vigorously.

This had been a hot issue at the formative meeting of AIEP members at the Connaught Rooms in September 1987 and it quickly found its way on to the agenda of the Association's Executive Committee. Cometh the hour, cometh the man. The Committee was blessed with having in its ranks the Honorary Secretary of the National Association of Water Power Users, Cdr George Chapman RN. Retired from the Royal Navy, George was an engineer and passionate about small-scale hydro power. On the small river which ran through his garden in south Devon he had installed a hydro-electric turbine, which powered his house, after which the surplus was exported to the South Western Electricity Board. George, who was a very clear thinker, was liable to become exasperated by text which was unnecessarily wordy, misleading or ambiguous – there was plenty of that to be found in the various documents that explained public policy as it applied to independent electricity producers, of course. Nevertheless, George, who was, in fact, in his element when faced with daunting amounts of detail, became the Association's rating expert. The Executive Committee's respect for him and his meticulous attention to detail was immense.

In February 1988, the government published the White Paper[17] which paved the way for the privatisation of the state electricity supply industry. It was a mere 16 pages in length[18]. The commitment to de-nationalisation was now clear and it would take effect in the Electricity Act[19] in the following year.

The state electricity industry was going to find itself intensely busy doing something that it would have deemed impossible a few years earlier. For months on end, teams of senior managers and civil servants would spend long hours in electricity industry and government offices trying to agree exactly how a privatised and competitive electricity supply industry should operate. Even as this work was going on, the electricity supply industry's top brass were trying to persuade the Department of Energy that it should not set its sights too high. *PR Week* (10-16 March 1988) reported:

Private power plan fight against CEGB

A David versus Goliath campaign - by a remote consultancy in rural Cornwall, aided by Britain's miniscule independent electricity industry – has beaten the CEGB's sophisticated attempt to defend itself against privatisation.

---

[17] Privatising Electricity. Cmd 322. February 1988.
[18] Contrast this with the White Paper on Electricity Market Reform in July 2011.
[19] Electricity Act 1989.

With the Government's proposals at the White Paper stage, and privatisation scheduled for 1990, the promotional battle looks set to become increasingly fierce.

CEGB boss Lord Marshall 'ferried Tory MPs in droves to Westminster's more exclusive restaurants to urge opposition to the CEGB's break-up, and Dewe Rogerson, *the PR agency was also hired to spread the anti break-up message' said the* Sunday Times.

While Chairman Lord Marshall has conceded that the board would not obstruct Government plans in principle, the power unions and allied supporters like the miners are likely to start applying the pressure.

The Association of Independent Electricity Producers has adopted an intensive but low-key lobbying campaign with the assistance of South West One PR, to put their case to opinion formers. The association was established last year on a shoestring budget because independent generators felt they weren't getting a fair deal from area electricity boards.

John Macadam, the treasurer of the AIEP, is currently preparing detailed recommendations for the House of Commons Select Committee on Energy. A teach-in for MPs has also been staged to keep Members informed.

David Porter, Director of South West One, *has also produced a monthly magazine for the association,* Independent Power News, *which has 2,500 readers in the UK and Europe. Ironically, one of its subscribers is Lazards, the merchant bankers who advise the CEGB.*

According to Porter, the AIEP will continue to lobby for independent generators – who have been allowed to produce electricity for regional boards since the 1983 Energy Act. 'The lavish lobbying techniques of Lord Marshall's gang were blown away by the prevailing winds of political opinion. We rejected the hysterical approach so often associated with small pressure groups and the combined forces of state-run industry and a multi-million pound ad agency could not prevent our success,' he said.

However well the AIEP may have been received politically, in truth the Association was only at the fringe of this process. The shape of the new industry and the way it would work was being determined largely behind closed doors and also behind closed doors, bankers engaged by the government were preparing for the sell-off. The independents were indignant, and in the late 1980s I shared that indignation. A quarter of a century later, having learned from those who were there just what effort went into the process and recognising what an achievement it was, I understand why we were kept at a certain distance. There must have been some consideration given to President Johnson's view about the side of the canvas from which it was best to have the enemy's urine flowing, but quite apart from the fact that the AIEP simply did not have the resources to participate, there were two huge political objectives that might not have been well served by having the Association at the table. First, the sell-off of the industry had to be successful. Shares in the ex-state companies had to look attractive and conditions that gave undue favour to their would-be competitors would not have helped in that regard. The second objective was that in a technical sense, the privatised industry should function properly. A seamless transition was required and frankly that transition had nothing to do with newcomers playing their part and everything to do with transforming the state industry, without putting supply at risk.

I have acknowledged the way that this transformation had to be achieved, nevertheless, the relationship with those who were already privately owned left much to be desired. One or two meetings were arranged, but as far as communication was concerned, it was more a one-way process than a true dialogue. The government and the incumbents were pursuing a highly ambitious programme and they could not afford to be diverted from the critical path. AIEP was able to make its views known to the news media, and that would ensure that the government could not dismiss totally the members' concerns. The aforementioned BBC *Panorama* programme on electricity privatisation centred on an interview with the Secretary of State for Energy, Cecil Parkinson. I reflect that I was probably much kinder to the Secretary of State when, later, I interviewed him for *Independent Power News* when he was visiting Cornwall.

From time to time, going into the news is helpful to a trade body, but later in my trade association life, I recognised that it is all too often indicative of a failure in the 'normal' process whereby an industry is able to comment constructively on legislation and regulation and try to influence it at its formative stage. I would make this point occasionally to the Association's membership at their AGM. Each year, we would assemble for the event the year's press cuttings and transcripts of radio and TV interviews concerning the Association – usually involving statements from me. It always looked impressive and the members saw it as evidence that the Association was working hard on their behalf. It was, of course, but once or twice at the AGM, I pointed out to the members that the Association was truly influential when it was on the front foot where legislation and regulation were concerned. That is, it was helping to find solutions or shape change without the issues necessarily being debated publicly. Being quoted in the press or interviewed on the *Today* programme usually meant quite the opposite – namely that a row had developed and achieving our objectives would be more difficult as a result.

'Lobbying' today is often misunderstood and has acquired a bad name. It is seen simply as self-serving and as often as not, sinister. It is, however, a vital part of the democratic process. Governments tend to involve themselves in far more things than they are able to manage properly and their enthusiasm frequently exceeds their understanding or their competence. All too often this results in unintended consequences. Initiatives by lobbyists, of course – proposals for legislation or regulation – must themselves be screened for unintended consequences, but governments' good intentions require at least as much scrutiny.

The AIEP had an early success, which, although it did not attract much publicity, was vitally important to many of the small electricity producers that pursued it – good for those small businesses and good for the credibility of the Association. To maintain, in the competitive market, the viability of the non-privatised nuclear power assets, a 'Fossil Fuel Levy' and 'Non-Fossil Fuel Obligation' were introduced. The AIEP was not slow to suggest that 'non-fossil' should also apply to renewable forms of energy. This was accepted and although, at the time, most of us felt that it was certainly not what the government had intended, I believe that the interpretation was encouraged from within the Department of Energy by the civil servant, Godfrey Bevan, who led the Department's work on renewables. The outcome was that the Non-Fossil Fuel Obligation (NFFO) included a support mechanism for renewables – indeed, historically, that is what it is remembered for, rather than for its support of nuclear power. Scotland, however, where the electricity market had not been liberalised when the market in England and Wales was, had many small electricity producers who were struggling with Energy Act tariffs and who had no access to the NFFO. The AIEP – with Stephen Andrews to the fore – took up the case and won the battle. There was an administered outcome for the small producers in Scotland and it provided them with an electricity wholesale price of 5.3p per kilowatt hour until 1998, which was a remarkable improvement on the payments they had received previously.

Key to the privatisation of the electricity supply industry and the introduction of a competitive market was the mechanism by which wholesale electricity would be traded – an activity which one or two senior figures in the state industry had declared to be impossible. Resoundingly, they were to be proved wrong, and the mechanism that was introduced would trigger important changes for the AIEP. The mechanism was the Electricity Pool of England and Wales – a half-hourly, day-ahead market enshrined in the 'Pooling and Settlement Agreement' signed on to by the parties that were to trade with each other. Representatives of the CEGB and the area electricity boards, later cap-badged with the companies that they would be transferred to, together with advisers and Department of Energy officials were destined to spend months of their lives working on the Agreement and the Pool Rules – everything from the principles of governance to the algorithms that determined prices[20]. The principles were essentially simple. Delivering that simplicity, however, was another matter.

It is not my intention here to describe the Electricity Pool in any detail. That has been done by people who understood it far better than I ever did. It is important, though, to explain its impact on the AIEP and the industry more generally.

Occasionally, there were meetings to discuss how the Pool would work and participants from outside the state industry were invited. Compared with the companies that were about to be privatised, however, they were at a huge disadvantage in terms of information and engagement. Their existence was at least recognised. It emerged that the Pooling and Settlement Agreement, in referring to the composition of the Executive Committee which would provide the day-to-day governance of the Pool, allowed for representation of companies that had not emerged from the former state industry. There were two seats of particular interest – one for a 'Group Representing Other Generators' (GROG) and one for

[20] An adaptation of the CEGB's 'GOAL' program, which determined the merit order for the state industry's power stations.

'Small Independent Generators (SIGS) … *should there be any*' (my italics). There were. Eventually one signed up to the Pooling & Settlement Agreement.

The Pool had begun operating well before the sell-off of the state-owned companies. Stephen Andrews, who had a keen eye on the way the body was shaping up, brought to AIEP confirmation that the organisation expected the seat for small generators to be taken up. He made clear to the AIEP Executive Committee how important it was somehow to take advantage of this. Recognising how demanding this would be if AIEP were to occupy the seat, Spike Pike went to the Department of Energy to meet the senior civil servant who was managing the project – Margaret Thompson[21], who would later become the Pool's Chief Executive. In a phone call to me after the meeting, it was clear that he had been impressed. Margaret was businesslike, direct and strong intellectually – characteristics which secured Spike's respect. Looking back, this seemed to have something in common with Margaret Thatcher's assessment of Mikhail Gorbachev in November 1990[22] – '*I like Mr Gorbachev. We can do business together.*' Before long, it was arranged that Spike should attend a meeting of the Pool Executive Committee. Rather, his attendance was to be arranged and I had responsibility for making that happen.

This did not go well. Having checked with the Department, I sent Spike to offices on the south side of the Thames, near the former Bankside Power Station. At Christmas Cottage in Herodsfoot, I received a phone call from Spike on the lines of 'I am where you have sent me, but no one else seems to be'. It emerged that the meeting had been relocated to a venue on the north side of the river. After further phone calls, I managed to redirect him to the right office. He arrived at the meeting a little late, of course, and as he always did, when asked to introduce himself

[21] Later Margaret McKinlay.
[22] Her interview with John Cole, BBC TV, 17 December 1984.

said 'My name is Pike. My friends call me Spike.' Spike was not comfortable at the meeting and probably did not feel that he was among friends. The mix-up over the venue could not have helped, but he told me later that he found the atmosphere rather too cosy, that papers for the meeting had been issued too late for his liking and that the participants seemed rather inward-looking. Years afterwards, one of the other participants told me that Spike's arrival that day had been a culture shock. The Committee had become inevitably rather cosy – a state of affairs induced by months of working hard together – and the newcomer, whose style worked so well at AIEP, came over as far from willing to adopt the culture of the incumbents. The AIEP resented the fact that the ex-state representatives had gone so far in making the rules of the game without consulting other players. They, however, under enormous pressure to deliver the de-nationalisation, found it impossible to engage seriously with small players who had no responsibility for delivery. These players were so small in relation to the companies emerging from the CEGB that the less respectful incumbents were apt to refer to them privately as 'bicycle generators'. As a result of all this, it would be a long time before any companies other than the ex-state businesses felt that they had ownership of the trading arrangements that were so important to them. Rather sooner than that, however, there would be consequences for me, arising from the Chairman's one and only appearance at the Pool Executive Committee.

I had regular early morning calls from Spike's car phone to my tiny office in Cornwall and a particularly important one of those calls went something like this:

'David, I think you should take up the seat at the Pool Executive Committee.'

'Me? I know absolutely nothing about it. I shall be eaten for breakfast.'

'No. You'll be fine. What's important is that we must make sure that you are properly briefed.'

The Director of the Association, Stephen Andrews, an electrical engineer, with a clear and comprehensive understanding of not just the industry itself but of the problems facing new entrants, would have been much better equipped than me to do that job. But Stephen's professional life was changing. He was leaving Orchard Partners to set up with his wife, Liz Reason – also a distinguished consultant – the energy practice Ilex Associates, and it had clients that were to become players in the Pool. Spike had a plan that was to be important for both Stephen and me.

At a rather tense meeting of the AIEP Executive Committee, held in the splendid offices of Tarmac[23] in a terraced Regency property, near London's Regent's Park, it was proposed that I should be nominated as the representative of the 'Small Independent Generators' on the Pool Executive Committee and that Ilex Associates should be given a contract to provide AIEP with advice on the electricity trading arrangements. The meeting was tense for two reasons. First, some members of the Executive Committee had understandable misgivings about handing the representation to a person with very little experience of the industry and second, for a young, relatively lightly-funded association, the contract with Ilex Associates would be a serious commitment.

The decision to go ahead was made. This was a brave decision and a defining moment for all concerned, not least the Association itself. Albeit late in the day, the AIEP now had a place at one of the most important tables in the new industry and the credibility that went with this would help to build its influence and to attract new members. The scene was set for a remarkable transformation.

---

[23] The PLC had a subsidiary which was involved in small-scale electricity production.

CHAPTER FOUR

MORE POWER TO
OUR ELBOW

Prompted by Spike's vision, there was to be another significant change at AIEP. In October 1991, after a two-year term, he was due to stand down as Chairman of the Association's Executive Committee. For me, this was to be only the second of many occasions when, with the support of the Committee[24], a new Chairman had to be found. But Spike did not see that as being quite enough for the Association. He and I discussed the succession and for him, the issue was not simply the choice of a Chairman. He said 'You do know that, when I go, you can't have the Association headed up by someone like me, with one megawatt of electricity on a rubbish dump? You need someone with more credibility and it's up to you to find them.' Not for the first time, Spike's thinking was ahead of mine, but I liked the idea of – as he would have put it – being left to 'pick up the ball and run with it.'

Neil Bryson became the new Chairman and with the full range of skills required, plus his deep involvement in the UK's first new combined cycle gas-turbine power station, he was ideal. In fact, he was an outstanding chairman, who would go on to be Chairman of the Electricity Pool. When Neil's two-year term with the

[24] Later, when the Association acquired limited company status, the Board of Directors.

Association ended, his colleagues asked him to serve for a third year and thankfully, he agreed.

But the task that Spike had passed my way was to find someone who was a recognisable public figure and whose involvement would help the Association develop and signal to the outside world its serious intent. I needed help with that and could think of no one better to get some advice from than the former Secretary of State, Cecil Parkinson MP. He no longer held ministerial office, having returned to the back benches when John Major replaced Margaret Thatcher as Prime Minister. I invited him to have lunch with me. It took place at the Park Lane Hotel in Piccadilly and I discovered quickly that although Cecil Parkinson and I had few things in common, there was at least one – we both used the hairdressing salon in the basement of the Park Lane Hotel. In Cecil's case, however – as photographs made plain – it was to rather better effect. He joined me for lunch immediately before an appointment with Jack, downstairs. It was not Jack, but his colleague, Toni, an Italian from Naples, who cut my hair, but in this small, friendly salon Jack's jokes were meant for everyone within earshot. Nevertheless, they seldom seemed to register with Toni, who was better with the scissors than at absorbing Jack's politically incorrect humour.

My discussion over lunch with this high-profile politician could well have begun with a review of Jack's latest pronouncements, but it did not. Cecil was genuinely interested in how things were working out for the independent electricity producers. Fortunately, there was a good story for me to tell and it led us eventually to the issue of the day, which was the search for the big name who might be persuaded to pledge himself, or herself, to the Association. I explained what the Association would expect of the appointee and the type of person that seemed likely to fit the bill. As the former Secretary of State for Energy and later for

Transport, Cecil knew the importance of trade association work and having run through, mentally, a few possibilities, he came quickly to a suggestion. He offered to put the idea to his former Energy Minister, Michael Spicer MP. Michael had been not only the Parliamentary Under-Secretary of State with responsibility for the electricity supply industry, but also the very Minister who had taken through the House of Commons the Bill for the privatisation of the industry – opposed, incidentally, by a young Tony Blair MP, with whom he developed a good and lasting relationship. I knew Michael only from one or two meetings in the Department of Energy, but he seemed to fit the bill well. This pleasant lunch ended with Cecil Parkinson confirming that he would talk to Michael.

A day or two later I had a call from Cecil's secretary inviting me to get in touch with her counterpart in Michael Spicer's office, to arrange a meeting. So, I found myself in Michael Spicer's splendid office[25] in the building 'Norman Shaw South', off Parliament Street in Westminster, discussing whether the new role at AIEP might appeal to this MP whose CV included having been a Minister in three government departments, the Parliamentary Private Secretary to Prime Minister, Margaret Thatcher and Deputy Chairman of the Conservative Party at a time when it was in the habit of winning elections – something to which his modernisation work at Conservative Central Office, on computer systems and on communications, had made an enormous contribution. Michael was interested, but understandably cautious. He had no paid, non-parliamentary interests and I think he was being careful to ensure that this little organisation, with its office in a cottage on a hillside in Cornwall, would not present him with any unpleasant surprises. I sensed, too, that he may have wondered exactly how the organisation was managed, with its limited resources. Aware that, not long before, as a Minister, he had enjoyed the support of a

---

[25] MPs do not usually have 'splendid' offices. Michael attributed his good fortune to having served as a Minister in several departments.

dedicated and highly professional team of civil servants, I assured him that the administration of AIEP would match anything that had been provided by the Department of Energy – a rash promise, perhaps, but as, at that time, virtually all of it would be down to me, it was one that I felt that I could live up to.

But there was a more fundamental issue that Michael wanted to clarify. Part of his caution had been concern about exactly what AIEP expected of him. 'One thing I won't do is keep getting to my feet in the House of Commons to raise issues on behalf of the Association' he said. 'It's a complete waste of time. It achieves nothing, because everyone in the House switches off whenever an MP who is known to do that sort of thing gets up to speak.' I understood and indicated that that would not be a problem, although I suspected that there were one or two members of the AIEP's Executive Committee – too busy with the day job to acquire much understanding of how Parliament and politics worked – who might have been concerned to hear his response. What we did want Michael to do was to provide a small and lightly-resourced association with much more credibility and provide good counsel when we were confronted with political challenges. We both knew that much would depend on how successfully the two of us were able to work together, though neither said so, in as many words.

I wanted to get on with it, of course, but appointing Michael Spicer was not a decision that I had authority to make. I arranged for him to join me for lunch with a few key members of the AIEP's Executive Committee, Neil Bryson, Philip Jackson and Spike Pike. We met at the Thistle Hotel in Westminster – not the best food in London SW1, but a convenient location and one where politics was on the menu every day. For his part, Michael showed a respectful interest in the work of the Association and asked questions about the issues, but also reiterated what he would not be prepared to do, namely keep getting to his feet in the chamber of the House of Commons to raise issues on behalf of the Association. With the possible exception of Philip, we understood that and accepted it. Pursuing issues in the House of Commons and putting them on record in that way is not entirely without its merits, of course. MPs do it continually, but as often as not, being 'on record' is as far as it gets. There are many different ways in which political decisions can be influenced and as far as AIEP was concerned, it was effectiveness that counted. Philip was no less interested in outcomes and he recognised that we needed a range of weapons at our disposal, though I suspect that he would still have liked to have seen Michael occasionally donning armour and AIEP colours and menacing his colleagues with our sword.

We appointed Michael Spicer MP as Chairman of the Association and a member of its Executive Committee, of which there was already a Chairman. In effect, he was the Association's President and later, when we concluded that it was confusing to have a Chairman of the Association and separately another Chairman for its governing body, we renamed the role and he became President of the Association. We should have done that in the first place and I cannot think why we did not. There were always more pressing concerns, of course.

I wasted no time in getting his name on our paperwork, nor in publicising his appointment. This was never going to make front page headlines, but it made government officials and journalists sit up and take notice and it was also good for the morale of the growing membership of the Association. Michael and I would be invited occasionally to visit a member company and as an experienced MP and former businessman and journalist, he was extraordinarily adept at understanding what concerned them and getting quickly to the nub of the issue.

As Chairman of the Association (later President) Michael also presided over the Annual General Meeting and used the occasion to make a speech that we released to the press. Over the years, a remarkably warm relationship developed between the wider membership and their President and this was always in evidence at the well-attended AGM. Although it gave its support in principle to the Conservative Party's privatisation of the electricity supply industry and to a competitive electricity market, the Association, of course, was not a party-political organisation. On the rare occasions when I was asked about its politics I would emphasise its neutrality and go on to say that I had no reason to think that the people within the Association's membership were any different politically from the electorate in general. Michael, who was known by everyone to be on the right of the Conservative Party, not only chaired the AGM with great style, but at the reception that followed, would be found circulating comfortably among the membership – members, including some of the very smallest, would travel from far and wide for the event. An unwritten part of the philosophy that made the Association successful was respect for the smaller players, and Michael understood that instinctively. It seemed to me to be in tune with the way in which, when later he became the long-standing and respected Chairman of the Conservative Party's 1922 Committee, he defended vigorously the role of that committee as a voice for the Party's back-benchers, resisting attempts by the Party leadership to have more influence over it.

However important Michael Spicer's role at set-piece events might have been, it was at our more frequent meetings to discuss Executive Committee (later Board) issues that I got to know him. Sometimes with the Chairman present, we would meet for dinner on the eve of a quarterly meeting and from time to time between those meetings. At the meetings of the Executive Committee or

Board, Michael's role was that of the effective 'Non-Executive'. He tended to ask the difficult questions – finance, politics, constitutional process or the wider interests of the Association – and stick at it until he received clear assurances. This made good use of him, being detached from individual company interests. In fact, the question of their 'detachment' was occasionally an issue for the Board members who had been nominated by their companies and elected as Directors to a Board whose legal responsibility was the interests of Association – as a company. Perhaps not surprisingly, some Board members would occasionally press for decisions which appeared to suit the interests of their own company[26].

But my meetings with Michael when we did not have a Board agenda to discuss were no less rewarding. Sometimes in a Westminster restaurant, sometimes in a dining room at the House of Commons and just occasionally in one of his clubs, we would meet to discuss an Association issue and its place in the politics of the day. Once or twice, I found myself in situations in which my parents would have been amazed to see me. Sitting next to Field Marshall Lord Bramall at the communal dining table at Pratt's and discussing a defence issue was one such occasion. Incidentally, I soon discovered that at Pratt's, every member of staff is called 'George'. That is nice and simple. Where to sit at the Garrick Club is less simple. On my first visit there I accepted Michael's offer of a drink in the bar and his suggestion that I should take a seat 'No, not there. It's Kingsley Amis's chair' he said. I jumped up and found somewhere more ordinary. Then I took out of my jacket pocket the folded piece of A4 on which the issues for discussion I had so carefully distilled. 'Ah, no. We mustn't do that' said Michael. 'We are not allowed to discuss business here.' Fortunately, I was able to

---

[26] I recall Dr Keith Miller, when he was Chairman of the Board of the Association, reminding the Directors, more than once, that when they sat on the Board, they were obliged to act in the interests of the company (the Association) rather than in the interests of the member company that had nominated them for the Board. That he should have done that was absolutely right, but it can, nevertheless, be a challenge for some Board members of a trade association.

remember well enough what the bullet points had been about, so, with the offending sheet of A4 back in my pocket, we were able to have our discussion over lunch without being seen to refer to anything as sordid as business paperwork.

In the early 1990s, Michael led the Conservative Party MPs that were opposed to the ratification of the Maastricht Treaty[27]. Constitutionally, this was a vitally important period for Britain, and those who remember it, or, have studied it, will know that at least one other MP is now recorded as having led the rebel group. There were, of course, sub groups within the merry band and that is where other claims may have some substance. But as diaries and biographies show, Michael's role was pre-eminent. For me, this was fascinating, but also of some concern, as far as his role in the Association went. We could not afford to have Michael's ability to participate in the AIEP's Executive Committee (later the Board) compromised by his political views and I do not think that, over the years, he ever put a foot wrong in that regard. He showed respect for the other parties, being prepared, occasionally, to joke about his own, or the Conservative Party's position and bringing to the table his immense experience of the wider political environment.

The months of conflict over the Maastricht Treaty, however, which strained the Conservative Party almost to breaking point, put Michael's role at AIEP to an early test. On 3 June 1992, when it had just been announced that, following a referendum, the Danes would not ratify the Maastricht Treaty, we had an Executive Committee meeting in London. There may have been some members of the AIEP Committee who were disappointed with the result from Denmark, but if there were, then they were in the minority and they kept their heads down. Those who did have anything to say were almost as pleased as Michael was – some because they sympathised with his views and others probably

[27] Treaty on European Union. 1992.

because, at that time, it was widely believed that the Danish decision would put the matter to bed and spare the British any further pain from an issue which had been so divisive. Later events proved them wrong about that, of course.

My personal sympathies were very much in line with Michael's position, and when he and I met for dinner during the time that that difficult debate was raging, as soon as we had worked through the electricity agenda, the conversation would turn to the Maastricht politics. Michael, renowned among his colleagues for his tact and discretion, gave nothing away of course, but I suspected that he may have been glad of the opportunity to talk through the issues with someone who had a sympathetic interest but carried none of the Westminster baggage. Once or twice, he was due to make an appearance on BBC2's *Newsnight* at the end of the evening and we ran through the likely questions and the traps that might be set. It was interesting and a challenge which I enjoyed enormously. A few years later, he reflected that the roles had been reversed – with energy issues becoming controversial, I would be in front of the cameras, including, occasionally, on *Newsnight*. On one such evening, we had just sat down to start dinner in Shepherd's when I received a call to go on that programme. I had been alerted about the possibility, but had left the office expecting an energy company Chief Executive to take the hot seat. He had been unable to do so and a BBC car collected me from Marsham Street at 9.30 pm – leaving just enough time to run through the direction of the questioning with Michael.

The provisions of the Maastricht Treaty – with a number of opt-outs – took effect on 1 November 1993. My sympathy for the efforts made by Michael Spicer and his colleagues in 1992-1993 is undiminished, but as time passed and European decisions began to have more impact on the UK's electricity supply industry, I found myself engaging increasingly with European legislation and its institutions. Much of that took place via the Association's membership of the pan-European electricity body, Eurelectric, for which I had great regard - not least because of its commitment to market-based solutions – but my dealings with the political institutions, which are rather remote from the people that they serve, led me to reflect that I feel much the same about government at the European level as I do about government of the UK. I would like it better if it were to do less and then make sure that what it did do, it did very well. Today, too much is attempted and too much is done badly.

CHAPTER FIVE

NEW POWER STATIONS, NEW RULES AND A NEW ISSUE

The government, keenly interested in the emergence of new players – albeit even more concerned to see the ex-state companies steer the industry steadily through the uncertain times ahead – saw interest in new investment as an endorsement of its pioneering changes. The existing small producers, such as those in AIEP, were in the 'nice to have' category, but more new players needed to emerge to signal that things had really changed. Not only new players, but players that would make substantial investments. Those investments seemed likely to be in 'Combined Cycle Gas Turbine' (CCGT) power stations, which were clean, could be built comparatively quickly and where the 'combined cycle[28]' made for more fuel efficiency. Natural gas, previously regarded as a premium fuel and not appropriate for use in power stations, had now been freed of this constraint. CCGTs also represented a step away from reliance on coal, which came from an industry which had a proven ability to challenge governments rather vigorously.

The press reported interest in a number of CCGTs, but one project began to pull away from the field. Neil Bryson, a man with

[28] Waste heat captured from the gas turbine in the first cycle is used to fuel a steam turbine in the second cycle.

extensive experience of the coal industry in the UK and abroad who was later, until 1987, a Department of Energy civil servant advising on coal, had looked at the 120 MW coal-fired power station at Roosecote, near Barrow-in-Furness, which the CEGB had closed down. His initial thoughts were that under private ownership, it could be reopened to burn coal from his own privately-owned mine and could be run more cost effectively than it had been under the CEGB. Before long, he concluded that gas from Morecambe Bay would be a better bet. With three other investors, Eric Ratcliffe, Ron Stone and Richard Stubbs, who had long experience of the electricity generation industry, and a substantial majority investment by the turbine manufacturer, ABB, the project went ahead. Lakeland Power built a 229 MW gas-fired plant, employing some 100 people, on the site of the former coal-fired plant which had once employed double that number for half of the capacity. It secured the first long-term gas supply contract with British Gas and a long-term power supply contract with NORWEB, its local Regional Electricity Company – vital for Lakeland Power, but a deal which was, nonetheless, controversial. The regional electricity companies, fearful of the dominance in the privatised market of the ex-CEGB companies, were keen to contract for generation from other sources. For their part, the ex-state generators were suspicious of such deals and apt to suggest that the REC contracts were 'uneconomic' – i.e. too generous to their new competitors.

Well before the plant was commissioned in 1991, Lakeland Power became a member of AIEP, increasing further the Association's credibility. Needless to say, the company was culturally very different from the privatised ex-state companies. It had to be. As the new plant was being built, the newcomers had to learn how the Pool would work and from time to time they were shocked to discover that the rules developed for the Pool did not allow for various circumstances that they would face as operators of a new CCGT. With the help of their advisers, Forstar Developments (a start-up business funded by ABB) they found themselves, in effect, having to propose drafting for circumstances that the ex-state players had not anticipated. The challenges that Lakeland faced and resolved made life much easier for the companies that followed them into the industry. The later participants probably had no idea how much smoother their route to market had been as a result of Lakeland's pioneering efforts.

I took over Spike Pike's seat at the Pool Executive Committee – the 'PEC' as it became known throughout the industry. It was daunting. Meetings, of which there had been at least 30 before the AIEP got its feet under the table, were now held monthly, usually on Thursdays, and they went on all day. The terminology was new to me, acronyms seemed to appear in nearly every sentence and it would have been impossible to stop proceedings to demand an explanation every time I was puzzled. Perhaps even worse was that many of the papers arrived by fax at night, giving us very little time to consider them. At Christmas Cottage, the fax machine (another £1,700 added to the investment I had already made in the computer, software and laser printer) sat on a side table in the sitting room. The sitting room was below our bedroom, with only the thickness of the 19th century floorboards separating us from the then highly advanced technology. The printing on to the thermal paper may have been almost silent, but the transmission of the paper through the machine was not. I remember one night lying in bed hearing 85 pages make their way slowly through the machine and the next morning, my wife, Judith, drawing together the huge coil of paper that had spread itself across the carpet, cutting it into A4 sheets and assembling a report.[29]

[29] I know that certain secretaries were reduced to tears by the volume of PEC papers and the way they were sometimes difficult to put together for a meeting.

All this would have been even harder to put up with had it not been for the success of the consultancy arrangements with Ilex Associates. Via a fax 'broadcast', in advance of each PEC meeting, John Macadam of Ilex received the papers too and I had a brief from him. Sometimes, however, I had already left home for an overnight stay in London on the eve of the PEC meeting and I found myself discussing the late agenda items on the phone in the hotel bedroom. At least John was prepared to explain clearly what the issues were, and I gradually began to pick things up. When John was not available, Stephen Andrews was. It was little wonder that they went on to become so respected and distinguished in what became a large field of energy consultants.

In fairness to my colleagues on the PEC, I should say that the other representatives of generation interests on the committee were reasonably patient with me and as time passed, we sometimes found ourselves holding the same view on some of the issues. In fact, when the Association grew and the Pool became more mature, there were many issues which united the generating interests, often in opposition to the views of the 'Public Electricity Suppliers' (PES) – the companies that ran the regional distribution systems for electricity and at that time, had a legalised monopoly of supply over domestic and all but the largest business customers. The PES had to buy their power from the generators and they were especially suspicious of the influence of the ex-CEGB generating companies who, understandably, were getting in tune with the commercial requirements of the new world much faster than the businesses that remained regional monopolies. Later, tensions would run high over the security that the Pooling and Settlement Agreement required the PES to put up, in order for them to buy wholesale electricity from the generators.

In due course I became Chairman of the group, comprising

generators, which the Pooling and Settlement Agreement termed the 'Major Default Calling Creditors' (MDCC). The wholesale trading of electricity put very large sums of money at stake and if monitoring showed that a supplier had been buying more electricity from the Pool than was provided for by its credit cover, the group would meet and ask that the cover should be increased. The companies affected did not like this as it was an expensive process for them and I recall, after one MDCC meeting, being telephoned by an anxious senior manager in a regional company to be enlightened about the huge charges they would incur if they asked their bank to provide a new letter of credit. The other side of that coin, of course, was that the generators stood to lose a lot if a supplier defaulted – a situation which was rare, but not unknown. When one regional company proved particularly reluctant to increase its cover, we consulted the Pooling and Settlement Agreement to see what further steps could be taken. The Agreement provided for such a company to be 'de-energised'. We were not entirely sure how that might be effected, however, nor was there the appetite to impose such a drastic penalty.

At the regular PEC meetings, we did not sit at the table positioned as opposing sides. It was not unusual for a PES representative to be sitting next to a generator representative. The PESs jointly had a contract for advice from the consultancy St Clement's Services. In front of each of them was the same brief. In that respect, the generator representatives were less co-ordinated. But early in the life of the Pool, there was one issue on which the generators were certainly not in agreement. It was the first major, Pool-related challenge to face the AIEP.

The generating companies that were signatories[30] to the Pooling and Settlement Agreement were obliged to trade all of their electricity output through the Pool. This did not mean that they

[30] Licensed generators – those exporting more than 50MW to the system after on-site demand had been met, or, with a facility of over 100MW regardless of export levels.

could not have agreements with the PESs outside the Pool[31] but that every megawatt hour of electricity had first to be traded through it. It was far from clear what this meant to smaller producers who were 'on-site generators' i.e. typically they used a combined heat and power scheme to make electricity which they supplied to their own company, or to clients on their site. To trade their output through the Pool appeared to mean that they would first have to sell their power into the Pool and be paid the Pool purchase price for it, then buy back the power that they needed at the higher Pool selling price. David Green, then the Chief Executive of the Combined Heat and Power Association, described this in an interview as being akin to asking a tomato grower to take his tomatoes to market, sell them and then buy back at a higher price the ones he wanted to eat. Not surprisingly, the independents found this proposal infuriating. Worse still, from their point of view, was that because their operation was usually heat-driven (the heat being used in industrial and commercial processes) rather than being produced in response to electricity demand, the electricity would be sold into the Pool at times when there was demand for delivering their heat. The industry, which values predictable and 'despatchable' production that can respond to changes in consumers' demand, used to refer to that less predictable and intermittent production as 'spilling' of electricity. At the time, being focused sharply on winning the argument, I did not realise quite how much the integrated electricity system depends on electricity production which is predictable and can be called upon when it is required, nor how much more valuable it is compared with the power that is simply dumped on the system when it suits the producer. I recall sitting up late into the night arguing about this with Dr Keith Miller, on the eve of a meeting of the Pool Executive Committee in Nottingham. Years later, in the summer of 2013, over

[31] They had such agreements in the form of 'Contracts for difference' (CfD), written around the Pool price.

a glass of wine, I revealed to him the little gap in my understanding of the situation over 20 years earlier. The principle continues to be relevant, of course, in the context of large-scale renewable energy systems putting electricity on to the system - not in response to demand, but when the wind is blowing or the sun is shining. In Germany, some gas-fired power stations have been blown off the system because the 'free', but subsidised, wind and solar power output has to be taken first. Some conventional plant, which is needed when the weather-dependent technologies are not producing, has been put out of business.

In the build-up to privatisation, the 'on-site' issue had been set aside as one which could not be settled quickly and would have to be added to a schedule of issues to be resolved later. Eventually, it found its way on to the Pool's agenda. The Pool members were unable to resolve it and it went to the regulator, Stephen Littlechild, the Director General of Electricity Supply at the Office of Electricity Regulation ('OFFER') for a ruling. AIEP schemed and lobbied hard. The lobbying was entirely transparent and straightforward. The scheming was more subtle. The second-largest of the two privatised ex-state generating companies, PowerGen, was rumoured to be interested in developing 'energy parks', where industrial and commercial customers would enjoy attractively-priced heat and power. They joined forces with the small generators on this issue and so did companies such as BNFL[32] which had a large combined heat and power scheme, and the well-established generating business of Slough Estates[33], which had been developed long before the electricity industry was nationalised and was one of the founding fathers of the AIEP.

---

[32] BNFL's generation status made it a member of the Pool's 'Group Representing Other Generators' and it had joined AIEP, where it was very active.

[33] Slough Estates (its energy subsidiary was later named 'Slough Heat & Power') had a 90MW, multi-fuel, plant.

Three propositions had emerged. Most of the Pool members opposed strongly any concessions to the on-site generators – an outright 'no'. At the time, the regional PESs, in particular, were anxious that there should not be an outcome which enabled on-site electricity producers, in effect, to shift their production 'off-grid' but still rely on the grid for voltage and frequency stability (without paying for it) and for back-up supply. Energy-intensive users, which had previously enjoyed hidden subsidies under the state-owned electricity system, were prominent in making the case for on-site generation.

Through AIEP, the 'Small Independent Generators' made very deliberately a strong case for the on-site generators to be excused the requirement to sell power to the Pool and then buy it back. We felt that neither of the extreme positions would be accepted, but a slightly more conciliatory position had been drawn up by PowerGen. Behind the scenes we worked with PowerGen to try to ensure that its proposal would be acceptable to the smaller generating businesses. It was – a great tribute to Paul Anthony, then of PowerGen, Peter O'Neill of BNFL, Philip Russell of Slough Heat and Power and AIEP's advisers, Ilex Associates. OFFER failed to resolve the issue and exercised its right to put the matter to the Secretary of State for Energy, John Wakeham MP.

I had gone to a meeting of the Pool Executive Committee, which I think may have been held at the offices of the Electricity Association at 30 Millbank, London SW1. As I was sipping my pre-meeting coffee, Margaret Thompson, the Chief Executive of the Pool, came over to me and whispered 'You've won the on-site decision.' It was to be announced later that day, but I acquired immediately a disgracefully smug grin, which stayed with me for most of the meeting. In fact, the decision was rather more in line with PowerGen's proposal, but perhaps Margaret had worked out that that was what we had been aiming for. Such moments had to be savoured. Winning a set-piece battle like that was not an everyday occurrence. But in an industry where the competing players were still getting used to the rules, this change to the rule book was short-lived. The cost of software changes made the PowerGen proposal too expensive to implement and the Small Independent Generators' 'netting off' approach had to be adopted anyway.

However imperfect the arrangements for electricity privatisation may have looked to the Association of Electricity Producers, the brainpower of the electricity industry staff and the civil servants involved, combined with an enormous level of commitment from all concerned, turned something once unimaginable into headline-making reality. The CEGB businesses and the Regional Electricity Companies may have been privatised at different times, but from 'vesting day', 1 April 1990, there was no looking back.

Small shareholders who bought in to the privatisation did well. The City of London did well. The government did well. So did the staff of the privatised companies. Before long, large numbers of them would leave the industry as it slimmed down, but even that was done with the minimum of pain and when some careers ended, others began as new drivers led to new roles, with staff adapting to them remarkably well. There were instances where new companies behaved like kids who had found the keys to the sweet shop and others where those companies' judgement of how to behave in the world of business was seriously flawed. I recall an AIEP member coming to my office to complain about the negative and far from business-like attitude of a Regional Electricity Company that he was trying to deal with over his proposal to connect a CHP plant to the distribution network. I reminded him that he had been sitting across the table from people for whom life in the world of private business was still very new and furthermore, they were people who may well have gone into the state electricity industry because it was *not* a business. I promised to look into it and I assured him that things would improve before too long. I said it with confidence, but mentally I had my fingers crossed.

Though there may have been plenty of problems for the new industry to resolve, perhaps most importantly, the lights stayed on. The next planned, and major, change - the novelty of domestic customers being able to switch supplier when they felt so inclined - was still nine years away.

The industry was finding itself in the headlines, however, but the debate was rarely about 'energy policy'. Instead, it was usually about the pay and perks of the industry's bosses – one of a number of issues for which the newly-privatised industry was wholly unprepared and which would cause it serious long-term damage.

The British constitution is often described as 'unwritten'. I have never quite accepted that argument. It may not be a single document and it may rely on some conventions, but from Magna Carta in 1215, much of it has been in writing, in the form of statutes and judgments. British energy policy from 1990, however, seemed to rely much less on the written word. There was no handbook. Even the White Paper of 1988, which led to the Electricity Act of 1989, comprised a mere 16 pages. The Pooling and Settlement Agreement, of course, was a huge document, but like so many of the industry's important documents, that was about how things would be done, rather than what we were trying to achieve. There were ministerial speeches from time to time, but there was no single source of reference. Unless, that is, one looks back to June 1982, when the Secretary of State for Energy, Nigel Lawson MP, had addressed the International Association of Energy Economists in Cambridge.

If there was any philosophy behind energy policy, that that was probably it, but it was the attitude of the later Secretary of State, Cecil Parkinson MP, and his Energy Minister, Michael Spicer MP, and the tone of their statements that set out the policy stall.

Immediately after privatisation, there was really very little to trigger debate about policy. The industry had been privatised (most of it); there was an independent regulator; the lights stayed on; a programme to complete the liberalisation stretching as far as 1998 was envisaged; there was plenty of generating capacity; a fix gave some protection to the coal industry by obliging the ex-state generators to buy home-produced coal; another fix supported the nuclear power industry, which remained state-owned until 1996; new gas-fired electricity production was being planned and there was a programme of support (the 'Non-Fossil Fuel Obligation' or 'NFFO') for renewable energy. Often, when speaking at conferences, I found myself being asked whether it was true that the UK now had no energy policy. I used to respond to the effect that we now had privately-owned electricity companies that depended for their very existence on making and selling electricity and that was as good a driver as any to deliver the commodity reliably and at a competitive price. In fact, it had been under state ownership that we had suffered damaging power cuts. This response was rarely received with enthusiasm, but neither did it provoke very many arguments.

To my initial surprise, I received the occasional invitation to speak elsewhere in Europe, where EU-led electricity liberalisation was being contemplated. Among the invitations was one from Wilfred Aspinall to attend a meeting of one of the groups of the EU 'sounding board' body, the 'European Economic and Social Committee', to debate liberalisation with representatives of Europe's industrial and commercial customers of electricity

(IFIEC). The response to my opening remarks at that meeting took me by surprise. I had spoken about the benefits of competition. Not only were the energy utilities opposed to that, but so were many of the big customers. In parts of Europe, they preferred to settle their energy prices through a political deal with the state-owned monopoly. Opposite me sat Jacques Plénard, the head of the major energy users' group in France. He replied first, saying 'Mr Chairman, what Mr Porter has said is a trap.'

Bienvenue à Bruxelles.

The conference audiences in Brussels were not persuaded by my enthusiastic presentations, either. Mostly male, mostly engineers and generally a little older[34] than a British electricity industry audience, they posed questions that had been routine in the lead-up to the privatisation in England and Wales and they were questions which, in Britain, we had dealt with. Needless to say, seething contempt usually greeted my answers. The way the privatised companies in Britain had reduced their staffing levels seemed particularly unattractive to them. At one event, in Brussels, I was challenged by a sceptical manager from the Belgian electricity industry. The questioning had been typically hostile and he moved on from the routine doubts about whether private companies would really invest in the industry, to the notion that there might be a European market for electricity, one day. 'But how could we trade with the UK, when you do not want to join a single currency?' he asked. 'We already have a single currency for electricity. It is the megawatt hour' I replied. They did not like the sound of this. Whenever I faced an audience of electricity industry monopolists, to a man, they used the same expression to describe what had happened in Britain – 'The British Experiment'. With controlled indignation,

---

[34] I can offer no statistical evidence of this, but the slimming down of the British electricity supply industry post-privatisation encouraged older rather than younger employees to leave, thus creating a 'younger' industry.

but intending fully to be heard, my usual response was 'One thing that I must make clear is that this is not an "experiment".'

Some 20 odd years later, they might have argued that they had been right.

CHAPTER SIX

AN ASSOCIATION GROWING AND AN INDUSTRY SLEEP-WALKING

It may have been corporate fatigue from the process of privatisation and the drive for cultural change, or it could have arisen from the complacency that can develop when people and organisations know that they are doing a good job. Perhaps it was both of those things, but whatever the reason, the new industry began to sleep-walk into problems from which it would suffer immense damage. That damage to its reputational fabric would prove to be so serious that an industry that is vital to the economy would find that its credibility would virtually drain away.

The electricity supply industry under state ownership had a certain amount of independence of the kind that public corporations were meant to enjoy, but it worked hand in glove with the politics of the day. It was in the news occasionally. Certainly when there were strikes; occasionally when electricity tariffs were announced and sometimes in relation to controversial nuclear power – for example, the 340-day public inquiry into the proposed Sizewell B power station provided many column inches as did, more generally, the six years between the planning application in

1981 and the Secretary of State's decision, in 1987. It is worth remembering, however, that, along with other parts of the public sector[35], the industry was steadily losing the trust of the public and was the subject of strong criticism by select committees of Parliament. In the UK, by then, there seemed to be little left of the 'Spirit of '45" invoked by Ken Loach in his rather emotional film of that name.[36] Some 25 years later, the industry is mentioned in the press virtually every day. Tweeting means more to humans than birds and trending occurs rapidly, instead of at a glacial pace. If an energy company calls for a 'conversation' with the customers, it will get one but one half of that conversation will be none too friendly in nature.

Individually, the privatised companies recognised fairly quickly the importance of communications. They had good professionals dealing with their relationships with the news media and they gradually built a public affairs capability for the interface with policy-makers. The companies new to the industry tended to give similar attention to communications, but being much smaller and sometimes conscious of the risk of becoming top-heavy, they devoted fewer resources to central services of that kind.

From an industry-wide point of view, things were very different. The Association of Independent Electricity Producers was flourishing; so too were the Combined Heat and Power Association and the British Wind Energy Association. The ex-state companies, however, had the Electricity Association (EA) to represent them.

The EA was not created because of a great will in the industry to have a strong, united voice. It was formed because a home had to be found for the 1,250 staff of the state industry's Electricity Council, which represented the top of the electricity supply industry pyramid. When the AIEP heard that the EA was being set up, it issued a complaining press release and the leader in *Independent*

---

[35] And, eventually the monopolies created in the early privatisations – the monolithic British Gas, for example.
[36] The Spirit of '45. Fly Film. Sixteen Films. 2013.

Power News was hardly welcoming: 'It may be no more than a glorified club, but it should not be used to keep the ex-state companies immune from the pressures of the real world.'

AIEP's concern was understandable, but it would become clear later that it had less to be concerned about than at first it had imagined. There were some things that, with what soon became 850 staff, the EA was good at. It became an important player on the European front and its work in Brussels was highly respected. It did good work on environmental issues, load research, health and safety management and industry standards and it produced an authoritative yearbook for the industry – the 'Electricity Industry Review'. But a fundamental problem facing the EA was that it represented the ex-state companies and there were new businesses coming into the industry that had a different culture, no connection with the past and no wish to establish one. So, it was not as representative as it might have wanted to be, although officially, it wanted a wider membership. It was also rather unwieldy and needed trimming down. Although, at first, the large number of staff may have felt relieved that they had been transferred to the EA from the Electricity Council, gradually they will have realised that the organisation was going to face huge changes and that they would be put through a lengthy period of uncertainty. The research wing EA Technology was hived off. So was the management of the industry pension fund.

The EA's 'inherited' Chief Executive was paid off and a new one recruited. This, finally, signalled some serious intent. Philip Daubeney, a senior executive with ICI with international experience, had come to the end of his career with the company and was signed up by the EA. Eloquent, authoritative and confident, he must have been recruited to bring some clarity of purpose to the EA and cut it down to size – its members were already concerned about the cost of funding the Association and they questioned the value that they got from it. I can only guess, but the members must also have been expecting that a leaner, more purposeful EA would be able to get to grips with some of the industry-wide communications issues that were finding their way on to the agenda. From where I sat, Philip certainly appeared to be delivering a leaner, fitter EA. There were fewer signs of the communications agenda being addressed as effectively, however. In fact, that was probably far too much to expect in a short space of time, especially when the EA was shrinking and the big companies were still learning to work with each other – within the parameters permitted by competition law. There were, understandably, tensions caused when the testosterone freed up in the privatised companies strained their still immature working relationships – relationships which often made it hard to agree a position on an issue as quickly as they needed to, in order to satisfy the news hounds. AIEP (and later the Association of Electricity Producers) was a beneficiary of this. I used to make a point of trying to respond to news enquiries quickly when it seemed that the EA was still thinking or consulting its members. Of course, it was often much easier for AIEP (and later, AEP) because our remit was less wide-ranging and we had grown organically, whereas EA was having to endure contraction at the same time as defining a new role for itself.

Later it became easier still, after the AIEP went through the extremely time-consuming, but invaluable, exercise of agreeing what its policies should be on a wide range of industry issues. The resulting document, approved in in 1993, was enormously helpful to me because it not only answered a long list of specific questions but was so comprehensive that it often provided a large part of the answer to questions that had not yet been asked. I found myself in the satisfying position of being able to comment quite freely with the backing of the membership; building a worthwhile relationship with press, radio and television journalists and in the process, almost certainly irritating the EA. Note that, except for endorsing a degree of support for renewable energy through the Non-Fossil Fuel Obligation, the answer to many of the policy questions tended to rely on a solution being market-orientated.

Philip Daubeney must have been concerned that the Electricity Association was not always having the impact which, for its size and importance, it should have had. In October 1993, he made Dick Fedorcio the Director of Communication at EA. Fedorcio came from Kent County Council and he had been President of the UK's Chartered Institute of Public Relations in 1992. The appointment of a big-hitter was a clear signal of intent, but perhaps there was insufficient agreement among the EA's members for clear and strong communication to be achieved – even by a leading practitioner. Dick Fedorcio was there for just over three years. In December 1996 he moved into consultancy and in the following year became Director of Public Affairs for the Metropolitan Police, where I believe he remained until March 2012.

As the associations ploughed their separate furrows, little progress was made with helping the industry to communicate on big, 'cross-cutting' issues. We did talk, though. Philip Daubeney and I would meet for lunch or dinner from time to time. Our thinking was in harmony on a great many issues and Philip and I got on well together. Our meetings were enjoyable occasions when we could discuss issues frankly. Now and again, we agreed to work together on an issue – successfully on the question of business rates for power stations, for example. On communications, however, we went our separate ways. I felt sure that that was what my membership – representing so many smaller companies and a greater variety of businesses than EA – would have wished. But what of the journalists? They may have been pleased to get an AIEP or AEP quote in a story, but they tended not to view the industry as a series of sectors, any more than most of the customers did. I sensed this from time to time, but did not feel particularly inclined to do anything about it, beyond occasionally commenting on issues which, strictly speaking, were a little outside my remit. I certainly had no brief to think more widely and in any case, I had very little time to do that. The job was demanding and the resources were slim. That is not a retrospective grumble – I confess that I usually liked it that way and I would hazard a guess that my office colleagues did too.

On Thursday 16 April 1992, things started to become even more complicated. The Pool Executive Committee was meeting at ICI's Wilton plant, close to the huge, soon-to-be-completed power station of Teesside Power. We were being given a tour of the construction site before the meeting and I was about to make a gesture of help – literally a shoulder to lean on – to fellow Committee member, Dr Graham Thomas, the Trading Director of the ex-state generating business 'PowerGen'. A big character in every sense of the word, Graham was warm and trustworthy, experienced, intelligent and greatly respected by his staff and colleagues, not only as one of the architects of the Pool, but as an exceptional manager. On this particular day, though, he had one of his legs wrapped in a black plastic rubbish sack to protect it from the construction site mud and the weather of the north-east of England. I think he had injured it playing rugby – something from which a duller, more cautious man would quietly have retired by then.

As we shuffled towards the door of the site bus, he said, 'I wonder if we could have a chat some time? PowerGen would quite like to join AIEP.'

I think I replied 'Bloody hell'.

The Association had not been set up to accommodate PowerGen nor, indeed, any of the privatised ex-state companies. Far from it. But the chat took place and before long, I had a similar request from the larger of the two privatised generating businesses, National Power and a discussion with another hugely respected industry figure, Dr Keith Miller, who, with Graham Thomas, had also been an architect of the wholesale trading arrangements which had made the privatisation possible. Elsewhere in this book I describe in more detail how the AIEP dealt with this challenge. Here, it is sufficient to say that they came to the Association because their companies were not satisfied with the support they received from the EA and being part of an association for power generation businesses seemed to offer them a voice that the EA could not provide.

I reported the interest of PowerGen and National Power to the Chairman of the Association, Michael Spicer, and the Chairman of the AIEP Executive Committee, Neil Bryson. It was soon on the agenda of the Executive Committee.

Michael Spicer, Neil Bryson and I met Graham Thomas and Keith Miller for lunch at Shepherd's restaurant, in Marsham Street, Westminster. They understood how serious an issue their membership would be for AIEP. It was only a few years earlier that those companies had been created from the CEGB and the memory of the AIEP members was still very clear. On the other hand, their stated intention was to use AIEP to strengthen the lobbying position of the generating sector and with their dominance of that sector, their own credibility depended on the other members of the Association being able to succeed. That, of course, was attractive. But could they be believed? Some members thought their intentions were far less honourable and that they would seek to put us out of business by wrecking the Association from the inside. Others thought they would dictate policy to the Association.

The difference in scale – generating capacity – between the two giants and the other members was huge. National Power had been privatised with 29,486 megawatts of generating assets and PowerGen with 18,764 megawatts. By way of comparison, the Foster family's hydro scheme at Achnamara by Lochgilphead was measured in hundreds of kilowatts, the Summerleaze landfill gas scheme near Beaconsfield was then one megawatt, Slough Heat and Power's CHP scheme was 90 megawatts and Lakeland Power's new CCGT, opened at Roosecote in 1991, was 229 megawatts. There was already a huge difference between the largest and smallest members of the Association, but with the two ex-state generators on board, it would become enormous. It was not only the amount of generating capacity, nor the market share that mattered. There was a cultural difference between those PLCs and the small businesses that made up most of the membership. The PLCs, though released from the public sector thinking of the CEGB, had a business culture commensurate with their turnover and the number of staff they employed. 'Risk', for example, meant something different for National Power, compared with its effect on investment by a small business, where even personal property might have been at stake. Decision-making was a different process, too.

It was clear to me, from discussions with the two companies, that they were deadly serious in their intentions towards AIEP. Furthermore, if they were to be rejected by AIEP, they would try to pursue what they wanted in other ways, and that could have had adverse effects on the Association. Equally clear was that, constitutionally, the AIEP had no grounds on which to reject their application. The companies were now independent – no longer state-owned. The only rational reasons for saying 'no' were the loss of the Association's purity and the possibility that, with a more diverse membership, its messages might have to be watered down.

But what about the benefits? However successful the Association had been, it had grown on the back of enthusiasm and goodwill and very little in the way of resources. That could change, with more cash being available to finance things like research and consultancy that established trade associations take for granted, but which AIEP had usually had to manage without. Then, there was the impact on prospective members. If AIEP membership gave them the opportunity to sit at the same table as the big players, they would probably find that attractive – there was a lot to be learned, especially as the two companies had played such a big part in creating the market which had such an influence on generating companies' activities. But perhaps above all, when an enlarged AIEP membership could reach agreement, the strength and representative nature of its argument promised to be considerable. Issues with National Grid, OFFER and the distribution businesses came to mind. So did European issues, which were in the hands of the Electricity Association. With National Power and PowerGen on board, although AIEP could not match the EA for resources, it would have much more clout. At times, it would be a thorn in the EA's side.

The matter was put to the Executive Committee of AIEP, where it was debated in a grown-up way and put to a vote. The vote was 7-4 in favour of the two companies joining, but with provisos. They were that the Association's rule of 'one member, one vote' (regardless of size) must continue to apply and we should have to re-visit the structure of membership fees to ensure that the scale[37] meant that the newcomers paid a substantial sum. As the Association's President, Michael Spicer, put it: 'If we are going to lose our virginity, we may as well get a handsome sum for it.' A further proviso, inspired by Michael Spicer, was that before we made any commitment, the principle of the two companies joining

[37] Cdr George Chapman worked this out with the aid of his slide rule.

should be discussed at the very top – with their Chief Executives – to make sure they were sympathetic to the deal.

Being part of an association with National Power and PowerGen in it was not what most members of AIEP had joined for, nor what anyone had expected. There were, however, no tantrums, nor any resignations. Instead, there was a level of expectancy – that it was going to be interesting; that it might not work, but that it would probably be exciting trying to make it do so.

The meeting with the two PLC bosses took place on Thursday 11 June 1992 at the Park Lane Hotel, Piccadilly. This five-star hotel, at the time one of the largest family-owned[38] hotels in London, had become the AIEP's unofficial London headquarters. An imaginative loyalty scheme made it possible for me to stay there at a remarkably low room rate and I used the hotel and its restaurant often. It was in the hotel's restaurant that I – accompanied by Michael Spicer if the prospective member warranted the presence of the former Energy Minister – would entertain prospective members over lunch or dinner. The restaurant staff, under head waiter Vito Belmonte, knew how to look after their regulars, and although the food would never have won a Michelin star, it was very good, albeit slightly old-fashioned cuisine, where lamp work and the trolley were still taken seriously. The relationship with the hotel grew even stronger because our President would occasionally be greeted by the owner, Clive Carr, who was known to him as the cousin of one of his constituents in West Worcestershire. As Michael often reminded me, AIEP, with a tiny office in a cottage on a hillside in Cornwall, punched well above its weight.

I booked a private room at the hotel for the meeting and lunch with the Chief Executives of National Power and PowerGen, to seal the deal for their membership. I also needed a room the night before. True to form, the hotel came up with the right answer –

[38] It was sold to the Sheraton Group in 1996.

the Lord Peter Wimsey suite, overlooking Green Park, and they would throw in the overnight accommodation – in the suite – for me. Not much to complain about there.

I had prepared in advance a brief for our guests. It provided a very short history of the Association and noted that, although 'as recently as 1988/89, AIEP was publicly sceptical about the scope for new generators to compete in the privatised industry… today it is firmly associated with the wave of new stations and also associated with what is perceived as likely "over-capacity" '. A few weeks before the meeting, a headline in the *Financial Times* had read 'Electricity surplus of 60 per cent is predicted'. National Grid's Seven Year Statement had forecast that, with a surge of interest in new gas-fired power stations, more than 10,000 megawatts of coal-fired plant would be forced to close. A copy of the press cutting and the letter from me, which had been published in the *Financial Times* on 28 April 1992 was included in the brief.

Michael Spicer, Neil Bryson (Chairman of the AIEP Executive Committee) and I met John Baker, Chief Executive of National Power and Ed Wallis, Chief Executive of PowerGen. It was business-like, but also very cordial. The two big cheeses knew Michael well from the period leading up to the privatisation of the industry, when he had taken the Energy Bill through the House of Commons. That was helpful, of course. They showed respect for the authoritative and diplomatic Neil Bryson, who had invested his own money in Britain's first CCGT power station at Roosecote – the dominant status of the two big PLCs meant that they needed to see smaller companies' projects succeed – and they had clearly had encouraging reports about me.

John Baker and Ed Wallis were hugely different as individuals; their companies were branding themselves differently and their personalities were reflected in the way those businesses were run.

John Baker was an Oxford arts graduate, who had been Corporate Managing Director at the CEGB and whose background in the higher echelons of the public sector meant that he was at ease with high-level politics and government. Ed Wallis was an electrical engineer and former power station manager whose role at the CEGB included the battle with Arthur Scargill and contending with the miners' strike. Ed was also familiar with government and politics, but compared with John, may have been less tolerant of its failings.

The two companies were the great beasts of the privatised electricity supply industry, but not without their problems. They were so dominant that they knew that their future would almost certainly involve them being scaled down – not the easiest thing to manage where shareholders and business plans are concerned. But in the here and now, they had to be careful how they handled that dominance - no bullying in the playground. Usually through no fault of their own, they would find that, in the eyes of the news media, it would be hard for them ever to do anything right. National Power was huge and therefore, almost by definition, 'guilty'. PowerGen was smaller and so keen to shake off the CEGB culture and let bright ideas flourish that it was occasionally over-imaginative. Its traders' approach to trading behind 'constraints' saw it heavily criticised by the regulator, for clever ideas which, rumour had it, led Chief Executive Ed Wallis to lay down the law, after someone suggested that what had happened was no better than theft. National Power's people were not unimaginative, but its rival somehow seemed to attract more attention. That is now all history. The companies' names have changed, their ownership has changed, the market has changed, the businesses are different and the boundaries of trading behaviour are now well understood. Nevertheless, the roots of today's problem of reputation and trust can be traced back to the way the privatised industry stumbled through its early years, with too little attention to communications and image issues.

The meeting at the Park Lane Hotel drew to a conclusion in the way that was expected. The companies were ready to join and see the subscription structure changed so that they paid what, for AIEP, would be large sums for their membership. Crucially, 'One member, one vote' would continue. There was one additional issue on which there was informal agreement. All concerned recognised that there were risks attached to them joining and one such risk was that they might withdraw from membership at short notice, perhaps leaving the Association with greater commitments than its reduced funding could sustain. They, therefore, offered to commit to membership for three years. All were satisfied and for AIEP, a new era was about to begin.

By the time of the AIEP's Annual General Meeting, in November 1992, National Power and PowerGen were members. Much as this raised the standing of the AIEP, it must have proved a great irritation to the EA. With those two huge companies being members of both associations, however, it did mean that we sometimes had to tell the world that EA and AIEP (later AEP) were complementary organisations that worked together. There was a certain amount of truth in this – but without debating it at any length, we seemed to map out our own territory fairly well and we managed to co-exist reasonably peacefully, although we were, inevitably, rivals. The relationship was not always easy for the industry's observers and commentators to grasp.

One day, after the two organisations had each given oral evidence to a select committee in the House of Commons, my colleague Nicola Steen and I were relaxing with some senior people from EA over a drink in The Atrium, in Westminster. A journalist that was known to all of us approached and joined the conversation. After a brief discussion about the issues of the afternoon he said, 'By the way, I've never really understood… what's the difference between your two associations?'

I had had to answer that question many times before, but in my drained, post select committee state, stupidly I tried to think of a new way of responding. I was too slow. Nicola replied whilst I was still trying to dream up the perfect answer.

'We have more fun' she said. Although, of course, there was more to it than that, the response could not be dismissed as flippant, for the look on the face of a colleague from the EA confirmed that she was right.

Other journalists and perhaps more importantly, politicians, would soon ask far more challenging questions, questions with which the industry was ill-equipped to deal. The electricity industry was not alone in this. The privatised gas industry attracted hugely unfavourable publicity between 1994 and 1996. The gas industry may have been different in that it had been privatised as a single entity – a decision that the Conservative government regretted later – but the warning for the electricity industry was there. The revolt by the shareholders of British Gas in 1995 had led to damaging tabloid headlines about the company's Chief Executive, Cedric Brown, who was likened to a pig with its snout in the trough. In fact, publicity-seeking protestors had brought to the company's AGM a 20-stone pig to be photographed 'feeding on a trough of share options'. The year before, Mr Brown's pay increase had attracted headlines and in 1995, the Gas Consumers' Council reported a doubling of complaints against the company. The wider share ownership resulting from privatisation seemed to do very little in the way of making voters more kindly disposed towards companies which, perhaps naively, they felt that they had once 'owned' anyway, when they had been public corporations. Did the state 'owning' an industry make it particularly responsive to the public's wishes? Of course not. Arguably, PLCs are at least as vulnerable in the face of public opinion as public bodies formed by government. That does not usually mean that they are any more loved, though.

Public disenchantment began to challenge the electricity supply industry.

Electricity prices for British industry; profits of the Regional Electricity Companies; lack of sufficient competition in the Pool and allegations about cashing-in from interpretation of the rules; remuneration packages of the senior people in the industry; data and billing problems with the 'over 100kW' industrial and commercial customers; marches to support the coal industry and coal-fired power stations; marches to oppose coal-fired power stations[39]; foreign ownership of energy companies; security of supply worries; rising prices for domestic customers and finally, by 2012-2013, an apparent lack of willingness on the part of the UK's energy companies to invest in the future of their own industry, all contributed to this.

The grumbling did not take long to start. It began with the larger industrial customers. Pre-privatisation they had very attractively-priced supply contracts which allowed for them to be disconnected when the system was under serious pressure, but there appeared to be an unwritten agreement with those customers that such disconnections would not actually occur. In the new world, from the very beginning of the liberalised market, the biggest users – those with over 1 megawatt of demand – were the first of the customers to have the right to choose the most competitive supplier, which included the opportunity to contract directly with the generating companies. With growing competitive pressure putting the squeeze on the UK's manufacturing and process

---

[39] The marches to oppose coal came much later and I recall a BBC regional journalist telling me that, in a private capacity, he had been in both the 'pro' and 'anti' marches.

industries, questions were being asked about prices paid by those big companies. More precisely, comparisons were made with the prices paid by their competitors in other parts of Europe, where competition and choice did not exist, but government-sponsored deals certainly did. Until very recently, the UK's major energy users had been accustomed to agreeing their tariffs in a similar way.

Their trade body, the Energy Intensive Users' Group, was led by its experienced and statesman-like Chief Executive, Ian Blakey. But it was the EIUG's Economic Adviser, Lisa Waters, who had begun her working life as an Energy Policy Adviser at the Confederation of British Industry (CBI), who became a stone in the shoe of the electricity supply industry and the government. Highly personable and very quick-thinking, Lisa often exhibited on public platforms more insight and confidence than the companies she represented. Her views, however, were a gift to journalists, who must have thought that the rich seam of stories emerging from the electricity industry and its customers was inexhaustible. The argument at that time was simple – electricity for these vital industries was overpriced because there was too little competition in electricity production and the trading arrangements (the Electricity Pool) did nothing to make the situation any better. There was undoubtedly too little competition, but the extent, if any, to which electricity was 'overpriced' was highly debatable and there were occasional studies into the subject. Later, they would show that the two price-setting companies had been careful not to set wholesale prices too high, which would have compounded their problems. Lisa herself was well capable of producing a thesis on pricing and she could debate her case in detail when required, but she knew when not to over-complicate things, preferring at crucial times to use the headlines from her analysis far more effectively. I recall chairing a conference when she was a speaker and made her latest 'overpricing' claim, which would quickly find its way into the press. The conference delegates must have seen my jaw drop when Lisa made her latest pronouncement about the alleged excesses of the generating companies. Jaws were also dropping in the Association's membership. My members were becoming increasingly disconcerted by the headlines and suggested that we should hit back with at least as much imagination as Lisa was using. There would have been little mileage in that approach. Even without search engines, social media and wiki-whatever, the alleged overpricing was already accepted wisdom. Our response came through the occasional worthy fact sheet and talking up the industry 'positives'. Alas, such things do not make headlines and restoring reputation and trust is a very slow and painstaking business.

It may have surprised or even disappointed some of our members, but Lisa and I managed to disagree with each other without engaging in any personal animosity. In 2000, my wife Judith and I were delighted to be guests at her marriage to Kyran Hanks. Today, we meet only rarely, but we remain friends.

Important though the EIUG was, the aggrieved companies, individually, were well capable of getting their case into the news. Probably the most vociferous was ICI. The company had its own generating station at Wilton, on Teesside, providing heat and power to its chemicals plant and on issues affecting small generators and combined heat and power schemes, ICI collaborated willingly with the AIEP. It did so very successfully on the question of on-site generation in the Pool, for example. It was, however, unwilling to become a member of the Association. For me, that was frustrating, but definitely not the end of the world. Our job was to secure the right outcomes. If, from time to time, that was achieved through collaboration with other businesses or organisations, it was the result that mattered most.

I am not sure that ICI ever stated exactly why it did not want to sign up. The decidedly mixed range of interests that AIEP represented may not have appealed to it. Probably much more important, however, was the fact that, although it had some power generation of its own, with production facilities for chemicals across the UK, it was a net buyer of electricity and it saw itself as being essentially on the opposite side of the table from AIEP members. The large users' claims about energy prices were often strident and in the case of ICI, they were sometimes made with reference to its chlorine plant at Runcorn, in Cheshire. With the de-merger of parts of ICI's business, that plant eventually came under different ownership. Before and after, however, it was regularly cited in the press as being on the verge of closure because of the level of its energy bills, compared with those of competitors elsewhere in Europe. It did seem to me to be on the verge of closure for rather a long time, though. Experienced people in the electricity supply industry were suspicious of ICI's statements and motives. It is not unknown for companies that are facing a decision about closing an old plant, or, switching their operations to a more efficient site, to deflect blame for the consequences to a third party, and what better third party than an energy industry that was already under fire from the news media and politicians? ICI sold the plant to Ineos Chlor, which announced in 2003 that the facility was to be modernised.

The public grumblings of the electricity industry's largest customers were not the only reason for the headlines which ground down relentlessly the industry's reputation and destroyed the trust of customers, opinion formers and policy makers. There were many other issues, and those stories would probably fill a book.

There was some settling in to be done when PowerGen and National Power joined the AIEP. For a long time, some of the Association's smaller members were uncomfortable with the notion that the giants of the industry would be sitting at the Association's table. They probably wished that it had never happened. It was easier, however, for those who were actually at the table – the smaller players on the Executive Committee and later the Board of Directors – to make the adjustment. It may have been less difficult for those who were small players in electricity, but whose businesses were subsidiaries of much larger PLCs. They understood big company culture. Slough Heat and Power, for example, was a subsidiary of Slough Estates, a PLC that had grown from a venture in the 1920s to become a FTSE 100 listed company. Not only that, but the company's Chairman, Sir Nigel Mobbs, was an important figure in the Conservative Party and sufficiently well connected to be able to pick up the phone and speak to the Prime Minister. Slough Heat and Power's contribution to AIEP discussions was always robust. In 1987, the MD, Fergus Wiggin had been prominent among the founders of the Association and his successor, Philip Jackson, who was prepared, at least metaphorically, to bang the table, became Chairman of the Board of the Association in 1994. Philip and Fergus also employed bright people, such as Philip Russell (formerly of Orchard Partners), who understood the world of electricity supply well beyond the 35 miles of network that his employer ran on the Slough Trading Estate and who could be found contributing on behalf of his company to the work of key committees of the Association.

There were other examples of small players in the Association being not quite what they seemed. For example, few would have known that behind the renewable energy company that Jeremy Sainsbury, from Scotland, represented so enthusiastically and effectively was shipping magnate Fred Olsen. Jeremy began his work with renewable energy managing the hydro-electric scheme at Forrest Estate, then, became involved in renewables more widely, including successful wind power schemes. At the AEP Board, he was not only a passionate advocate of renewables and Scottish interests, but someone who could also see the bigger picture, which helped him to command the respect of some of the bigger players.

I was once responsible for putting Jeremy on a live television programme. Through no fault of his, it did not go as well as I had expected. One Friday, having returned to Cornwall the night before from a meeting in Scotland, I took a call from Tyne-Tees Television asking if I would appear on a popular children's television programme in Newcastle-upon-Tyne on Saturday morning, to talk about renewable energy – a live and apparently rather lively two-hour show which was networked. I could not face the rapid turn-round and the journey north that would have been required, so I promised to find them someone else, but not without first checking the format. It all sounded straightforward. The guest from the Association would meet Jenny, Lewis and Nobby and answer a few simple questions. It would be fun. No trick questions. Nothing complicated. I rang Jeremy, gave him the background and he kindly agreed to step in. When I watched the programme, however, I was horrified to discover that 'Nobby' was, in fact, a talking sheep, who tried in various ways to embarrass the guest and generally to steal the show. Afterwards, Jeremy swore never to forgive me. Fortunately, he did not mean it. He soon did forgive me and I wondered whether meeting Jenny Powell had more than made up for him being savaged mentally and physically on national television by that rather boisterous 'sheep'.

Jeremy's predecessor as Chairman of the Association's Scottish Committee was Patrick Gordon-Duff-Pennington, who not only had a small hydro-electric scheme at Ardverikie but was very well connected, both in Scotland and in Westminster. When the Scottish MP Brian Wilson was Energy Minister and he was giving a speech at the reception before the AEP's Annual Lunch in 2002, Patrick chipped in with a jocular remark. Brian Wilson replied 'I see that we have the landed gentry represented here today'. It was all in good fun. The two had very different backgrounds, but respected each other. Patrick was a hard-working, public spirited and warm hearted man, who understood politics, but seemed to have little time for party politics. He gave a lot of his time to hill farming interests and chaired the Deer Commission for Scotland, but he was also keenly involved in the Industry and Parliament Trust, which he explained as follows '...a non-party charity dedicated to education of Parliamentarians too often ignorant of businesses, large and small, for whom they legislated, which in their turn were equally ignorant of the Parliamentary process.' In 2004, I was privileged to be invited to the launch of his memoir 'Those Blue Remembered Hills'[40] and was deeply touched to see that he had included in it a generous reference to Judith and me. He also wrote, of himself, 'I went back to Muncaster, and tried not to return to the SLF office. There's nothing worse than old has-beens revisiting the site of their former glory, wasting everybody's time, drinking the office coffee and giving unwanted advice.' He was right about that and these days I try to keep away from my former office.

I had an opening remark which I used when talking to new members of staff at AEP about the electricity supply issues in Scotland – 'Scotland is different'. It was, and still is. Not only was competition in electricity supply introduced more slowly in Scotland, but faced with a perceived threat from the English, or, an apparent injustice, different and even competing interests in Scotland were prepared readily to unite as a common defence force. I recall the shock that PowerGen felt from the opposition when the company wanted to construct a gas-fired power station at Gartcosh, near Glasgow. It was never built. I write as someone

[40] Those Blue Remembered Hills. Patrick Gordon-Duff-Pennington. The Memoir Club. 1994. ISBN 1-84104-054-1.

whose father's parents were Scottish. Such links seem to mean rather less today.

The range of interests in the Association was remarkable. Gas-fired generation came to have enormous importance. But the members not only embraced technologies such as combined heat and power (CHP), wave power, small-scale hydro-electric power and primitive (by today's standards) wind power, but also highly innovative waste-to-energy projects. I went to the official opening of the Elm Energy used-tyre-burning project in Wolverhampton and had great respect for Anne Evans from Connecticut, who served on the AIEP Executive Committee and whose drive and determination made that project possible. If you meet her, ask her about the challenge that she faced in persuading a bank from the far East to help fund a project that looked attractive, but suffered from the 'disadvantage' of being led by… a woman.

Rupert Fraser and his father Simon ran Fibrowatt, which developed the technology of burning chicken litter to run small power stations. They invited me to be the guest of honour at the ground-breaking ceremony for their Thetford plant, where, with the help of local schoolchildren, I buried a time capsule. Having succeeded in the UK, they took their innovative biomass technology to the United States.

What the traditional AIEP members faced across the table in the 'new' AIEP were not corporate monsters, but individual people. No instructions about how to 'get on with each other' were ever issued to any of the players, large or small. Although this was no love-in and some of the tensions between large and small would never be dispelled, respect grew. The Association chairmen of the time carried huge responsibility and Neil Bryson's term of office was vitally important. So successful was he that he was asked to serve for a third year, when the convention had been that the Chairman served a two-year term. Fortunately, he agreed.

There were some fundamentals that bound the members. They all had an interest in getting a decent price for the electricity they produced; they all shared concerns about the networks, how much it cost to connect to them and use them, about costs generally and about the effectiveness of the trading arrangements. Without seeking explicitly to do so, they also learned from each other. The small businesses learnt more about the Pool, for example, although anything wrong with it would always have been deemed to have been the fault of the big players, who had created it. The big players will have noticed that their micro-sized counterparts had different ways of doing things – usually somewhat quicker ways. They would also have noticed the importance to many of them of bringing renewable energy on to the system and of getting more recompense for the services a small plant could provide when it was connected to a local distribution system. That issue, and more importantly, the government's desire to have much more renewable energy and more combined heat and power plant located on the distribution systems, gradually raised concern among the biggest companies, which prompted a discussion between the CEO of a major generating company and me and in the months that followed, led to some important policy work on the role of generation 'embedded' in the distribution system and a significant report being published by the Association and submitted to government.

We produced many other reports, of course, which were helpful to the members; typically on renewable energy issues – usually helped by *Green Land Reclamation* – and on market issues, with the help of *Ilex*. These were often financed partly by government, through its 'Energy Technology Support Unit' (ETSU) – a financing arrangement that, with the passage of time, now looks rather odd.

There were disagreements and of course, there were meant to be. Over time, it was not the smallest players who were apt to cross swords with the giants. The trickiest arguments were likely to be between the big players and the growing ranks in the middle, who were building new gas-fired power stations. Later, the greatest challenges were in trying to get agreement between the six largest companies. The world likes to see them as virtually identical. They are not.

It was never perfect, but at times, it was fascinating. There was some collateral damage. Some companies left the Association to throw in their lot with sector-specific renewable energy associations, where they would eventually find themselves, again, sitting down with the big players – with renewable energy businesses set up to take advantage of the renewables support schemes. The loss of some of the members would have happened, anyway – membership 'churn'. But somehow it all worked. When asked how it worked, I would refer to an unwritten rule that I had made up, namely that 'The elephants should try not to tread on the mice and the mice should resist the temptation to bite the elephants when they were passing by.' There was more to it than that, of course. It all depended on people, and this was never clearer to me than the day when I reported to a saddened Board of Directors the untimely death of Cdr George Chapman, who, as the Honorary Secretary of the National Association of Water Power Users and the builder, owner and operator of a small hydro-electric scheme in his Devon garden had been, in 1987, one of the first members. At that Board meeting, Graham Thomas of PowerGen said of George Chapman 'He was a great guy'. The minutes of Association Board meetings were invariably formal and businesslike, but on this occasion, Graham's comments went into the minutes, verbatim.

By the time National Power and PowerGen joined AIEP, my wife and I had just finished building a new house on land which we had purchased behind Christmas Cottage at Herodsfoot. Compared with our two-bedroomed terraced cottage, this was a much bigger house, with an even better view over the valley of the West Looe River. It needed to be quite big to take advantage of a site of almost one and a half acres, and we had clear ideas about how to make use of the space. There was an annexe for Judith's recently-widowed mother, who came to live with us, and a big office to cope with the growing work of AIEP. We were especially looking forward to having plenty of office space as the six-foot-square office at Christmas Cottage had become an uncomfortable constraint and some equipment was spilling over to other parts of what was a small but charming property. If friends came to supper, the first task, that afternoon, was to move the rather hefty photocopier off the kitchen table.

A large part of the planning of the new house worked out well. One particularly important feature – the office – was certainly beneficial, but not for very long. National Power and PowerGen thought, quite reasonably, that the Association should have an office in London. I knew their suggestion was sensible, but I could see that the implications would be painful. Just as we were moving into a large, new house, with a great deal of work still to be done and my elderly mother-in-law to be settled in to an annexe and cared for, I found myself announcing that I would have to move to London for most of the working week. Most weeks I managed to get home on Thursday evening, but occasionally, that was impossible. I am well aware that far worse things than that can disrupt the lives of families, but it was, nonetheless, a difficult time.

With the help of Western Industrial Finance, a member of AIEP, we took up a lease on part of their offices at First Floor, 41

Whitehall. The location was excellent and the address certainly sounded good. It was at the Trafalgar Square end of Whitehall, above a café. For a first London office, it was better than most. But a mouse would occasionally sit on the photocopier and gaze at the staff, and one Monday morning we came in to find that we had been burgled. The burglars found nothing that they might have valued and for reasons that I will never understand, they left some cash for us on the counter of the reception area. I cannot say that we were eternally grateful for the donation, as it would barely have paid for a snack in the business downstairs. We thought they had also photocopied parts of themselves – as I believe some modern intruders like to do. Despite the presence of 'prints' that were more extensive than those at most scenes of crime, I do not think the case attracted much interest from the Metropolitan Police. The incident may well have traumatised the resident mouse, though.

For a week or two, I began my AIEP working life at 41 Whitehall on my own. I soon found myself a 'temp' who told me that she was related to Peter Tatchell[41] and also that her name was listed in the credits on 'Watership Down' and that she was 'between jobs' in the film industry. Priscilla and I worked well together for a few weeks, but my London home at this time was whichever Forte hotel could offer the best DB&B package deal for three nights, so I lived out of a suitcase and usually went home on Thursday evening. But temporary accommodation and a temp to help in the office clearly had to be just that… temporary.

Finding a personal assistant was more urgent than finding accommodation that would serve me better than a hotel room, so I rang Susan Hamilton, who had been a friend of Judith's at school. Susan ran the employment agency which bears her name to this day and one of her managers sent a few people to be interviewed. Neil Bryson, who was then the Executive Committee Chairman,

[41] Peter Tatchell – a political campaigner, probably best known for his work as a gay rights activist

and I were unanimous that I should sign up Mrs S A Morris[42] ('Sam'). Sam's career background looked first-class, but very unluckily, she had been made redundant and was delighted to get the job. It was the beginning of a highly successful working relationship, which was to last for 14 years. More than that, Sam was someone the members would get to know and rely on for that time, too.

Sam had not been in the job very long before we were discussing recruitment of some support staff. We had computers – my contract with the Association required me to provide mine – but they were used mostly for word-processing. I had email, but as most of the Association's contacts did not, this was not something that played much of a part in office life. So there was, of course, a lot of 'clerical' work, printing, copying and collating of documents, labelling, stuffing and stamping envelopes and reliance on the Royal Mail. Plenty of phone calls, too.

Sam found two assistants from a government training scheme for young people, and she chose well. Sarah Beck and Peter Williams were bright, personable, glad to have a job and keen to learn, which they did rapidly. Eventually, they both went on to far better things. I lost touch with Peter, who I believe progressed in IT, but I remember Sarah moving to Morgan Stanley with the very best wishes of everyone who had worked with her at AIEP.

It was essential that we should be able to cope first with the basics at the Whitehall office, but in 1994 I was pressed by the two largest members to indicate when I was going to find someone to help with the policy work that AIEP was now immersed in. I needed that prompting.

In the spring of 1994, Neil Bryson and I conducted interviews for a job I termed 'Assistant – Research and Information', but in an organisation as small as AIEP, I knew that any successful

[42] She later re-married and became 'Sam' Inns.

candidate who could offer more than that would be encouraged to do so. We got exactly that kind of person. In May 1994, Nicola Steen, who previously had been working at the Royal Institute of International Affairs at Chatham House, started work at AIEP. She was a great asset to the Association and contributed hugely to its success. Nicola would prove to have a lot of influence on the Association in her seven years as a key member of the team. Intellectually strong, used to keeping abreast of vast amounts of information and researching issues in depth, she brought more to the Association than I had any right to expect from one person. But if she were to go down in the Association's history for one thing, it would be her influence on its policy towards the global warming issue. Nicola was to stay for seven years and it was apt that when she left, it was to join CO2e.com, a company that was involved in the trading of carbon emissions. I see her only rarely now, but when we last spoke, she was leading a scheme to provide people in the third world with clean cooking stoves[43] – a project that had grown from the climate change mitigation agenda, but which also offered huge health benefits to those who would no longer have to cook and live in smoke-filled conditions.

For a few months, I had been struggling to resolve the question of where to live in London. The answer seemed likely to be in a rented flat, although I considered buying one. That, however, would have required me to get a mortgage and finding a property at the right price would probably have meant that I would have to live much farther from the office than I thought was desirable. At the time, although we had moved in to the newly-built house at Herodsfoot, we still owned Christmas Cottage and were letting it. Completing the construction of the new property, however, had required us to take out a small mortgage and I would have had to persuade a bank to lend much more, against an income which came

[43] Coincidentally, when I last heard from Rachel Hunter, who was the AEP's Communications Executive (2009-2012), she was also working on such a project, but through a different organisation.

from my company, *South West One Ltd*, with which AIEP had placed a consultancy contract. It all looked somewhat challenging and I had no intention of being cavalier about it. Comparatively recently, before we left Christmas Cottage, I had witnessed the value of that little property rise in a very comforting way, only for a property crash to see it lose about 40 per cent of its peak value in the space of about a year. Having climbed to a certain height on the ladder, I did not want to contemplate slipping back if there were to be a repeat of the dip in the property market.

I began looking at rented flats. I remember being attracted by an advertisement to view a studio flat in Kensington. The apartment block was very smart and the location was appealing, but the studio was barely what it purported to be. At first, I could not see where a bed would go, but that was clarified before I could ask. With a sweeping movement of her hand, the agent pulled down the bed from its recess. Very clever. But the foot of the bed was perilously close to the shelf where the television rested. 'So, where do I sit if I want to watch TV?' I asked. 'Er… on the foot of the bed' came the reply.

There were others to see. Nothing appealed, least of all the ones that were too grubby to contemplate living in. But eventually, I fell on my feet. I saw an advertisement in the *Evening Standard* for a one-bedroomed, rented flat in Pimlico. I responded immediately and found to my astonishment that it was at Dolphin Square. 'Astonishment' because Dolphin Square was the home of Peers, MPs and one or two celebrities and more importantly than that, it was known to be hard to get into – the landlord for this 1930s block of about 1,100 flats was, at that time, Westminster City Council, but the management was delegated to a trust, which was reputed to be very fussy about who lived there. Employment in central London was one prerequisite, the others were the subject of speculation. I was often asked 'How on earth did you get in there?' But it was almost perfect for me. The office was half an hour away on foot and there was the Victoria Line from Pimlico for wet days. There were a few shops, a launderette and a restaurant and also a leisure centre, with a magnificent 60-foot swimming pool, which I often used when it opened at 7 am. Despite its size, the apartment complex was very quiet and secure and it was the sort of place where people said a polite 'Good morning' when one passed them in the corridor.

Judith grew to like it there, too. Having first arranged for her mother to be looked after at home in Cornwall – a far from trivial matter – she would occasionally come and stay for a day or two and with Dolphin Square as her base, enjoy the usual attractions of London. I was to be a tenant at Dolphin Square for 19 years.

As for 41 Whitehall, we stayed there perfectly happily until 1998 when, needing more space and having viewed a range of properties, we were attracted to premises offered to us by a member company, BNFL Magnox. They were vacating the first floor at 17 Waterloo Place SW1 – period offices in a listed building little more than five minutes' walk from our Whitehall office. The offices were ideally located and they looked just right. Getting a date to move in proved a challenge, because the basement was bristling with the company's communications equipment and getting it out and relocated seemed to be riddled with problems. We renewed our lease in Whitehall in order to give our new landlords time to get their affairs sorted out and finally found ourselves across the table from the BNFL Magnox property managers, agreeing the finer details. We comprised a team of two. I was accompanied by Graham Thomas, the Chairman of the Association's Board of Directors. Graham was very good to have at one's side in a negotiation and especially so, that day.

Among the issues to be discussed was the furniture. I wanted to buy the BNFL Magnox furniture, as it had been purchased only a few years earlier, specifically for those offices - a perfect fit, in terms of quantity, quality, size and style. The BNFL Magnox team had already pointed out that they had spent some £40,000 to £50,000 on this and had listed it in some detail in the particulars. In my budget, I had allowed a maximum of £10,000 for furniture, but Graham, who, in his spare time, had a keen interest in antiques, told them authoritatively that it was completely worthless. 'You would have to pay to get it taken away' he said. I think I chose to look out of the window at that point, but when they recovered from the shock, it was agreed that the Association would acquire the furniture for £100.

The offices had been owned by part of the Harrods business and in 1999 I ended up in the room which, before BNFL Magnox had moved in, had apparently been occupied by the late Dodi Fayed. But there was more to 17 Waterloo Place than a decent office for the Chief Executive. It had a very presentable board room, which meant that members could meet at the Association's headquarters, instead of in member company offices or in hotel meeting rooms – hugely important for the sense of belonging that would help the trade association function well.

Staffwise, we grew a little more at Waterloo Place. One reason for that was the growing influence of gas on the electricity market and the likely arbitrage between gas and electricity. It was Philip Jackson who pressed, quite properly, for that to be addressed. An 'Electricity and Gas' committee was set up, run by Nicola Steen and advised initially by Ilex Associates. Later, we recruited a former employee of National Power, Julie Cox, to advise on gas issues, at which she excelled. Nicola Steen's work grew and she recruited Danielle Lane as an assistant. It was a good move. In what I think was her first full-time job, Danielle thrived and before long, the inevitable happened; she moved on, first to Centrica, then to the Crown Estate and later to Dong Energy as the UK Head of Public Affairs. Sarah Merrick was appointed to replace Danielle. She thrived, too. Sarah became the Association's Head of Renewable Energy, then moved on to the wind power company, RES and later to head up the UK public affairs work of Vestas. That career route was a good one for talented young people at the Association.

Alastair Tolley joined us to help the staff that developed policy, then became Head of Renewable Energy before moving to Eggborough Power to do their public affairs work. Laura Schmidt moved from a similar role developing policy to become our Communications Executive, which provided a stepping stone to a communications job at the European Commission. After we had left Waterloo Place, Rachel Hunter succeeded her with style, before moving on to a bank and then to a company promoting healthier and environmentally-friendly cooking facilities in the third world. Brendan Murphy joined us from EDF Energy's retail business to support the senior staff, before moving on to consultancy. Unfortunately, in an organisation as small as the Association, however talented the individual members of staff, it was often hard to offer them the internal career moves that they deserved, so, from time to time, departures were inevitable. It was a great credit to the more experienced people – among them, at various times, Julie Cox, Gwyn Dolben, Steve Johnson, Andy Limbrick, Nicola Steen, Malcolm Taylor and Barbara Vest – who advised and encouraged the younger members of the team.

It was at Waterloo Place, one morning in May 2007, that my Personal Assistant, Su-Yen, having brought in the day's post, handed me an unopened letter from 10 Downing Street – a letter which was so emphatically marked 'confidential' that I assumed immediately that it was about security issues relating to the industry and I put it aside to read when we had finished dealing with the more routine things. When Su-Yen had left the room, I opened it and discovered that it was not what I had thought it to be. I found to my astonishment that No 10 had recommended to the Queen that I should be appointed OBE. This had to remain in confidence until the Queen's Birthday Honours List was announced on 16 June 2007.

On 18 October 2007, with Su-Yen, my previous PA, Sam Inns and my wife Judith as guests, at Buckingham Palace, I received the OBE from Her Majesty the Queen 'for services to the power generation industry'. It was a wonderful occasion, even though, looking back, I was in something akin to a trance when the moment came to meet the Queen and I am ashamed to say that, afterwards, I could not recall fully our very brief conversation. I was the fortunate recipient of the honour, but it would not have come about, of course, without the dedication and commitment of the many wonderful people who had worked for, or, supported and encouraged the Association in the 20 years that it had been in existence. I shall always be deeply grateful to them all.

In September 2008, the Association moved again – 147 paces (mine) up Lower Regent Street, to Charles House, where we leased a modern office with much more meeting space. Later, this would become the home of Energy UK, although AEP had occupied only the basement and Energy UK would need that and the top floor of the building.

Before it left Whitehall, however, a constitutional change had faced the Association. The title 'Association of Independent Electricity Producers' had become established and it was good enough to get us the access and recognition we wanted. But from time to time, I was asked what the Association's name signified. It may have been clear enough to us, but apparently not to the rest of the world. This suddenly became an issue. Early one morning, I was in BBC Radio Four's waiting area for the *Today* programme at Broadcasting House, sipping the kind of coffee that was welcome at the time, but would not be acceptable in our high streets today, when the programme's famous host, John Humphrys, appeared. Before returning to the adjacent studio, he stopped for a brief chat, to let me know how he was going to start the interview with me. I was grateful. That kind of guidance always helps, because the interviewee can begin to think about the response and settle in to the discussion more confidently. On air, in the studio, however, it did not go quite as planned. The first question from John Humphrys was not what I had been expecting. Instead, he asked 'What do you mean by *independent* electricity producers?' 'Media training' for interviewees tells us not necessarily to answer the question, but to focus on the message that we want to convey. That morning, however, I gave a straight answer, which led to another question about AIEP and the outcome was that a substantial part of the interview was given over to a discussion about the Association, rather than the topic that had prompted the BBC to ask me to take part in the programme.

Later, I discussed the matter with our Chairman, Philip Jackson, and I suggested that it might be time to drop from the Association's name the word 'Independent'. After all, there was no longer a state industry from which to be independent. The Board agreed and on 1 July 1995, the Association became the Association of Electricity Producers. We had already changed our legal status to that of a company limited by guarantee.

When the Association publicised its change of name, we

explained that 'Independent' was now confusing and we took the opportunity to circulate a reminder of what we were pursuing. It read:

AEP argues for:

- Better awareness of the competitiveness and success of the new industry.
- Fuel and technology choice to continue to be market-driven.
- An end to regulatory fixes in the generating sector (e.g. the pool price cap) which damage investors' confidence.
- Realistic prices for producers (sufficient to sustain new investment, when needed, including that to meet environmental standards).
- Effective choice of supplier for domestic and small business customers in 1998.
- Competitive solutions to the industry's trading problems.
- Better opportunities for locally-based generation.
- Improvement of NFFO arrangements for renewable energy technologies.
- Implementation of Europe's single market in electricity – this means enabling competitive British electricity businesses to secure worthwhile access to our European trading partners' markets.

That final bullet point was somewhat naïve. The British market was very accessible. So much so that, on those occasions when it was suggested to me that the UK was not a 'good European', I would counter that suggestion by pointing out how open our market was. EdF (France), E.ON (Germany), Iberdrola (Spain), and RWE

(Germany) would buy major British energy businesses and have a huge influence on the industry. British companies did not make their mark across the Channel, however – other markets proved to be less accessible than had been hoped.

CHAPTER SEVEN

PLENTY TO DO AND A DISTRACTION OR TWO

Even in a liberalised market, there was no shortage of issues for this small but growing association to address in its new life in London SW1. In the first few years, they could be summarised as:

■ Keeping an eye on the way the trading arrangements in the wholesale electricity market (the Pool) were working, responding to changes and sometimes proposing them.

■ Trying to make sure that the conditions and the charges imposed on generating businesses by the network monopolies – for connection to and use of the system – were reasonable.

■ Pressing for changes to the government's support scheme for renewable energy (in the early 1990s, that was the 'Non-Fossil Fuel Obligation' – NFFO) to make it more attractive for members to develop renewable energy schemes and proposing entirely new support arrangements for the longer term and trying (successfully) to secure comparable terms for renewable energy schemes in Scotland, where, initially, there had been administered wholesale prices, rather than a competitive market.

■ Considering and agreeing ways of addressing the agenda for the newly-emerging issue of global warming.

- Responding on behalf of the membership to consultations from government departments and regulators.

- Responding in the news media to criticism of the electricity generating industry.

This was a substantial agenda for an office comprising, in the first few years, a Chief Executive, a Personal Assistant, a Research and Information Assistant and two junior office staff.

Interestingly, in one form or another, all of these issues remained on the Association's agenda throughout its life. The Pool was replaced by new trading arrangements and the NFFO by the Renewables Obligation, later supplemented by a Feed-In Tariff for smaller-scale schemes; the global warming issues came to dominate political thinking about the industry and the consultations that demanded a response became a virtual torrent. In the midst of all this, criticism of electricity generation and supply (occasionally, the networks, too) grew incessantly.

Renewable energy

The early support for renewable energy, the 'NFFO', was welcomed by the AIEP, despite the Association's attachment to a technology-neutral, competitive market. NFFO, after all, was a modest intervention, the success of which would not make a huge impact on the competitive market, nor on the system generally. Moreover, through a tendering process, it at least made the beneficiaries conscious of the need to develop technology that had some prospect of becoming competitive, and more than mere R&D funding could, it acquainted developers with the electricity market. It was, however, bureaucratically cumbersome and hard for many developers to live with, because of the intermittent timing of the tendering rounds. There were occasions when AIEP and other associations had to tell the government that with no announcement of a further round of bidding, renewable energy businesses were finding it hard to keep their staff employed and might not be able to wait much longer for a tendering opportunity to be announced. I was never convinced that the politicians and civil servants had any real understanding of business stresses like that.

NFFO also had a limited shelf-life, principally because it put a legal obligation on 'Public Electricity Suppliers' (PES) to contract for the power, the additional cost of which – i.e. the amount exceeding the wholesale market price for electricity – was funded by the 'Fossil Fuel Levy' paid by suppliers of electricity from non-renewable sources. The problem with the PES being defined in the legislation was that they were due to be abolished in 1998[44], when customer choice and competition among electricity retailers was expected to be introduced. AIEP was well aware of the significance of that and began work, led by Nicola Steen and the Association's consultants *Green Land Reclamation*, where Andy Limbrick – whose highly professional input on environmental issues would later prove so important to the Association – took the lead, to bring forward thinking about how it might be replaced. Having published a renewable energy policy review in 1995, two years later, we published *Renewable Energy: building on success[45]*, which mooted a 'percentage obligation' – a measure well in tune with a competitive market, in that the obligation would be for the purchase of renewable energy regardless of technology; the suppliers upon whom the obligation fell would want to contract with the cheapest producers first and if there was insufficient renewable energy production available, the price would rise and vice versa. As AIEP was shaping up its ideas on this, Nicola Steen tested reaction to it

---

[44] In fact, the many challenges associated with retail competition meant that its introduction was delayed until 1999.
[45] RenewableEnergy – Building on Success. Association of Electricity Producers. 1997. ISBN: 1 900395 06 1

at regular meetings of a round table of renewable energy interests (an informal group, not part of AIEP) and was, at times, disappointed with their reaction. They did not like the sound of anything quite as market-orientated and argued that in the absence of known, government-supported prices, renewable energy projects would be 'unbankable'. Not only that, but the proposed approach would favour 'near-market' technologies and offer little to those that might well be promising, but still required more research and development. The AIEP's response to the latter point was that if our policy-makers wanted to support less-developed technologies of that kind, they should do it through a separate, more conventional subsidy mechanism.

Despite the misgivings of the renewable energy sector, the government appeared to like the look of the 'percentage obligation' and in 2002, it was at the heart of the Renewables Obligation[46], the legislation that eventually replaced NFFO. That was a strong signal that the market continued to matter to the government. In 2006, however, the government announced its intention to reform the Obligation. 'Banding' was introduced in 2009 to provide different levels of support to different technologies depending on how well-developed they were. Depending on one's point of view, this was either a political loss of faith in the market approach generally, or, a recognition that such an approach would not provide sufficient incentive to bring forward the huge investment required to meet the demanding and binding renewable energy target for 2020, imposed by the EU Renewable Energy Directive, proposed in 2008 and confirmed in 2009. We often hear of the UK government's aspirations for renewable energy, but rarely (from Westminster) that the target for 2020 is a European one which is legally binding upon the UK.

---

[46] Renewables Obligation (RO). The RO required licensed UK electricity suppliers to source from eligible renewable sources a specified proportion of the electricity they provide to customers. The proportion (known as the 'obligation') was set each year and increased annually to provide 'headroom' to encourage further production.

'Embedded' generation

The value, or otherwise, of small-scale electricity production that was connected to a local distribution system, rather than the national transmission system, was an issue that was hard to resolve. It mixed engineering problems, commercial considerations, emerging energy policy and when debated, it exposed vested interests which were difficult to contend with. When a new member of staff joined the Association and found themselves facing up to some of the policy challenges, I would usually say, at some point 'Remember, nothing in this business is "technical" – it is all commercial.' The advice was deliberately exaggerated and it would probably offend electrical engineers, but there is more than a grain of truth in it. For example, if a network owner specifies that a connection to the network has to be in a particular place, or to a particular standard, it is not entirely disinterested. It has its own commercial interests in mind as much as any other. In that respect, National Grid and the Scottish network owners are no different from the distribution companies in England and Wales.

The integrated electricity system in Britain had been developed so that most power production was connected to the high-voltage transmission network – in road transport terms, roughly equivalent to the motorway network – and conveyed to the 'A and B roads' on the lower voltage networks of the various regions, where most industrial, commercial and domestic customers were connected. This was an unashamedly centralised approach, with power flowing from the centre 'outwards' to where it was consumed. In geographical terms, of course, power flowed roughly north-south, because most production was in the north and most demand in the south, but the principle of production being centralised remained.

In National Grid's management of the transmission network

and at the local level, the distribution companies' management of their networks, customers have much to be thankful for. It does not always look that way, however, from the point of view of the prospective producers of electricity – especially the smaller ones – and the situation after privatisation was not encouraging. Some of the distribution companies were far from ready to help smaller-scale producers to connect to the system and even when they were, the charges could seem penal. Worse, in some ways, was that it seemed to be up to the producer to choose a suitable point for connecting to the distribution system, and whether or not to allow the connection was in the hands of the system owners. Some AIEP members would come to the Association to complain that a distribution company had said no to their proposal and had invited them to rethink it, but without suggesting where on their network the connection there might be a better opportunity. This seemed starkly at odds with the network owners' approach to the location of new demand. The atmosphere in some of these discussions was said to be poisonous, and even more toxic when some of the regional companies had not only distribution and retail interests but generation businesses of their own; more than once I received complaints about 'PES' behaviour, to the effect that 'These people are not business-like'. A change of culture would not happen overnight.

Even when the engineering details of a connection were agreed, the commercial arrangements could prove to be a show-stopper. Some networks wanted their entire costs (connection and perhaps system reinforcement) paid for in a lump sum. Others were prepared to spread the cost over a period of time. The commercial issues did not stop there, of course. If a project developer stumped up millions to pay for connection of a project and reinforcement of the distribution system, should a later proposal for a connection in that area be able to take advantage of the reinforced system and in effect, free ride on the first company's payment?

At every opportunity, the Association made the case for locally-connected electricity generation to get a fair deal from connection arrangements and to be rewarded for the benefits that it provided – not least that power available locally for customers should not incur charges for using the transmission system. National Grid was not always comfortable with this and it would point out that the PES networks were in no sense electricity 'islands' and that they depended not just on the power they imported from the transmission system but on the stability they offered nationwide. National Grid seemed to keep a close eye on this 'embedded' generation and from time to time would argue that, with its responsibility for managing the system and keeping it stable, it needed to have some degree of control over such plant. We always countered that this was unreasonable and that without justification, National Grid was looking to extend its sphere of influence. Privately, I and perhaps some of the members could see that National Grid might have had a point when an influential cluster of small generating schemes appeared just beyond the boundary of the transmission system.

The energy politics of the time suggested a substantial growth in small-scale generation at the local level – there was a government target for combined heat and power schemes and also, with the support of the Non-Fossil Fuel Obligation, for renewable energy. The potential impact of this was beginning to cause some tension in the big generating companies and among the Association's members.

I had in the diary a visit to the then Group Managing Director of PowerGen, Deryk King. He had clearly been briefed that the growth of 'embedded' generation was an issue on which the

Association appeared to be going with the flow of the tide, without a great deal of thought about where it was going to end up, or, what it would encounter on the way. He had a point. We needed a strategy. On my return to London, I discussed this with our Head of Electricity Trading, Steve Johnson. Steve, who had been employed previously by PowerGen, understood big company thinking. Steve had also been closely involved with the smaller players in the Association and had earned their respect. He set up a working group to identify carefully the embedded generation issues and in what seemed to be the absence of any awareness of those issues at a senior level in government, to make proposals for dealing with them.

Steve managed this with distinction. Not only did he get the best out of the working group, where he had access to the great expertise of Stephen Andrews of Ilex and Guy Nicholson of Econnect, but he built a network of contacts outside the group, which included Catherine Mitchell[47], then in the Energy Group of the Science Policy Research Unit at the University of Sussex, and Philip Baker, an official at the Department of Trade and Industry.

The outcome was a report, approved by the Board of the AEP, which, if adopted, would help to put smaller-scale generation on a more equal footing in the industry; it showed, if it needed to, that the large and small players could work together successfully in the Association, and was a textbook example of the value of trade association work. I was pleased with our work and so were the members of the Association. But it also revealed a trap that busy trade associations are liable to fall into. The report went to the government and to the regulator, but for many months, nothing happened. It lay in 'reading' or 'pending' trays at a time when officials were busy with bringing domestic customers the right to choose between competing suppliers and the challenge of

[47] Catherine Mitchell moved to Warwick Business School and later became Professor of Energy Policy at the University of Exeter.

reviewing the industry's arrangements for trading electricity. To say nothing of issues like the future of coal-fired electricity production. I was guilty of thinking 'job done', but it was not. The hard lesson was that, however compelling the report, it would not be acted upon without a great deal of follow-up work, where government and regulator could be asked how it would be implemented, who would be doing it and by when. They were busy. We were busy. So at first, it did not happen. If you wanted something to happen, simply sending a report to the Department of Trade and Industry and the regulator was not enough.

The introduction to the report read:

The Association wishes to promote a broad review of the current arrangements for the connection of plant and for the apportionment of the costs of system security. It believes that there are fundamental flaws in the current arrangements that create inappropriate incentives on suppliers and result in unfair or unequal treatment of generators.

Such a review would be particularly appropriate as it fills a gap in the current industry review processes in respect of the relationship between the wires businesses and the competitive energy market traders. It also comes at a time when industry licence changes are under consideration and at the start of the PES price review by OFFER.

A key aim of the review would be to promote consistent treatment of all customers of the transmission and distribution systems with respect to carrying the costs of system security and the connection of their demand or generation. More effective integration of the commercial operation of the interconnected wires networks would be promoted by ensuring costs and benefits of each connection are appropriately recognised. There is significant interest in the development of small scale generation and supply at present. Appropriate trading arrangements need to be in place as soon as possible to ensure that the many hazards of retrospective adjustments are avoided.

The Association has carried out its own review using the experience of members. The intention of the review was to bring forward proposals to identify whether there are any inappropriate or unfair advantages in connecting and operating plant to a REC network compared with the National Grid. It became clear that there are fundamental inconsistencies in the treatment of different connectees that need to be addressed.

The review concentrates on the England and Wales networks. The Association is already supporting separate discussions on developments in Scotland.

The findings were summarised like this:

1. *The industry should operate in a non-discriminatory manner for all connections whatever the voltage, whether the connection is for generation or demand and regardless of asset ownership.*

2. *RECs should make clear their policies and procedures for connection of generating plant. The industry should establish standards for the application of connection charges that ensure consistent treatment throughout the network.*

3. *Competition in the provision of connections should be enhanced. Work defined as 'non-contestable' by individual RECs should be subject to monitoring and regulation.*

4. *REC wires businesses should be required under their licence to publish sufficient network information to assist the understanding of key network issues (cf. transmission licence holders).*

5. *The service standards for each connection should be agreed and there should be appropriate redress when the standard is broken.*

6. *Customer wires component charges should reflect the effect of the nature and location of their demand on the system. It should not be possible to avoid the wires component cost of system charges unless the customer is totally disconnected from the system. Where ancillary services can be provided this should be appropriately rewarded.*

7. *The security benefit that embedded generation gives to the transmission and distribution networks should be recognised in the charging methodology as well as the costs imposed on transmission and distribution.*

8. *There should be a clear hierarchy of responsibility for system security that ensures that there is transparency of technical information across the REC/NGC or other network boundary. Generation that is not centrally despatched should only be obliged to deal directly with the network to which it is connected and that network operator should have an obligation to act on behalf of the generator customer where necessary.*

9. *The system planning standards do not fully reflect structural changes in the electricity system. The review in progress at present should ensure consistent treatment for all generation connections and take due account of these changes.*

10. *RECs and other network operators should be liable for the wires component of security costs in their network and also for network boundary transfers such as reactive power flow. All network operators should be required to promote an active trade in system security products with customers, generators and other network operators to optimise security and minimise cost.*

The word 'active' in paragraph 10, above, became important. Steve Johnson's work on these issues resulted eventually in the concept of the 'active' distribution network becoming common parlance in the industry, including having a place in the 'smart' concepts that began to be discussed years later. Sadly, for AEP, its work in this area was seldom acknowledged, but it was, of course, the outcome that mattered.

Some 16 months after AEP had submitted its proposals, in November 1999, the DTI and Ofgem set up an Embedded

Generation Working Group. It was a response to the government policies that expected to see significant growth of renewable energy and CHP by 2010 and its remit embraced the issues that AEP had put on the agenda in 1998. Chaired by Dr Brian Wharmby of Ofgem, it reported in January 2001 in the form of a consultation document[48]. I was formally a member of the group, albeit once it was up and running, Dr Malcolm Taylor, Head of Electricity Trading at AEP (he had taken over from Steve Johnson) became the AEP's active representative on it.

In the light of all this effort, it was somewhat ironic that the government's 2010 targets for renewable energy and CHP were not met. Those targets had been for:

- 10,000 MW of CHP by 2010.

- 10% of electricity from renewable sources by 2010.

In a manner not unlike that adopted for industrial production targets in the Soviet Union, the renewable energy target was raised and extended to 2015. Much more important, though, would be the impact of the EU Renewable Energy Directive 2008, which set a target for the UK of 15 per cent of energy from renewables by 2020. But 'energy' includes fuel for transport and heating, where the scope for change by 2020 is limited, so this implied that the burden for achieving the change would fall on the electricity generating industry and at least 30 per cent of electricity would have to come from renewables by that date. That was nothing if not ambitious.

Combined Heat and Power (CHP)

The CHP target was interesting too, not least because it shows how meaningless such targets can be and how naïve governments can be when they set them. Despite the Labour government's CHP

[48] http://webarchive.nationalarchives.gov.uk/20100919181607/http://www.ensg.gov.uk/assets/21_10_2002_main_report.p

Strategy, CHP did not grow at the rate that had been expected. Gas prices, on which the CHP forecast had been based, had increased significantly and roughly 3,000 megawatts of CHP which had been expected to be built had been put on hold until industry confidence returned. An expectation of rising wholesale electricity prices and the impact of the EU Emissions Trading Scheme were expected to boost the prospects of the technology, however.

The CHP strategy may have been drafted to ease some government embarrassment – not simply because the target looked unlikely to be met, but because the government itself had helped to create the conditions which had damaged the industry's confidence. CHP users may not have liked the Pool particularly, but it provided a half-hourly reference price against which they could contract to sell their power, and for larger schemes, big enough to be Pool members, it provided an immediate market for their power. The abolition of the Pool in favour of NETA, in 2001, was not good news for CHP, nor any generating technology whose output was less predictable than most – NETA was specifically designed to favour predictability and penalise those who could not deliver (or take) the power that they had contracted to provide (or take).

CHP, which had to meet the schedules of those who used its heat, would not be encouraged by this. In fact, quite the reverse. The AEP which at first had opposed NETA, quickly accepted it and decided to 'work with it' when it became clear that its introduction was inevitable. It informed the government in written comments that CHP and renewable energy schemes, which could not predict their output, would be seriously disadvantaged and that the government needed to think hard about the unintended consequences of NETA.

This was not just in the form of written comments. On 10 July 2000, the Association hosted a reception on the Terrace of the

House of Commons at which the Energy Minister, Helen Liddell MP, was the Guest of Honour. The Chairman of the AEP's Board of Directors at that time was Richard Rigg, a former army officer and a perfect gentleman, who was blessed with good manners, but did not allow them to dull his cutting edge. In his speech that evening, he left the Minister in no doubt that the government had a problem to sort out and of course, in time-honoured fashion, that the AEP was available to help solve it, if required. I do not recall being asked to help to sort out that little difficulty and should probably count myself lucky that I was not. It was very hard to see a meaningful solution which was truly compatible with new trading arrangements that had been put in place specifically to increase competition in the electricity wholesale market and drive down prices. It was one of many examples where there was – and still is – a huge conflict between the three main strands of energy policy (security of supply, driving down prices and meeting environmental objectives) and our policy-makers try to be all things to all men. This was not good for investment in CHP, or indeed any other generating technology. Even worse when it dawns on investors that the politicians tend to be consistent in saying that they want to achieve all three of those objectives, but inconsistent in the emphasis they give to each of them. That aspect of public policy is right at the heart of so many problems faced by the electricity industry in Britain. It is, of course, replicated at EU level, and this exacerbates the problems.

Distractions

With the large companies absorbed into the AIEP and things running well, there were nevertheless some serious distractions from time to time. It was not too long before I was sounded out about the possibility of moving to the Electricity Association to become, in effect, a deputy to Philip Daubeney. The expectation seemed to be that I would bring some new thinking to an organisation that was struggling to shake off some of the shackles of its earlier role and implant some of the AIEP culture into the larger association. I think it might also have been thought that some of the members would follow me, but I felt that that was most unlikely. It was flattering, but I decided that the risk of being unable to bring about any change at EA was too great and that I would miss the excitement of working with AIEP and its growing membership. Nor did I want to give up being the top dog in the organisation, even one which was tiny, compared with EA. So, with all due courtesy, I turned down what had been an informal invitation to move to 30 Millbank.

Then, there came proposals for a merger with the EA. In 1995-1996, I was asked if the Association would consider entering into some form of merger with the Electricity Association. For the members of the EA, I could see the attraction of a merger. Some of EA's members would have expected it to add fire power to their organisation and perhaps help to change its culture. For others, however, it would have meant that AEP would no longer be a thorn in EA's side. The former had a certain amount of attraction. The latter had none. But this was not a proposal that I could respond to. It would be a matter for the Board and then the wider membership. We declined the invitation, but not before some difficult discussions which Philip Jackson said later had 'blighted' his two-year chairmanship of the AEP's Board. Unfortunately, Philip's assessment was probably right. It was hugely disruptive for an association as small as AEP to engage itself in an issue where its very identity was at stake and at the same time, continue with the day-to-day work that its members expected it to do. Both of those things were addressed, but the process was painful and Philip, who was a strong character, was frustrated by that.

The AEP Board set up a team to discuss the proposal with the EA. We met Philip Daubeney and his senior managers a few times and engaged in genuine discussion about what their members wanted to achieve and how a merged association would work. It was clear, however, that for this to be a 'merger' we had to overcome the problem that one party was huge and the other tiny. One was well-resourced, the other was not. But the two associations shared some large and influential members and each party owed something to those members to explore properly what might be achievable. There were many difficulties associated with this, but there was one over-riding obstacle for AEP. As an independent body, it made its own decisions under a governance process agreed by its members on a 'one member, one vote' basis. The problem running through the discussions with the EA was that it was hard to see how the generating sector could continue to make decisions and take positions in the interest of its membership when there would be, at the top of the new organisation, a governing body that included parts of the industry – retailers, for example – that would often take a different view.

At one point in the series of meetings, the EA seemed suddenly to be offering a federal structure where the generators' independence would somehow be maintained. Subject to the detail of this being spelled out, Michael Spicer and I were prepared to continue discussions on that basis. George Rufford, however, did not share that view and there followed a bitter disagreement which saddened Michael and me and in truth, probably George too – we had always been very close on the key issues that faced the industry. Thankfully, that disagreement was not long-lasting and events would soon leave it behind.

Discussions continued and one evening, with the merger issue coming to a head, the two teams were meeting at the offices of the Electricity Association when the AEP team asked for a break and a chance to talk alone in a private room. On the AEP side, we all knew, from what we had heard from the EA, that there was not enough on offer for us to be able to recommend to AEP's Board that we should take things any further. We gathered around the table in a room off the main meeting room and were immediately of one accord – we should say 'Thank you, but no thank you'. It was then just a question of how we told them. If we had been in any doubt about the decision, something was about to happen that would have helped us to make up our minds. There was a knock on the door and the Chief Executive of one of AEP's member companies, who was part of the EA negotiating team, came in on his way back from a comfort break. 'I shouldn't do it, if I were you' he said. The response was immediate. 'Thanks. We weren't going to anyway!'

So, we broke it off. Later, I thought a little about the impromptu advice that had been given to us and why it had been proffered. I wondered if the AEP Board members from the big companies had been asked to brief their Chief Executives before the negotiations; they had advised those bosses that there was much that they valued about their membership of AEP and that the companies should not risk throwing out the baby with the bath water. Whatever the reason, we put the merger negotiations behind us and I concluded that, even though it had caused some tension in our own ranks, we had been right to have the discussions and equally wise to reject the proposal. For the EA, however, it must have been frustrating. The EA, understandably, had been trying to strengthen its position and embrace a wider range of interests, to reflect the changes that had occurred in the industry. It had also been known to want to embrace gas supply interests, but there were few signs of that happening. Centrica, for example, which had been formed from the British Gas demerger in 1997, had always seemed unwilling to join the EA and frustratingly for me, it appeared to be in no hurry to bring its generating interests into AEP. That did not happen until 2007 and not until there had been a great deal of discussion with the Association. I think that the problem – even then – was that Centrica did not want to be associated with the companies who had acquired a less-than-desirable reputation.

Some time after the dust had settled, Philip Daubeney asked if I would consider leaving AEP to join him in a senior role at the EA. An attractive package was laid out which I had to consider very carefully. I was in my mid 50s by that time and of the many interesting benefits on the table, it was the attraction of the electricity industry final salary pension that made me think hard. Compared with the highly uncertain payback from the private pension schemes I was contributing to, it had huge appeal. But I could not convince myself that I would enjoy the work as much as I did my role at AEP, where, reporting directly to the Board, I enjoyed a huge amount of freedom. There was a risk that I would be limited in what I could do at EA, which would mean not only that I might not have enjoyed the day-to-day work, but that when Philip retired, I might not have made by then the impact necessary to be confident of securing his job. I thanked Philip and told him that it was flattering, but I wanted to stay at AEP. I don't think that he was very pleased and I could understand that. Short of offering me his own job, there was probably little more that he could have put on the table.

But this issue could not be eliminated. It seemed to have the durability of Japanese knotweed. In 2001, at an 'issues of the day' meeting over dinner between AEP and the EA in a Mayfair hotel, the approach of Philip's retirement was mentioned and out of the blue, from Philip's EA member colleague, came the announcement: 'We would like David to take over from Philip when he retires.' This was flattering, but also embarrassing. Michael Spicer called diplomatically for a break when he and AEP Chairman, Keith Miller, had a swift conversation in the gents' lavatory. In the days that followed, I was offered a new, much-improved contract at AEP. I was deeply grateful for that and the efforts made by Keith Miller and Michael Spicer on behalf of the Board, and I turned down the EA again.

Philip's departure was, indeed, approaching. Headhunters were appointed to find his successor and I found myself under consideration. I felt that this time, it could be different. This was not a situation where I would be a deputy who would be overshadowed, or could disappear without trace. If appointed, I might actually have enough influence to bring about a better and more acceptable relationship between the associations.

I was interviewed by the headhunters in the comfortable surroundings of a period office in Westminster and was quite pleased with the way that the discussion went. I had plenty to say about the way the industry was represented and how things could be done better, and I had a track record I was proud of. They were rightly interested in all of that, but it was clear to me that doubts remained and that they were to do with my lack of experience in managing a larger organisation. I had thought a great deal about how I would go about that and I explained it to them carefully, but this did not alter the fact that I had no record of having managed an organisation over ten times the size of AEP.

A week or two later, I received a holding letter from the headhunters saying that they wanted to look at more candidates. It did not actually say 'We regret to inform you…' but I did not like the sound of it and wrote immediately to say that they could take me off their list.

Eventually, I heard that Jenny Kirkpatrick, a former Chairman of the Gas Consumers' Council and Director of the Electricity Consumers' Council had been appointed. On the grapevine, the gossip was that the EA wanted to signal that it was taking more seriously the retail issues and the expectations of customers generally. It was, nevertheless, an appointment that surprised many people.

I had a pleasant dinner with Jenny at the OXO Tower in March and she started work at EA in April 2002. At that dinner, there were hints of a challenge to come and it was not long before the jungle drums were sounding another message, namely that she had been asked to sort out once and for all the relationship between EA and the AEP. Some of the gossip suggested that this meant more merger talks. Some suggested that it meant putting the upstart AEP in its place. But the upstart organisation extended to her the same courtesy that it had given to her predecessor. Among other things, this meant that Jenny was invited to be a guest at November's Annual Lunch of AEP. Later events would suggest that her presence there would prove helpful as far as the AEP was concerned.

Jenny launched a review of the energy trade associations, with a view to bringing about change. At AEP, we assumed that this would mean a strengthening of the role of the Electricity Association. The consultancy Enstra was engaged by Jenny to carry out the work. A copy of Enstra's confidential report found its way to my desk, courtesy of a senior member of staff of a company that was a member of both EA and AEP. I read it with the same attention which many years before as a restaurateur, I had given the annual publication of the *Good Food Guide*. The report, which gave a lot of emphasis to interviews with influential people in and around the industry, had little to say about the EA that would have given its members and staff much comfort. AEP, however, came out of it rather well. Among other things, the report said that AEP had more focus than EA and that it was also more nimble, in the sense that it seemed able to respond quickly in the news media when issues arose.

Not long after her visit to the AEP Annual Lunch, Jenny Kirkpatrick visited some of the members of EA, including Edison Mission – a company that was a member of the EA, though not prominent there, but was an active member of AEP. One of the senior people from that company told me later that, having seen the huge number of people at the AEP lunch and the support that the association seemed to attract, Jenny felt that it was inconceivable that her review should pose any threat to AEP. Of course, in practice, she could not have got rid of an independent body such as AEP, even if she had wanted to, but had she been minded to do so, she could perhaps have tried to persuade those EA member companies that were also members of AEP, to leave the smaller, more narrowly representative organisation. But she saw that as a non-starter.

What she eventually recommended to the Board of the EA, however, astonished us. She proposed that it should be broken up, in favour of representation through three sectoral bodies – the Association of Electricity Producers (AEP), Energy Networks Association (ENA) and the Energy Retail Association (ERA).

As soon as I heard of the EA's intentions, I rang Michael Spicer and George Rufford, both of whom had been on the front line in the earlier merger talks. Michael was amazed. George was more sceptical. He had never been able to see the post-privatisation organisation as anything other than a re-incarnation of the Electricity Council, for which he had little respect. Indeed, George would enjoy making the mistake of referring to the EA as the 'Electricity Council'. This was calculated mischievousness, of course. But George was understandably guarded. His response to the news that the EA would be wound up was more or less 'I'll believe it when I see it.'

Jenny Kirkpatrick, who was disappointed at the reaction of many of the EA staff to the closure plan – she told me more than once that they had 'circled the wagons' – engaged help with what would be a complicated winding up of the business. Duncan Sedgwick, from a senior position at PowerGen, was seconded to the EA to manage the task. The job would certainly not have appealed to me, nor, I suspect, to many other people. The organisation had emerged from decades of life as a state industry body and there was a great deal to be unravelled. Duncan managed this with great style and it was a role from which he moved to one of the bodies that succeeded the EA – the Energy Retail Association. The three associations – AEP, ENA, with Nick Goodall[49] as Chief Executive, and ERA – pledged immediately to work together effectively and signed a Memorandum of Understanding to that effect. When we met EA to discuss the restructuring, however, we had been surprised to see a fourth box on their diagram. It was placed above the three sectoral bodies and the name pencilled in to that box was 'Energy Association'. The AEP representatives, however, could not sign on to the idea that they would somehow report to a 'superior' body and the idea was dropped. I reflect elsewhere that our alternative proposal for addressing the 'cross-cutting' issues that faced the industry was rejected and at the time, we were blind to the risk that failing to resolve that issue might present.

The Electricity Association finally closed down on 30 September 2003. The Energy Networks Association and the Energy Retail Association then came into being and the AEP continued to represent the generating sector, albeit now without the confusion of having the EA also representing the generation interests of the

[49] Nick had previously led successfully the British Wind Energy Association.

larger companies. The tiny organisation, which had begun its life in a six-foot-square office in a cottage on a Cornish hillside and had been funded initially by small companies had outlived a much bigger association that had been put in place with huge state industry resources. For AEP, the winding up of the EA was momentous.

New responsibilities – a bigger role in Health and Safety

When the demise of the Electricity Association moved from mere speculation to a formal decision and the AEP was about to emerge undisputed as the trade organisation representing electricity production in the UK, the Board of AEP had to look hard at what the EA had been doing in the field of generation and compare it with AEP's own activities. AEP, for example, had been strongly involved in electricity trading issues – engaged in the work of the Electricity Pool, for example – but largely excluded from European issues[50] and it was much less involved than was the EA in the health and safety agenda, which AEP had begun to address only in 2001. The Board considered a long list of activities and did it through the eyes of an organisation which had always prided itself on its low-budget approach to its work and a reluctance to get involved in anything which distracted it from its main ambitions.

Faced with a report from me and a long list to consider, the Board was asked to do some serious 'box ticking'. Most of this was fairly predictable. There were many activities which were deemed 'nice to have', but far from essential. No doubt many of the former staff of the EA would have been hurt to hear how their work was dismissed. But I was in for a surprise. I assumed that stepping up the 'Health and Safety' work would get a 'tick' fairly readily and I recommended the appointment, by AEP, of someone to undertake

[50] See Chapter Eight.

that work for the generating sector of the industry. No one present took a tabloid newspaper's extreme 'elfnsafety' attitude to the proposal, but some were cautious on the grounds that it was the member companies that had the real responsibility and that there was even some risk of the Association attracting liability if it became too involved.

My expectation of AEP's role was that it would provide a forum in which health and safety issues could be discussed, different companies' experiences reported and the adoption of best practice encouraged. I was also concerned that we might give the impression that the Association was not interested in health and safety. AEP President, Michael Spicer, helped by underlining that to avoid liability generally, the Association had always made clear that it did not give advice and that it could make that equally clear where health and safety was concerned. We moved forward on that basis and decided to engage someone in a part-time capacity. The Chairman of the Board, Mike Bowden of Innogy had been characteristically helpful by seconding one of his team to take up the role and later, Stephen O'Neill, a specialist consultant, became the first Health and Safety Adviser to AEP. He gave the role the impetus it warranted.

In the event, the Energy Networks Association, which had taken on the Electricity Association's Health and Safety staff, became the industry's leading player on Health and Safety issues, much as AEP had taken the lead on the European policy front. So long as AEP had a seat at the table when it mattered, I was content with that, although at times I was made aware that the Health and Safety Managers from the generating businesses were less comfortable with taking a back seat. It was not, however, something over which a turf war would have been beneficial to either party. In fact, quite the reverse.

Although I had no wish to over-egg the AEP's health and safety work and I would have been, as much as anyone else, a critic of the more extreme 'health and safety gone mad' culture, I had always recognised the importance of the subject, not least because I knew that power stations were places where serious health and safety challenges had to be addressed and that companies took very seriously the need to manage the risks they presented to staff and visitors.

If I had harboured any doubts, however, they would have been dispelled later by two serious events. On Friday 30 June 2006, there was an accident at E.ON UK's coal-fired power station at Ratcliffe-on-Soar, in Nottinghamshire. An engineering consultant and an insurance company representative were severely scalded and taken to hospital when there was a sudden burst in the bend in a metal pipe carrying water at very high temperature. However bad 'severely scalded' may sound, it cannot convey fully the horror of such an accident. A burst of steam escaping under pressure from a split in a pipe could kill a person in an instant. Fortunately, on this occasion, it did not, but it was nevertheless serious for the individuals concerned. It was serious for the business, too. The power station was closed for a lengthy period, which meant that the company incurred losses that must have amounted to tens of millions of pounds. The Health and Safety Executive (HSE) launched an investigation, of course, and the focus turned to the particular type of pipework involved – 'cold-formed bends'. Somewhat to my surprise, the Association was invited by the HSE to draft a protocol for addressing the threat posed by the failure of cold-formed bends and how to address any safety issues arising from their use elsewhere in the industry. This was done and the proposals were accepted by the HSE – a tribute to the Association's members, who were clearly seen by the HSE as being trusted to carry out this task and to Percy Smith, seconded from RWE npower, who led the work for AEP. After making rather tentative steps into the field and employing one part-time professional – at first, by secondment, Mike Rock and the later, by secondment, Percy Smith, before AEP engaged Stephen O'Neill - the Association had acquired credibility when it counted.

There was, of course, press interest in the incident at Ratcliffe. The local BBC TV and radio journalists, hearing that a major power station in their region had closed down, began to ask whether the loss of the power plant meant that there would be power cuts in the Nottingham area. I was able to reassure them that the integrated nature of the power system meant that we could keep the power on in Nottingham. It was, however, a reminder – as if one were needed – that we should not take for granted journalists' understanding of the way that electricity supply works.

The second occasion when safety issues featured strongly on my agenda was in March 2009. I received a letter from a coroner in South Wales who was investigating the tragic death of a contractor in an accident at a power station site. An inquest jury had found that a number of different factors had contributed to the fatality – a fall from height – and the coroner wanted to know what steps the Association had taken to ensure that lessons learned from the incident had been communicated to the rest of the industry. Fortunately, the company concerned and our Health and Safety specialist, Stephen O'Neill, had been extremely diligent and I was able to respond with chapter and verse, explaining what steps had been taken to make members aware of the circumstances of the tragedy and to try to ensure that it was not repeated elsewhere.

Whereas competition law quite properly imposes severe penalties on companies that collude on matters such as pricing, exchange of information on health and safety issues is to be encouraged and what might appear to be, at first sight, a 'talking shop', is to be valued.

One day, in a live television interview to discuss the invasion of a power station by environmental protesters, I remarked that '… a power station is not an adventure playground.' The comment was meant to hint that some of the protestors' antics were childish. But I was also trying to say that these are not safe places for people who do not know how the risks in power stations must be managed.

CHAPTER EIGHT

EUROPE

As AEP began to mature and become established, the Board found itself discussing issues which could be traced not just to Westminster, but also to Brussels. Not only that, but the much talked-about European market for electricity appealed to many of the members, especially the larger ones. It appeared to offer the opportunity for companies to take their experience of the liberalised market in Britain and exploit it elsewhere in Europe. But for some time, it was as much as AEP could do to keep up with public affairs in Westminster, let alone take on a wider European role. In any case, the UK's Electricity Association already had a European role and even an office in Brussels. Discussion with the companies that were members of AEP and EA led us to the rather obvious starting point that liaison with the EA on this issue would be better than nothing. It was, but it was not enough. Its role in Europe was one of EA's selling points, just as AEP's engagement in the Electricity Pool, for example, was a selling point for the smaller association.

Philip Daubeney invited me to visit EA's man in Brussels, Stuart Hercock[51]. He was experienced, helpful and sympathetic, but even he operated with rather fewer resources than I had imagined – Stuart was a one-man band and if he went to visit the European

---

[51] An entertaining and interesting man, aligned politically with the Labour Party but outside politics, like me, a motorcyclist, Stuart sadly succumbed to cancer in May 2010.

Commission, the EA's Brussels office was served by an answering machine. It was none of my business, but other large European countries had small (in the case of France, apparently, not so small) teams in Brussels and I felt that Stuart should really have had an assistant of some kind.

The biggest generating companies were helpful, too. Hilary Watson[52], who did some of PowerGen's public affairs work and was well regarded by Chief Executive, Ed Wallis, was particularly sympathetic. Hilary was very professional and good to work with and however imperfect they may have been, the various loosely-stitched efforts at liaison were better than nothing. For about a year, the Association also took on, as a consultant, Wilfred Aspinall of the EU Economic and Social Committee, but the budget was getting tight and we had to terminate that arrangement. Philip Daubeney kindly got me involved in the UK's team that was responding to the European Commission's thoughts on how the market should develop and more especially to fight off the proposal (French-inspired, I think) that there should be a 'single buyer' for wholesale electricity. I recall being able to confirm at a meeting in Brussels that the Association would contribute £1,000 to the fund to do this work – not a huge proportion of the total bill for a consultant's report, but a signal of our backing for the effort to secure an open market and of our being a little more fleet of foot than some other participants, who had to report back to and consult with their seniors.

As it developed, the Association began to feel less comfortable with the idea of being dependent on the Electricity Association for access to debate at Eurelectric. The EA had no obligation to involve AEP and despite some overlap in membership it had little to gain from giving us more involvement. Not only that, but EA had a membership which included generation, supply and networks

[52] Later became Hilary Apps.

interests and from Brussels, it must have looked highly representative of the UK's electricity industry. It could not pretend to represent, however, the many smaller companies that belonged to AEP – companies that had never been part of the state electricity industry. I did some research on Eurelectric and discovered that in some European countries, there appeared to be more than one organisation enjoying membership. Not only that, but where there was more than one listed, they appeared to be small, rather than larger, entities. I was encouraged and I went to see Paul Bulteel, then Secretary General of Eurelectric, to find out how AEP could join. Paul is a gentleman and I was received cordially, but my search for a side door into Eurelectric was closed off. The memberships that I had discovered and had drawn Paul's attention to were 'historique' he told me. The organisation had reached recently a decision to restrict future membership to one representative trade body for each country and in view of that, he proposed that I should talk further with the EA to ensure that it would address AEP's interests. I was not overjoyed with that response and nor was the Board of AEP when I reported back to them. We discussed the issue with the EA, but had little confidence in the idea that it could speak effectively for AEP.

But sometimes the unexpected happens.

Jenny Kirkpatrick's arrival at EA as successor to Philip Daubeney, had made some of her senior staff rather anxious about the way that the EA would be organised and run in the future. Very soon after starting work at 30 Millbank, she had commissioned a review of the electricity trade associations, including EA's role as the largest of them. I could not be sure how that review would pan out, but the uncertainty presented an opportunity. That came when I heard that Gwyn Dolben, who headed up the EA's European work, was unsettled. I knew Gwyn and had attended meetings with him and I had great respect for his work. He was a consummate professional, who was fluent in French and German and had a deep understanding of the European institutions and of energy's place in European public affairs. Eurelectric membership or not, I wanted him at AEP and I had the backing of the then Chairman of the AEP Board, Mike Bowden of Innogy.[53] Mike, a lawyer, was imaginative and hugely supportive and served as Chairman for three years, instead of the usual two.

It took a little time, partly for delicate contractual reasons, but also because I had to make the case to the AEP Board. Unusually, it took me two meetings to do that. The Board agreed that the Association needed to up its game on the European front, but began talking of 'trawling' to find the right person. I knew who the right person was, of course, and I feared that he might be snapped up by one of the energy companies if we did not act soon. Finally, I said to the Board 'Think of it in terms of a football team. It is a good team, but there is a key position to be filled. I don't need to look around. I know who would fill the gap perfectly. It would be like signing David Beckham.' That was totally different from my usual way of putting issues to the Board, but they agreed and Gwyn's immense contribution to the Association over many years showed that they were right to do so. Not everyone was happy, however. When I told Jenny Kirkpatrick, she was angry with me.

When the Electricity Association was closed down, the AEP took up the UK's membership of Eurelectric. We had to show that we were representative of the UK's electricity supply industry however and this meant reaching an agreement to share certain things with the Energy Retail Association and the Energy Networks Association.

I became a member of the Board of Eurelectric and found the work there more interesting than I might have expected. It was

[53] Dissatisfied with the value for money that it offered, Innogy (previously 'National Power') had resigned from the EA. This must have damaged EA's credibility and contributed to the decision to wind it up.

often challenging to reach agreement with the interests of so many different countries to take account of, but the staff of Eurelectric were both professional and enthusiastic and their success rate was impressive. Even more so because they were drawn from all over Europe and business had to be done in the language of Eurelectric – English. Once in a while, the views of members or staff could get lost in translation, but fortunately such occasions were rare and if, to the Englishman at the table, it suddenly became clear what was meant, it would not have been appropriate to correct another member's English. Indeed, bearing in mind the language skills of the average Briton, it would have been inappropriate, even embarrassing. The Board meetings were chaired by the serving President of the association (a Chief Executive from one of Europe's major energy companies) and I recall that, early in my time there, one President would seek confirmation of a Board decision and seeking to put on record the unanimity, would state 'We have agreed anonymously.' He did an excellent job and we all knew what he meant.

As is the case with many trade associations, a great deal of Eurelectric's work was concerned with important issues that were often low-key. Equally often, this entailed responding to another organisation's agenda – typically that of the European Commission. From time to time, however, Eurelectric would get its teeth into an important issue and take a high-profile position on it. The debate about global warming had been growing and Eurelectric thought that the industry, with its vested interests, was probably seen as an unhelpful obstacle to change. Under the leadership of its Secretary-General, Paul Bulteel[54], and with great commitment from the UK's Dr Bill Kyte (E.ON and Chairman of the Eurelectric Environment Committee) and John Scowcroft (Head of the Environment Unit at Eurelectric), Eurelectric conducted a study to determine what

[54] Later (from 2007) Hans Ten Berge.

Europe's electricity supply industry would have to do to achieve, by 2050, the reduction in carbon emissions that the EU policies demanded. Using computer models constructed by Professor Pantelis Capros of the National Technical University of Athens, this was a comprehensive study, which concluded that the industry could achieve a very low level of carbon emissions by 2050 – provided that Europe had a properly-functioning energy market and all low-carbon technologies were to be deployed (perhaps a gentle way of saying that nuclear power needed to be part of the solution)[55]. In a presentation to the World Energy Congress, in Rome in 2007, Paul Bulteel reported:

The resulting message is a positive one: with the right policies that include a long-term visibility of carbon pricing to allow integration of climate change impacts in investments and business strategies, it is possible to substantially reduce greenhouse gas emissions without unreasonable costs to the economy, and at the same time to reduce oil and gas dependency.

Further work on the subject led to Eurelectric's next report on the issue – *Power Choices*[56]. Under the Presidency of Lars Josefsson, who was Chief Executive of Vattenfall and new Secretary-General, Hans Ten Berge, Eurelectric took another step forward on the issue. The author of a book on the response to climate change[57], Lars wanted the European electricity industry to be seen as an agent of the changes that Europe's policy-makers wanted to achieve. A significant step was taken on 18 March 2009, when 61 chief executives of energy companies across Europe put their signatures to a declaration which, with some ceremony, was handed over to the then Energy Commissioner, Andris Piebalgs. The declaration

[55] The Role of Electricity: A new Path to Secure and Competitive Energy in a Carbon-Constrained World. Eurelectric. 2007.

[56] Power Choices: Pathways to carbon-neutral electricity in Europe by 2050. Eurelectric. 2009.

[57] The Future in Our Hands: How the Threat of Climate Change Can be Dealt with in a World where Everyone is Entitled to Development. Lars G Josefsson, Christofer Fager. Vattenfall AB. 2006.

committed them to action towards a sustainable energy future and called on EU and national policy-makers to provide a framework conducive to achieving that goal. I was there. It was a most impressive event and one which put Europe's electricity supply industry on the front foot.

In the build-up to the publication of the *Power Choices* report, I attended a meeting of the Co-ordination Committee of Eurelectric. I learned a lesson – humour can be lost in translation, too. We were tidying up the final draft of *Power Choices* when I realised that around the table, people were describing differently what was envisaged for 2050. It was variously described as 'decarbonisation', 'zero carbon', 'low carbon' and 'carbon neutral'. To me, these expressions were not identical in meaning and there was a risk of misunderstandings, so I thought it was important that we should agree on one of them and use it consistently. Eventually we settled on 'carbon-neutral', but not before I had foolishly attempted to illuminate the discussion with a little irony. My colleagues asked why the precise wording was important to me and I explained that there were subtle differences in meaning between the terms which were being bandied about and the scope for misinterpretation. So, I said to the Committee 'Look, in 2050 I shall be 103 years old and I will not want the BBC ringing me up to ask why we have not completely "decarbonised".' Except on the face of fellow Brit, Bill Kyte, there were blank expressions all around the table. They had taken my comment literally and must have concluded that I had unrealistic expectations of longevity.

On a more serious note, within a few years, it was clear that, although they had welcomed the Eurelectric declaration, Europe's policy makers were prepared to overlook the conditions which Eurelectric applied to the achievement of a carbon-neutral industry by 2050. Among other things, by 2014, instead of implementing emissions reductions *without unreasonable costs* (Paul Bulteel, 2007, above) muddled policy-making and lack of certainty was already contributing to concerns, from industry and domestic customers, about rising energy bills.

In 2008, I was greatly honoured to be made Chairman of Eurelectric's 'Energy Policy and Generation' Committee. It was a challenge that I enjoyed immensely. In some respects, the challenge had things in common with my work at AEP – for example, a wide range of different interests to satisfy. But this was on a different scale and the debate, with perhaps 30 people around the table, could be demanding. I was fortunate to have invaluable help from, at first, Juho Lipponen and later Susanne Nies as Head of Energy Policy – professional and knowledgeable people who were supportive and wonderful to work with. The energy policy 'triangle' – security, prices, carbon emissions – of course, was just as big an influence in Brussels as it was in London and many of the debates that I had to chair were down to the different weight that policy makers, or energy companies, applied to those three objectives, the conflicts between them and their impact on energy companies. In my last year as Chairman of the Energy Policy and Generation Committee, the apparent insensitivity of policy-makers to some of the market issues and their effect on investment troubled me. After the financial crisis of 2008, it seemed that the EU was pursuing much the same policies in 2012 – including conflicting ones – as it had been before 2008 and no one seemed to be considering whether these remained viable. I wrote to the then President of Eurelectric, Fulvio Conti[58], to express my concern. Mr Conti's response was to ask me to set up and chair a task force on the investment issues and report back. With the help of Hans Ten Berge, Susanne Nies and her team, we did exactly that and it was gratifying that its membership embraced various interests from outside the mainstream of the industry, to include banking and finance, a think-tank and consultancy expertise.

[58] Then Chief Executive of ENEL.

The work included a survey of 45 senior people from European energy businesses and among other things, it found that 44 of the 45 did not think the volumes of investment implied by current policy would be achieved. The report's recommendations signalled that the EU and governments should think more clearly about the impact of policy, resist the temptation to make piecemeal decisions and focus on getting the energy market working instead of announcing targets for everything. It found that political and regulatory risk was hampering investment decisions and when the report[59] was launched in Brussels on 6 December 2012, it became clear that some of the European Commission staff did not like its findings. Responding to the report, a representative from the Directorate General for Energy argued that the Commission was delivering exactly the regulatory certainty that the industry wanted. A later presentation from a financial analyst, however, demolished the Commission's complacency. He highlighted the reality of the current financial standing of European energy companies, pointed to the negligible value of expensive generation assets and contrasted this with the high value of cheaper, stand-by generation assets. The message was that here could be seen an unintended and little-known consequence of public policy.

In 2012, at my last meeting as Chairman of Eurelectric's Energy Policy and Generation Committee, my colleagues were very kind to me. I was presented with gifts. One of them, I was at first not aware of. A group photograph was being taken and as we all smiled for the camera, I sensed that something was going on behind me. I turned round to find that Susanne Nies was holding behind me a blue and gold EU flag, in which, in the photograph, I would appear to be draped. Knowing that I harboured some scepticism about the institution, they expected me to protest, and I delivered the response

[59] Powering Investments: Challenges for the liberalised electricity sector. Eurelectric. December 2012.

they wanted. It was, however, all good fun and indicative of what had been a warm and productive working relationship, and one I valued immensely.

CHAPTER NINE

'NO ENERGY POLICY'

Although at privatisation, the high-level thinking was that in future the electricity supply industry would be making most of its own investment decisions without being steered by the heavy hand of government – and the privatisation itself was an astonishing achievement – the market, immediately post-privatisation, was far from 'free'. In fact, it featured:

- regulated prices for domestic customers (full customer choice did not come until 1999 - a year later than originally planned);

- a special transitional deal for the largest industrial and commercial customers;

- a deal to ensure that the ex-CEGB generating businesses continued to buy indigenous coal;

- a levy to support existing nuclear power plants (which proved impossible to privatise until 1996);

- an obligation (the 'Non-Fossil Fuel Obligation' or 'NFFO') triggered by the need to find a way of supporting nuclear power, but also designed to finance through a levy renewable energy projects that were successful in a tendering process;

- in Scotland (until 2002), regulated wholesale and retail prices, rather than a market price and

■ regulated prices in Northern Ireland, where retail competition
   was absent until 2010.

But the mood music was about the industry's freedom and those
that did not like the sound of it would assert that the country no
longer had an energy policy.

The Energy Minister, Tim Eggar MP, decided to pay an official
visit to the offices of the Electricity Pool and just before the end of
a tour of the Pool offices building, he enquired of his host, the Pool's
Chief Executive, Margaret Thompson, 'Remind me. [60]What is my
role in all of this?'

'You don't have one' she replied.

There was every reason why a Minister should not have had a
role in the wholesale trading of electricity, but Mr Eggar may have
been surprised at just how hands-off the Minister was expected to
be. In the post-privatisation era, however, that was the context in
which the liberalised electricity industry operated. Some 25 years
later, the industry would find itself being moulded increasingly to
suit the wishes of government. Indeed, by 2012, companies would
find it almost impossible to make any significant investment in the
industry without some kind of support or assurance from the
government. Worse still, the level of trust in each party – industry
and government – would have fallen, making the two parties stare
harder at each other before companies entered into any long-term
commitments. In the 1990s, however, with a regulator to ensure
that there was competition and that the network monopolies were
run fairly and efficiently, and a political commitment to the
phasing-in of customer choice, it was hard to see why the
government would need to concern itself with electricity
production and supply. Customers wanted the electricity very badly.
Companies would respond to that demand and earn a return on

[60] Minister of State for Energy 1992-1994, Minister of State Energy & Industry 1994-1996.

their investment by doing so. Competition (backed by strong competition law), good market rules and customer choice would ensure that customers got the best possible deal.

So, what was the problem?

There was no problem, save that over a number of decades, British voters had been encouraged to believe that government would take care of more and more aspects of their daily lives and provide, or procure for them, a wide range of services. These days, our governments not only try to protect us from the 21st century equivalents of Philip II, Napoleon Bonaparte and Adolf Hitler, but increasingly even from the impact of our own behaviour. Despite their well-documented cynicism about politics and those that practise it and the unintended consequences – not least, the cost – of so many political decisions, voters' memories tend to be short, so they still appear to have a surprising amount of faith in the ability of their elected representatives to deliver what they promise. But it is not hard to see why it would be difficult for a government to tell its electorate that it was not taking some responsibility for electricity – a commodity upon which virtually all of modern life depends.

Electricity, of course had been the government's responsibility for so long that state ownership had come to seem a natural state of affairs. Even with the industry in private ownership, for a Minister to go on the *Today* programme and say 'We can leave all this to the market' would have been career-limiting - whether he believed in what he had said or not. And even politicians who are kindly disposed towards market solutions are apt to harbour some misgivings. They are not alone. I have lost count of the number of times I have been told that markets do not always work. I tend to reply that more often than not, they do seem to work, but that the problem for those who argue that they do not work is that, although they can see clearly that they do, they do not always like the outcome. As far as politicians are concerned, I wonder whether markets make them uncomfortable because, when they work, it means that there is less for the politicians to do.

The privatised electricity industry may not have been quite as *laissez faire* as it could have been, but nevertheless, its freedom worried many politicians and commentators. Between the White Paper of February 1988 and the Electricity Act 1989, prominent figures were arguing that the industry could not or should not be privatised and liberalised. But when that change had become a fact, most seemed to come to terms with it and commit themselves to making it work. Some, however, continued to question whether the new industry could offer the security and reliability of the state-owned monopoly. I recall speaking at a conference at what was then the Institution of Electrical Engineers[61] and having to deal with questions on the lines of 'Who is in charge of the industry?' and 'Who will make investment decisions?' It seemed that some highly-qualified people did not accept the idea of an electricity industry driven by what customers wanted.

It was argued by many that eventually there would be a problem with investment. I comment later on the particular investment problems of 2010 onwards, but I do not attribute them to the privatisation of the electricity industry, rather to the uncertainty created by conflicts in public policy – uncertainty fed and watered by the way that the muddled management of the climate change agenda was allowed to conflict with the need to maintain secure supply and keep prices as low as possible.

In the 1990s, though, the gently expressed concerns were not about whether electricity companies would respond to demand from customers, but whether they would make new investments in a way which was sufficiently timely to avoid shortages of supply. Those concerns were not expressed more boldly, of course, because

[61] It became the Institution of Engineering and Technology in 2006.

at that time, there was ample capacity. Not only that, but the Electricity Pool provided a capacity payment and signal – a calculation involving 'Loss of Load Probability' (LOLP) and based on a notional 'Value of Lost Load' (VOLL). This, however, was controversial and resented by the large industrial customers. They disliked having to help to finance a capacity payment which provided reward for the plant that was made available to provide some security beyond the level of actual demand and they were sceptical about its value as an investment signal. On that, they may have had a point.

I have always found it hard to accept that generating companies might not invest in sufficient new plant to meet expected demand. It is their business. They like doing it. They are good at it and they know that, although too much capacity could be damaging to them, if they failed to invest when it was important to do so, they would find themselves at the mercy of politics.

Eventually the sceptics came up with another concern, namely that the companies would invest, but that they would all pile into the same technology – gas-fired power production – and as North Sea gas output declined, this would put security of supply at risk by making the country over-dependent on imported gas. This argument gained ground when companies did invest heavily in combined cycle gas turbines, although, however close it might have come to a crisis, the generating industry had never lost its gas supplies. Those who feared that there would not be enough gas, or not enough gas at the right price, could not have asked themselves why any company would build an expensive new power station for which they did not expect to be able to buy fuel in the future. Nor did they ask who might be better placed than the energy companies to make a judgement about the future availability of fuels. Surely, it was not government they had in mind?

This argument about 'over-dependence', however, was given more credibility by one or two companies who expressed concerns publicly about it. Occasionally, the issue found its way into public statements by AEP. I was not challenged about them, but if I had been pressed about the implications of this issue for public policy, I would probably have fallen back on the simplistic argument that diversity of fuels is important (the AEP represented users of virtually every generating fuel and technology) and we should not reject coal, nuclear power and well-developed renewables. But what the warning from the companies was leading to was the intention, on the part of some of them, to think about investments not only in gas-fired stations, but in new coal-fired plant and perhaps even nuclear power. Those that were big enough to enjoy diversity in their generating assets, did not need to be told by a government that diversity might be a good thing. Elsewhere, here, I mention the proposal by E.ON UK to build a new coal-fired plant and E.ON UK was not the only company with ambitions of that kind.

In an industry where generating capacity was plentiful – and new entry was being encouraged – until the implications of the EU Large Combustion Plant Directive[62] became clear, the debate about security of supply was largely academic. Debate about competition and prices, however, was more sensitive and rarely out of the news.

At that time, domestic customers were not able to choose between competing suppliers. They were supplied by the ex-state, regional electricity companies at prices which were regulated. The wholesale price, however, was based on prices in the Electricity Pool of England and Wales – the half-hourly, day-ahead market around which contracts for difference were written. Electricity contracts for energy-intensive users – industries such as steel, chemicals and paper – were linked to the Pool price and

[62] Large Combustion Plant Directive 2001/80/EC.

determined in a market where, although it was growing, competition was limited. Wholesale prices were controversial.

In February 1994, the regulator, Stephen Littlechild, Director General of Electricity Supply, secured an agreement with the two major generating companies, National Power and PowerGen that they would ensure that pool prices were capped at £24 per megawatt hour (time-weighted) or £25.50 per megawatt hour (demand-weighted) at October 1993 prices and that they would seek to sell respectively 4,000MW and 2,000MW of their generating capacity. The AIEP was deeply concerned about this decision. So concerned that it took legal advice – I recall going with John Macadam to discuss the legitimacy of the decision with the renowned barrister, Michael Beloff QC. Although we were fascinated by the QC's opinion and not least by the way it was delivered, we were disappointed by his view that the Director General's decision was probably legal. Of course, to lay people such as ourselves, this regulatory decision had seemed highly questionable. But bidding to keep prices within the cap and the required divestment of plant were both achieved, the latter taking effect through the sale of plant to Eastern Group (later Energy Group) in June and July 1996. Not surprisingly, that regulatory decision of 1994 made headlines. When it was announced, I was interviewed by BBC TV and I appeared on the news saying 'The regulator's decision is perverse…' The divestment of plant was probably inevitable after the way in which the industry had been privatised and almost certainly would improve the industry's health. The requirement that the two companies should cap the pool price, however, seemed to give them authority to collude and the cap on prices looked to be anything but healthy for other producers in the market. Newcomers needed a higher wholesale price than did their competitors - the incumbents with assets that had been paid off.

In 1997, faced with a constant stream of adverse publicity about the Pool, the Association of Electricity Producers published a short report on the Electricity Pool – 'The Electricity Pool 1996-97: a review'. It drew attention to falling prices, more competition emerging at the margin and record availability of power stations. Published to put a few facts on the table, it made no headlines, but it made interesting reading. It still does. The period that the report referred to had followed an extraordinary one in the new industry's short history.

The AEP's report in June 1997 showed that, contrary to the expectations of the industry's critics, when the regulatory brakes were taken off at the end of the agreement, prices did not go up. In fact, they went down. Prices fell in absolute terms by 3.7 per cent and in real terms by 8 per cent in a period when demand rose by 4.8 per cent. The AEP report went on to say 'Pool price volatility has increased steadily since 1992, reflecting market uncertainty. Demand volatility has remained broadly constant over the same period.' No wonder that, when journalists challenged me about pool prices, I would sometimes say to them that, despite the volatility that sometimes grabbed the headlines, I would have loved to have been able to buy my domestic electricity at the pool price. The intensive users that did have pool price-related contracts may have squealed when the price peaked, but they knew what they were doing. Day to day, it was sometimes hair-raising. Over a year, however, it probably served them very well.

The Pool prices were published every day in the *Financial Times*. Along with those of other PLCs, of course, so too were the share prices of the privatised electricity companies. When the Pool Executive Committee held its monthly meeting away from London and an overnight stay meant that members met at breakfast, the first topic of discussion for the REC representatives seemed to be the business pages and more specifically, the share prices of the privatised companies. They were shareholders, of course and the share prices were still something of a novelty. At the meeting itself, however, the price that interested them was the Pool price. As buyers in the market, they were sensitive to any proposals by the generating companies that might push prices up and when prices reached levels that they deemed too high, they would express concern at Pool meetings about 'high' Pool prices.

I felt strongly about that issue and I tried to persuade the PEC not to make a value judgement of that kind. 'There are no "high" Pool prices, any more than there are "Low" Pool prices,' I would say. 'There is only "the Pool price".' I felt that, whereas the PEC should concern itself with whether or not the Pool mechanism was working as it was meant to, in the absence of any suggestion that it was not, it should avoid falling into the trap of implying that the price was somehow wrong – that would have been a gift to its critics. On one occasion, this came to a head in a way that astonished many of those around the table. The Pool prices were submitted to the *Financial Times* by the National Grid Company[63] and on a day when prices had risen to what I think had been an unprecedented level, it was too much for National Grid's Pool representative, who declared that he was minded not to publish the figures. Heated debate ensued.

The Pool became increasingly controversial. One way or another, the generating companies that traded in the Pool seemed always to be under investigation by the Office of Electricity Regulation (OFFER). Bright, highly-motivated, young people trading electricity for the generating companies knew the importance of keeping within the rules, but were keen to exploit them to the maximum. The challenge of trading electricity from behind 'constraints' on the system was a case in point. Constraints?

[63] Owned jointly by the RECs until 1996, when it became independent.

An integrated electricity system, however well run, suffers from physical weaknesses – bottlenecks, breakdowns, over-crowding in particular areas. But these problems have to be managed by those who control the grid. Putting too much power on to a part of the system that cannot use it is a serious matter. As demand and supply fluctuates, the frequency of the system, for example, has to be kept within a certain range or customers' electrical equipment will be damaged. All this is managed with immense commitment and professionalism by National Grid. But however much industry players may appreciate the skill with which the grid is managed, those who generate power are at risk from bottlenecks on the network. They may be ready and willing to produce electricity but through no fault of their own, can be denied access to the system and therefore find themselves unable to sell their product. So, the Pool rules – and indeed, the trading rules after the Pool era – allowed for constraint payments for power that, because of system problems, could not be delivered to the customers. Under the Pooling and Settlement Agreement, such payments were charged to the electricity Suppliers as part of a package of costs that was added to the Pool price in the form of 'uplift'. This part of the bill from the Pool was disliked intensely by those companies and scrutinised carefully by them.

Generating companies could see opportunities in constraint payments and PowerGen in particular got itself into deep water with OFFER for the enthusiastic way in which it interpreted the rules. Looking back, companies were bound to test the limits of those rules. Indeed, if one wanted a vigorous and healthy trading environment, testing the rules had to be part of it, as did the risk of being summoned to the Director General's office.

It has to be said, however, that the reporting of regulatory battles did nothing to enhance the reputation of the industry and it was a gift to the naysayers who had never been comfortable with the privatisation, let alone those who thought that there was now 'no energy policy'.

CHAPTER TEN

THE LIGHTS
GO OUT - SHOCK

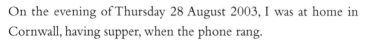

On the evening of Thursday 28 August 2003, I was at home in Cornwall, having supper, when the phone rang.

'David, it's John Ingham at the *Daily Express*.'

My heart sank. When a tabloid journalist rings, the spokesman for the electricity generating industry has to be on full alert. That's because even the most reasonable and carefully-worded comments could well be found in print the next day, in a context that it would have been difficult, perhaps impossible, to have envisaged at the time of the conversation.

'Hello, John. What can I do for you?'

'Do you remember when the lights went out in New York, I called you and you said that it couldn't happen here?'

'I didn't quite say that, John. I said that it was most unlikely to happen here.'

'Well, I think it has happened.'

'Why? What's going on?'

'The power is off in my office. The lights are out and the computers are down.'

'Ah. Take a look out of the window, John and see if other buildings are affected.'

'I have. There doesn't seem to be power anywhere and I can see Blackfriars Station and nothing is moving there.'

'Someone has probably put a digger through a cable' I said. 'I'll find out what has happened and I'll get back to you.'

I rang London Electricity, thinking it must be their problem. They doubted it and suggested that I spoke to National Grid. In the meantime, my wife had switched on Sky News, where the Mayor of London, Ken Livingstone, was being interviewed. His annoyance at the inconvenience caused was perfectly understandable, but well in advance of any investigation, he was ready with an explanation. He blamed a lack of investment by the privatised electricity industry. In fact, when the investigation was eventually completed, we learned that the cause was a moment of human error when a relay of the wrong size had been fitted in a National Grid sub-station. When something unexpected happened, National Grid brought that sub-station into use and the relay failed, tripping the power off.

Power was restored remarkably quickly – to the credit of National Grid and the people that ran London Electricity's local network – but in the meantime, people were stuck in lifts, 60% of the London Underground network came to a halt, stations were evacuated, traffic lights failed, commuter train services to Kent came to a halt, businesses were plunged into darkness and hospitals had to switch to stand-by generation.

However brief it may have been, this was an important moment in the history of the UK's electricity supply industry and a big influence on public policy for the industry. It was a big moment for me, too. I seemed to field more press, radio and television enquiries about the London blackout and its ramifications than for any other issue that I dealt with over a period of 25 years of commenting. After the London incident, the calls to my office continued for three weeks and towards the end of that period, some local radio stations were still producing programmes about security of electricity supply and what should be done about it. As AEP President, Michael Spicer used to say to me from time to time, 'Where electricity issues are concerned, the press are interested in two things – Will the lights go out? What does this mean for prices?'

There is, of course, nothing better than a power cut to awaken the interest of customers who take their power supply so much for granted. Rare it may be, but we all know the feeling when we get home, press the light switch and nothing happens. We make our way to the drawer where we think the torch is kept and press another light switch on the way. Yes, we do – it does take time to sink in. There is no light and there is silence. No fridge humming, no television chattering away, no kettle burbling and not even a gentle hum from a computer. At this point, we might even consider it worth paying more for our electricity. In my role at AEP, of course, I would have been torn to shreds by the press if I had been heard to say anything remotely like that.

CHAPTER ELEVEN

THE LIGHTS
GO OUT – DRAMA

In 2003, the Current Affairs department of the BBC began planning a series of dramatised documentary programmes which would, in the words of Peter Horrocks, BBC's Head of Current Affairs '...*take some of the most complex policy problems which face our politicians today – such as an ageing population, the tax and spend dilemma, the energy crisis – to explore them, explain them and at the same time turn them into engaging television … The approach we decided to take was to analyse these issues by looking into the future and dramatizing the possible outcomes of the actions, or inactions, of today's politicians. We've called it war-gaming the future.'*

The topics chosen by the BBC were related to energy; inequality in society; the ageing population and division between 'baby boomers' and the young; the changing role of women and the obesity 'epidemic'. The first of these programmes – and in entertainment terms, probably the best of them – would prove to have considerable impact on political thought about the UK's energy industry and electricity in particular.

I was invited by the Producer, Dai Richards, to take part in the programme. The discussions with the programme researchers were interesting and they led to my being filmed for an entire afternoon in a penthouse suite at what was then the City Inn in John Islip Street, London SW1. There was a wonderful view over the Thames, towards south London and the sun shone all afternoon. My role was to be one of the 'expert' witnesses and I wanted to fulfil it honestly, but knowing that hours of filming would be distilled into no more than a few minutes of the broadcast, I also wanted to try to make sure that straightforward answers were not cut and pasted so as to become alarmist comments. That kind of challenge ran through the huge number of radio, TV and newspaper interviews that I did for AIEP, AEP and finally, Energy UK. Representing the many different companies that make electricity, I had always to try to ensure that I did not increase concern when faced with a possible crisis, real or imagined. After all, it was my members that were at risk of being blamed. The other parties – government and regulators – are far better at deflecting blame than accepting it.

I went to the BBC's very enjoyable reception to launch the series on the evening of 3 March 2004 and heard flattering comments from the BBC team about my contribution. That concerned me – journalists' ideas about what is 'good' were sometimes at odds with my own thinking. I need not have worried. In the event, the 'honesty without anxiety' approach was reasonably successful.

The first 'IF' programme was broadcast on Wednesday 10 March 2004. The story was set in the winter of 2010. As the BBC trailered it:

'A terrorist attack on a gas pipeline in Russia has a disastrous effect on Britain, which by then is heavily dependent on Russian gas to generate electricity. IF paints a scenario of a future in which the south east of England is plunged into darkness. Householders are left without water or electricity, traffic is gridlocked, tube trains stranded underground and airports closed.

As the situation worsens, emergency services are affected and people's lives are put at risk.'

However flawed some of the fundamental assumptions may have been, the programme's attention to the impact on (fictional) individuals and the apparent feasibility of the 'cause' of the problem (terrorism) gave it great impact. It featured in the press, of course, and little more than a week after the television broadcast, the programme was being referred to in the House of Lords, where an Energy Bill was being debated.

This is Baroness Miller of Hendon's statement:

'My Lords, this is a totally new amendment. It is a simple amendment that I, my noble friend Lord Jenkin of Roding, the noble Lord, Lord Ezra, and the noble Baroness, Lady Miller of Chilthorne Domer, tabled because of our disappointment at the lack of any assurance in the White Paper, in our debates in Grand Committee or anywhere in the Bill that there is a clear government policy on the security of the future supply of electricity. Over the past year or more, there have been numerous debates and questions on the subject in your Lordships' House and in the other place. There has never been a clear answer.

'Many of your Lordships will have seen the television programme last week. I sincerely hope that the Minister watched it carefully. In it, participants repeatedly asked who was responsible for the security and continuity of the electricity supply—in other words, "Who is responsible, if the lights go out?". Answer came there none from the Government, either in the programme itself or in the discussion that followed, in which the Government declined to participate.

'I entirely agree that the Government are not at the beck and call of any TV producer who asks them to appear on a programme. Secondly, the scenario set out in the programme could have been described as a little

hyperbolic. However, the fact is that nobody seems to accept responsibility for ensuring that there is no breakdown in one of the three most basic of the essential services required in a civilised and advanced country: fuel, especially electricity.'

This TV programme caused quite a stir. Unrealistic it may have been, but it touched nerves that were already sensitive as a result of the events that occurred in the previous year – the power cut on the eastern seaboard of the United States, including New York; the blackout in Denmark and part of Sweden and the loss of power to the whole of Italy. More significantly for the UK - the loss of supply for about 40 minutes in central London on 28 August 2003.

CHAPTER TWELVE

MISUNDERSTANDINGS AND MISLEADING MESSAGES

One of the problems the industry faced as it found itself in the spotlight was the lack of understanding on the part of policy-makers, journalists and commentators about the basics of the electricity supply industry – let alone the various policies that affect the way that it operates.

When Ratcliffe-on-Soar power station was out of action for a lengthy period of time in 2006, the BBC interviewed me about the concern locally that the lights would go out in nearby Nottingham. The role of an integrated electricity system was not well understood.

When the winter weather early in 2014 caused power cuts in the south of England, a well-known presenter on the BBC *Today* programme asked whether some people in a village from which a live report was being made might not have lost their supply because they had chosen different suppliers from those customers that had been cut off.

It is not just with regard to the way that the electricity system works that there is a risk of misunderstanding. The way policy is applied is not always given the attention that it deserves, either. I saw on the regional TV news a report about a West Country school which, by installing a solar photo-voltaic (PV) system, had amassed large amounts of money which it was putting towards extra textbooks. The head teacher also enthused about the way the school's PV system was teaching the pupils about energy. The school was not only saving money but displaying green credentials. The reporter was equally enthusiastic, but he did not choose to ask how this minor economic miracle was being financed. Had he done so, he might have stumbled upon the fact that other electricity customers – including those least able to pay – were financing the school's savings by funding, through their bills, the payments under the Feed-In Tariff.

Nor, in the way that reporting is carried out, is there much evidence of understanding of business economics when energy companies publish their financial results. On 21 May 2014, when energy company SSE had reported its results, at 8 am on BBC *Breakfast News*, the second headline was '*Also this morning, big profits for the energy company SSE…*' We heard later that the profit was £1.55 billion. Was that 'big'? To make a judgement about that, a business reporter might have been expected to refer to what had been invested in the company and what turnover it had achieved. It is rare, of course, for such comparisons to be made. Energy companies seem to be expected to provide a secure supply, good service and low prices and invest massively in the technologies that politicians and journalists favour, but profitability is not something that attracts approval. The tone of the reporting tells us a lot. In television news studios, energy company profits tend to trigger gloom and long faces on reporters, whereas profits in other industries make for more upbeat reporting. But perhaps those favoured industries should also be on their guard. In the UK's news media, the lauding of success is often the first step towards criticism of the successful.

It is, of course, no good blaming the news media, nor even the politicians, for their failure to understand engineering, or even the business of investment. They each have their agenda and they have to win their audience. The electricity supply industry should have won its audience, too, but it failed. I was part of that failure in that, although I believe that AEP had a good record in terms of responding to criticism, on reflection, it spent too little time ensuring that some of the simpler facts of life of the electricity supply industry were understood by the policy-makers and those who influence them. And, of course, even if we had had the time and resources to engage in an 'education' programme, the generating sector was but one part of the industry.

When it did try to communicate, all too often the industry failed to do as well as it might have. It should have remembered the pros and cons of 'KISS'. 'Keep it simple, stupid' is a valuable mantra, which is best understood in the fields of engineering and design. As customers and users of different goods, we know almost instinctively when KISS has been applied successfully, although we tend to take for granted the effort that goes into the design of a good product. Communicators also fare better when they understand the principle. But in the electricity industry, perhaps too readily, we fall into a trap which may well have led to us reducing the public's understanding of the industry and its challenges. The trap is that of over-simplifying to the point of misleading the audience. As Albert Einstein is reported to have said: 'Everything must be made as simple as possible. But not simpler.'

As far as the public's understanding of the electricity supply industry is concerned, policy-makers, regulators and industry communicators seem to have remarkably low expectations. It is clear that people can cope with the challenge of online gambling, mobile phones, 'apps', internet shopping, foreign travel, rents, mortgages, banking, social media and home entertainment systems, but are deemed to be incapable of understanding what a kilowatt hour is. Electricity bills are usually said to be too complicated, and choosing between a range of competing tariffs - where, of course, there is plenty of help available from price comparison websites - has led not just the regulator, but at one point, even the UK Prime Minister, to opine that the customer is faced with too much choice and that the range of options should be regulated away.

I was surprised to find that even some of the cost-conscious and savvy buyers of energy for business would like things to be simpler. At a lunch attended by industrial and commercial buyers of energy, I was sitting next to the guest speaker, the then Chief Executive of Ofgem, Callum McCarthy, when one member of the audience complained that his firm was faced with a choice of too many different tariffs. Almost in the manner of Victor Meldrew, but taking care only to whisper, Callum said to me 'I cannot believe what I have just heard.' Nor could I. If choosing an energy contract is too challenging for industrial energy buyers, they should get help. The Major Energy Users' Council helps its members with that sort of thing. It is not alone. Having been a judge for the 'Energy Live Consultancy Awards'[64], I am aware of the many excellent professional advisers that will help their clients secure the best deal. That must surely be a better option than calling for choice to be reduced?

But sometimes, we try too hard to simplify things. The typical news release that announces a new power project always tries to keep the story simple, but may turn out to be misleading at the same time. Here is a nice, simple statement:

'When it is completed, the 576-megawatt project will provide enough electricity for 400,000 homes.'

Yes, but not if the occupants of those homes all decide to switch on an electric kettle at the same time. The 576-megawatt

---

[64] The Energy Live Consultancy Awards. Energy Live News. www.energylivenews.com

production facility would allow each of those 400,000 houses to consume up to 1.4 kilowatts. That is enough for when the family's appliances were simply ticking over – the fridge, the freezer, the computer, the phone chargers, the appliances on standby and perhaps a few other things – but not enough to boil the kettle, do the ironing, cook the dinner or run an electric shower, and nowhere near enough to be doing all of those things at the same time. The electricity supply industry in Britain has been so successful that its customers do not expect their consumption to be constrained – they expect any or all of their appliances to work when they plug them in and switch on.

That includes days when millions are watching the same television programme and they boil an electric kettle at the end, or during an interval. Probably the best-known 'television pick-up' of this type was at the end of the football World Cup Semi-Final between West Germany and England on 4 July 1990, when an additional demand of 2,800 megawatts had to be met, although, curiously, not quite as rapidly as the managers of the system had expected. The grid controllers were surprised that, at first, nothing seemed to happen – the England team's armchair supporters, must have been numbed and immobilised by the defeat in the penalty shoot-out and for a few moments, there was no increase in demand. By now, of course, we know that, when it comes to a penalty shoot-out, the kettle may as well go on as soon as the need for penalty kicks becomes apparent.

Strictly speaking, that press release about the 576-megawatt power station is just about correct. But it becomes misleading if readers conclude that the 400,000 homes could rely entirely on its production. In the interests of simplicity, it does not mention that power stations are not always able to produce electricity – they close for maintenance, sometimes they break down and if they are powered by an energy source which is weather-dependent (e.g. wind or sunshine), then they may or may not be able to deliver power when the customer wants it. In an integrated electricity system, where customers not only want the fridge and freezer to run continuously but also want the hairdryer (and any other appliance) to work when they switch it on, there has to be steady production to keep the 'always on' things running and sufficient other plant that can respond as soon as it is required – to increase electricity production, or, scale it down when demand drops. Until there is a significant breakthrough in electricity storage technology, electricity stands out as the prime example of a 'just-in-time' product, and the integrated system that Britain enjoys is a good example of how to deliver this precious commodity reliably. The principles behind this are much the same, regardless of the industry's ownership structure.

A '576-megawatt' power plant means nothing to most customers. A power plant to supply 400,000 homes does at least paint some kind of a picture. But what are lacking are the other facts of life in electricity supply. Demand rises and falls, sometimes predictably, sometimes less so. To deal with those changes, a kilowatt hour of electricity will have a different value at different times. Even in the state-owned industry, under the 'Bulk Supply Tariff', there were seasonal, time-of-day elements – lacking in detail compared with today's market, but nevertheless signifying the importance of the issue. The CEGB needed a mix of plant to manage the system. Under private ownership, a mix is still required, but deciding what should run and when it should do so is commercially-driven and some of the key elements of pricing are now visible, for those that are interested.

But what of that electricity production that cannot respond to demand, because it depends entirely on wind or sunshine?

When the Association of Independent Electricity Producers was formed, in 1987, with, even at that time, renewable energy interests in the membership, there were no commercially-available photovoltaic panels turning sunlight into electricity, and although there were a few pioneering wind turbines, their impact was hardly measurable. Since then, things have changed enormously. Everyone is now familiar with the sight of a wind farm, or at least, pictures of them. In fields in some parts of the country there are 'solar farms', and in most areas there are photovoltaic panels to be seen on roofs. Make no mistake, these technologies do produce electricity. That is not an issue. But what they look like has become an issue, and whether they represent value for money is also an issue. Those are serious matters. The issue of visual impact, however, tends to concern people who, for years, have been enjoying the benefit of electricity from power stations which they have probably never seen. They are happily located in someone else's back yard. It is nonetheless serious. So is the question of value for money. It is far from trivial, because the extra cost of developing and running these technologies is added to customers' electricity bills, and that includes the customers who are less able to pay. I will return to those matters, but first I should say that this is another area where, in the interests of simplicity, customers have been misled. In this case, the blame may lie more with government than with the electricity industry, but both should be in the dock over this.

What matters most is that we have the means of electricity production to satisfy demand. That, of course, has to be paid for and where reliability of supply is concerned, an 'off-grid' means of electricity production will not usually be able to offer as much reassurance as a location on an interconnected system. From time to time, we hear how a local community would like to become 'independent', producing and supplying its own electricity – usually with renewable energy in mind. As part of the price for their independence, a few of these may well be willing to endure some 'down time' – breakdowns, repairs and maintenance – and go without the benefit of their appliances, entertainment systems etc. But those people are in a tiny minority. Today, most people want something better than a third world level of reliability. Importantly, so does the third world, of course, although we should not under-estimate how important a rooftop array of photo-voltaic panels can be to a remote, third-world village, miles from any grid – powering refrigeration, they could mean that the village has access to life-changing vaccines and medicines which would otherwise be unavailable.

Most want more than that, though. I recall, in June 1996, an official visit to the AEP by delegates from Ghana, who were looking to increase their country's generating capacity and strengthen their power network. When Nicola Steen and I started to talk encouragingly about renewable energy, they listened politely but then made clear that they wanted to move beyond unreliable supplies to something '…like your system.' Closer to home, on a visit to see the very likeable and highly respected then Chief Executive of Guernsey Electricity, Ian Watson, I discussed with him the reliability of the electricity cable which linked the island with an electricity supply from EdF, in France. The answer was that it was highly reliable, albeit, like everything else, not 100 per cent of course.

'Then, do you still need your diesel-fuelled power station?' I asked.

'You sound like a regulator, David' he replied. 'Can you imagine the impact on this island's international finance businesses if we were to suffer major power cuts?'

In 2013, friends living in a rural location in Cornwall were confronted with a planning application for a 50-kilowatt wind turbine, over 100 feet high, in a field close to their house. They were deeply concerned and they wanted to discuss it with me. The turbine was the subject of an application under the 'Feed-In Tariff' and the planning application referred to the way it would help the county meet its renewable energy objectives, reduce carbon emissions, provide enough electricity for... etc. Although my friends did not want to look at the windmill from their sitting room window for the rest of their lives, they imagined nevertheless that it would be providing the area with a large amount of electricity, which they assumed would be important to the region. I began explaining what 50 kilowatts meant, but I sensed that I was not making things as clear as I had wished. 'I shall check the rating label on my electric kettle' I said. 'Three kilowatts' I told them. 'In that case, if the wind is blowing, the turbine would be able to power about 17 electric kettles like mine' I said. 'Only 17 electric kettles?' they replied. 'Well, perhaps 20 electric kettles if they were less powerful, 2.5 kilowatt ones.' In its way, that was just as misleading as the claims regarding the numbers of households that a power plant will provide for, but it was nevertheless highly accurate. They, of course, were somewhat surprised and the thought of their cottage being overlooked by this structure for about 25 years, whether it was operating or not, did not please them. Most people they spoke to were as surprised as they had been. Had it been a roof-top wind turbine, of the kind that used to be sold in DIY stores, their expectations would probably have been lower. But this was what they considered to be a big piece of power-generating equipment – important for the nation's power supply.

My friends in Cornwall, of course, are not the only intelligent people in the country who have little knowledge of electricity supply. After E.ON UK proposed building a new coal-fired power station on the site of its aged plant at Kingsnorth, in Kent, the more extreme elements of the environmental lobby launched a sustained attack on the existing power station, with the intention of closing it down. In August 2008, with a camp near the plant and a menu of stunts, including climbing the power station chimney, they attracted huge publicity. As Chief Executive of the Association of Electricity Producers, I was interviewed by press, radio and TV and participated in a live report on *Channel Four News*, where I was confronted by the formidable Caroline Lucas, then a Green Party MEP. But it was not my engagement with the news media that is relevant here. E.ON's staff told me that the local radio station had done some 'vox pop' interviews with local residents about the proposed new power plant, asking them if they would like a new power station on the site of the one that was due to close. Some said yes – the old plant had been a feature of the local landscape for years and a valued source of employment and they welcomed the prospect of that continuing. Others, of course, said no. When asked by the interviewer what they would build instead, some replied 'a wind farm'. The interviewer went on to ask how many wind turbines they thought would be needed to match the output of the proposed new coal-fired power station. There were various replies and they included 'Ten' and 'about twelve'. The proposed new coal-fired plant at Kingsnorth would have produced 1,600 megawatts. I am not sure what the typical output of an onshore wind turbine was at that time, but let's assume that a state-of-the-art machine would have produced 2.5 megawatts. To match the capacity of the coal-fired plant, instead of ten or twelve turbines, some 640 of them would have been required and even then, they would have been productive for little more than a third of the time that the coal plant would have been.

My thoughts, here, should not be interpreted as an attack on wind energy. What I am questioning is the muddled development of policy. When the wind is blowing at the right speed, wind turbines produce electricity perfectly well and the industry has made enormous strides in advancing the technology. So effectively, in fact, that it symbolises renewable energy in the UK. Energy policy, however, has stimulated the construction of large wind farms well in advance of policy-makers and the industry being able to make best use of wind power with the technology currently at our disposal. Not only that, but this has occurred under trading arrangements that policy-makers introduced in 2001[65], with the intention of driving down prices by bringing the cheapest and most competitive technologies to the fore and, in the process, rewarding predictable power and penalising producers who could not deliver when demand required them to. Policy is not muddled from the point of view of those that make it, of course.

When the political aspirations for technologies such as wind power were modest, so was the scale of the problem of accommodating weather-dependent production on the electricity system. But as aspirations grew and targets got bigger, someone should have been able to say to policy-makers that until we have a large-scale and cost-effective method of storing electricity, technologies that produce electricity only when weather conditions are right – rather than when the customer wants it – present a huge challenge to our electricity system. If they are to be built, then we must also have available plant that can respond to demand, either by keeping ageing fossil-fuelled plant on the system or building new plant that can respond when required, or both. There is, of course, a substantial cost attached to doing that. But this message was probably not delivered strongly until the thoughts of E.ON UK were quoted in *The Guardian* on 4 June 2008:

One of Britain's leading energy providers warned yesterday that Britain will need substantial fossil fuel generation to back up the renewable energy it needs to meet European Union targets. The UK has to meet a target of 15% of energy from renewables by 2020.

---

[65] The New Electricity Trading Arrangements ('NETA'), which replaced the Electricity Pool of England and Wales in 2001.

E.ON said that it could take 50 gigawatts of renewable electricity generation to meet the EU target. But it would require up to 90% of this amount as backup from coal and gas plants to ensure supply when intermittent renewable supplies were not available. That would push Britain's installed power base from the existing 76 gigawatts to 120 gigawatts.

Paul Golby, E.ON UK's chief executive, declined to be drawn on how much the expansion would cost, beyond saying it would be "significant".

There are several reasons why the industry – AEP included – was slow to speak on this issue. First is that over the years, out of respect for the democratic system from which they derive so much benefit, our energy companies have tended to be sparing with any public criticism of government – in this case, the European Union's Renewable Energy Directive, where the 15% target for renewable energy implied that over 30% of the UK's electricity would have to come from renewable energy by 2020[66]. The second reason is that UK energy companies, large and small, had enjoyed the degree of certainty that investment in renewable energy provides when legislation offers prescribed prices. Unless a scheme is very obviously flawed and doomed to fail, an energy company's board of directors might be hard put to explain to shareholders why it was *not* proposing to invest in technology that the government provided strong support for, albeit by compulsory charges on customers' bills. The third reason why the industry was slow to make reference to the problems was probably its poor reputation and the lack of trust in it on the part of policy-makers and the public. Almost certainly, it would have been portrayed as protecting vested interests and living in the past.

There have been attempts to make things simple, but so much so that they have been misleading. The outcome is that instead of

---

[66] There were reports suggesting that Prime Minister Tony Blair accepted this on behalf of the UK because he had assumed mistakenly that the 15% was related to electricity.

simple messages giving people a better grasp of the issues, the public's understanding is at times almost in the realms of childish fantasy. It is not just government and the electricity industry that are guilty of this. Lobby groups that are opposed to the industry and critical of energy policy find over-simplified messages very handy, and the news media are not always as probing as they should be. In November 2013, when RWE npower Renewables shelved its plan to build, in the Bristol Channel, what would have been the UK's biggest offshore wind farm, the BBC regional news programme *Spotlight* reported that among the concerns about the abandonment of the scheme was the challenge of keeping the lights on. Many journalists seem blissfully unaware of the extent to which a wind farm is able to 'keep the lights on'.

In August 2006, a 'Camp for Climate Action' descended on the coal-fired power station at Drax, in Yorkshire, intent on closing it down – at least temporarily. At 3,900 megawatts, Drax was the largest coal-fired power station in western Europe and it provided, typically, about seven per cent of Britain's electricity. The 'Camp for Climate Action' attracted a lot of publicity and when the impressive Chief Executive of Drax Power, Dorothy Thompson, had been interviewed and there was not very much more that could be said by the company, I was rolled out to comment. One such engagement was a live appearance on BBC Radio Four *You and Yours* on 31 August 2006. I was in the studio at Broadcasting House with the programme's host, Winifred Robinson. The spokesperson for the Camp, Alice Cutler, spoke 'down the line', from somewhere at or near the site. After an introductory discussion there followed comments that, if we use coal for power generation '…we're all going to be toast…' and we should be looking at '…the end of, you know, the end life on earth really…' Those were contentious enough statements, but an earlier one that the camp was '…

organised as an example of the way we want to live' was interesting, too. I should point out that life at the Camp for Climate Action was based on micro-scale intermittent energy supplies, compost lavatories, pedal-powered laundries and strictly vegan food. Without having conducted a survey, I would suggest that the way most people want to live is different from that and it involves an assumption about reliable and responsive supplies of electricity.

In 2008, there was a glimmer of hope for those who favour simple explanations, but not at the expense of losing sight of the facts when Professor David MacKay[67] published *Sustainable Energy - Without the Hot Air*.[68] Professor MacKay wrote his much-acclaimed book because he was fed up with judgements about energy technologies being steered by adjectives, rather than facts and figures and concerned that people are expected to have views on energy policy without access to a simple mathematical understanding of the issues. Among the large number of endorsements for it was this one, from Professor Martin Rees FRS, then President of the Royal Society:

'Energy policy is crucial for the world, and a wide public should be engaged in debate and decisions on these issues. But such debate must be grounded in realistic numbers and good physics. All the key principles are clearly and accessibly explained in this book. David MacKay has performed a great service by writing it.'

I invited Professor MacKay to be the Guest of Honour and speaker at the Annual Lunch of the Association of Electricity Producers on 5 November 2009. The big audience – a wide range of electricity generating interests and an even wider range of guests – enjoyed his short talk very much and he was a great pleasure to talk to over

[67] Chief Scientific Advisor at the Department of Energy & Climate Change (DECC). In addition to his role at DECC, David is Professor of Natural Philosophy in the Department of Physics at the University of Cambridge.

[68] Sustainable Energy – without the hot air. David J C MacKay. www.withouthotair.com/

lunch. The Professor's refreshing approach to the big issues enables debate to start on common ground, even though, with the best will in the world, before coming to conclusions, we must wrestle with so many different assumptions and our prejudices are rarely buried entirely.

It was encouraging that Professor MacKay was taken on as an adviser at the Department of Energy and Climate Change, but as Margaret Thatcher famously said in her television interview with Brian Walden, 'Advisers are there to advise, Ministers are there to decide'.

CHAPTER THIRTEEN

MARKET ABUSE – A BATTLE WITH THE REGULATOR

The privatisation of the state electricity industry's generating business owed much to careful design and a great deal to a political accident. A key element of the design was that one of the privatised businesses had to be big enough to absorb the costs and risks of the CEGB's nuclear plant. The political accident was that the City could not see how to sell off those stations and a new state-owned generating company, Nuclear Electric, had to be set up to accommodate them, until a way could be found to privatise that company. Nevertheless, there were initially two big ex-state generating companies – known as 'Big G' and 'Little G' at the planning stage and National Power and PowerGen in the implementation. In terms of competition, this was far from ideal and there was huge unease in the Association of Independent Electricity Producers about the implications for other players – existing and new – who would be dwarfed by these giants in the generating market. Some commentators called for a break-up of those companies, to create a number of smaller generating businesses. The political timetable did not permit that; there was probably a sense that less would be likely to go wrong in terms of security of supply and the share sale would have been a much trickier proposition. Arguably, existing and prospective independents would not have been as well served, either. They were usually price-takers, rather than price-setters and much fiercer competition from day one could have been decidedly unhelpful.

State-owned Nuclear Electric was a full participant at the various industry tables, including the Electricity Pool, but without having to face quite the same commercial pressures that National Power and PowerGen were adapting to and being usually a price-taker, its psychology would always be different. National Power and PowerGen, however, worked hard at building their brands – one, the UK's biggest generating business with all the style and responsibility that went with that status and the other, in the 'we try harder' mould, once adopted by *Avis* in the car rental market.

Very soon, the operation of the generating sector had its critics. It was always likely to find itself in the firing line. From the outset, it supplied electricity direct to the energy-intensive industries and the customer-facing, 'retail' part of the industry – at least for domestic customers – did not become competitive until 1999 (a year later than planned), until which time domestic prices were regulated and did not attract the attention that they would later. A reputational virus took hold very quickly and although the market has changed enormously since the early 1990s, it continues to infect the industry.

It was the Electricity Pool that began to attract attention. Large industrial customers, who had been the first to be able to take advantage of competitive buying of electricity, did not like what the Pool delivered. Journalists latched on very quickly and although many of them found it a struggle to understand the mechanism, that made the situation worse, rather than better. Few of them understood either that in the early days of the Pool, the market was distorted by long-term contracts to buy British coal, contracts which the two major generating companies had been required by the government to sign at privatisation. One way or another, the accepted wisdom was that the Pool was manipulated and the outcome was a succession of reports by the regulator, OFFER. The Pool was at quite a disadvantage in these exchanges of fire. It was an unusual entity in that it was not a company, merely an agreement between the parties who were required to belong to it, with oversight from the Director General of Electricity Supply ('OFFER'). With some of the complainants within its own ranks, as buyers, and initially very little specialised communications machinery with which to defend itself (and always a huge agenda of important development and operational issues to be addressed) it was at times a sitting duck.

It was not the fault of the Pool that there was an imbalance of market power in the generating market and it could do nothing about that, beyond ensuring that the Pooling and Settlement Agreement was adhered to and that the Pool's rules were applied. It did that, of course. The organisation was led with great diligence and integrity by its first Chief Executive, Margaret Thompson,[69] whose huge intellect and drive kept it moving forward when lesser mortals would have been dragged down by the weight of the issues and the volume of criticism.

By the time Neil Bryson[70] became Pool Chairman in 1996, the mechanism was running well. Margaret Thompson's determination and the efforts of the members had ensured that the Pool would perform as it was meant to, although that was not always enough to impress the industry's critics. By 1995, Margaret had moved on to a senior role at Scottish Gas and later at Centrica and Andrew Claxton had become Chief Executive. Andrew, like his predecessor, possessing great intellect, came with an MBA from Stanford

---

[69] Later became Margaret McKinlay.
[70] One of the developers of the first UK CCGT project (Lakeland Power) and former Chairman of Association of Electricity Producers.

University and 11 years' experience with McKinsey & Co. As a member of the Pool Executive Committee, I was astonished at how he absorbed so rapidly the way that the Pool worked. He also had a good sense of humour – a valuable weapon to have in the armoury, especially on those occasions when intellect, education and experience may have been tested in the face of a range of competing interests.

With Andrew's support, Chairman, Neil Bryson persuaded the Pool members to bring the issue of the Pool's image and reputation up the agenda. Clive Moffatt of Moffatt Associates – an experienced and sympathetic practitioner – was engaged to help address some of the PR issues. But sensing the danger that the Pool was in, from the barrage of adverse publicity, Neil's ideas went much further than improving communications. Key to his thinking was that the Pool was seen by its critics as self-serving and not in touch with what its customers wanted and in response to this, he proposed that governance of the Pool should be taken away from its members and vested in an independent board. The members were not easily persuaded of the wisdom of this, but eventually, the proposal was accepted.

I felt that the Pool now had a strong platform from which to do much more than merely defend itself. It had a positive proposal which acknowledged much of the criticism of the organisation. The Pool, however, was making these decisions at a time of huge political change. In the background, OFFER, having published its concern at price-setting in the Pool (in the first three years, the two largest companies set the price for 90% of the time) was looking to reform the Pool and on the front pages, the Labour Party was looking very likely to win the 1997 General Election. In June 1997 it did just that and in the build-up to the election, it criticised the Pool. That may not have been headline-making, but it was all part of the political mood – a mood which demanded great changes. The fact that regulated divestment of plant following a Pool price cap (1994-1996) had extended the range of price setters in the Pool cut little ice. Politics was in the driving seat.

The new Labour Energy Minister, John Battle MP, spoke about the review of the Pool at the Pool conference. He was about to leave promptly at the end of his speech, rather than take questions – a bad omen – but Chairman, Neil Bryson asked him to stay for questions that his officials would probably have preferred him to avoid.

But the Pool had what should have been a trump card – its proposal to hand over Pool governance to an independent body. We needed to make sure that the Minister understood the importance of this and a meeting in his office was arranged. Neil Bryson, Kevin Lee of NORWEB and I were the Pool team. We were received cordially and were listened to. The idea that the Pool would hand over its governance to an independent body should, surely, make the Minister and his officials sit up and take notice? They listened politely, but there were very few questions and this left the Pool's team of three feeling uneasy. I felt even more uneasy because sitting opposite me, Jonathan Green, Director, Electricity and Energy Utilities at the DTI, whom I knew fairly well and had worked with for some time, looked decidedly uncomfortable with what we had to say. It would later become clear that, however compelling the Pool's idea might have seemed to us, it did not fit the political agenda.

The new Energy Minister (his functions also included Science and Industry, incidentally) asked the Director General of Electricity Supply (OFFER) to review electricity trading arrangements. Eventually, it became clear that the OFFER-inspired 'Pool review', with DTI support, was actually about the abolition of the

Electricity Pool and its replacement with 'New Electricity Trading Arrangements'. The industry was to lose control of the governance of its wholesale trading mechanism, but not in the way the Pool itself had proposed. The organisation had been sleep-walking in that direction and although Neil Bryson's awareness and leadership had aroused the Pool members and put a great idea forward, it was too late to address the extent to which the Electricity Pool was disapproved of.

Perhaps bizarrely, one of the Labour government's criticisms of the Pool was that it had favoured gas-fired plant at the expense of coal, to which the party had, of course, a deep-seated allegiance. In 1998, it instituted a 'Review of energy sources for power generation' and imposed a moratorium on new gas-fired power stations, unless they were also CHP schemes[71]. Prospective developers of new CCGT stations were furious, and the intervention was an early sign that the liberalisation had proved rather too liberal for some political tastes. The government's review however, a consultation, referred to reform of the wholesale electricity trading arrangements '...to provide for proper competition in generation...' At the same time, it talked of the importance of taking action to secure diversity in power generation (i.e. protect coal-fired production) for fear of permanent closure of coal-fired generating capacity in the coming few years (incidentally, this was something that the EU Large Combustion Plants Directive would bring about, later, but for different reasons).

The Association of Electricity Producers, faced with the consultation on energy sources, was to find its long-standing preference for market solutions put to the test. This well-understood philosophy of the Association had been carried forward from its predecessor, the Association of Independent Electricity Producers.

---

[71] A CCGT would have some heat to spare, but its location would be determined by factors such as proximity to the grid, availability of a gas supply and, access to cooling water. Once those prerequisites have been satisfied, there is rarely any scope cost-effectively to make use of surplus heat, which requires construction of a network of insulated pipes and most importantly, customers that can use it and will pay for it.

If there was an exception to it, that lay in its acceptance of some support for renewable energy. That, of course, was a more comfortable exception whilst it represented only a very small part of the market and more so in that, a step on from raw research and development, the mechanism was orientated towards giving supported schemes some contact with the commercial reality of the electricity market-place.

The Association's response, dated 16 February 1998, was on 'The government's review of energy sources, including fuel diversity, sustainable development and the role of coal' and it included the following paragraphs, which point to the lack of clarity beginning to emerge in energy policy a mere eight years after the liberalisation process had begun and only seven years after the privatisation of the state-owned generating interests:

This review comes at a time when virtually every significant feature of the electricity supply industry is under scrutiny. The government is examining utility regulation, clean coal technology, renewable energy, electricity trading and now security of supply, fuel diversity and gas-fired power generation. At the same time, the Electricity Pool of England and Wales is carrying out a review of the Pool. It is important to note that these reviews appear to have been prompted by different pressures and concerns, some of which may well conflict with each other. This means that it is difficult for the Association to make detailed proposals about, for example, fuel diversity, without knowing the government's precise intentions in respect of the United Kingdom's contribution to any future reduction of anthropogenic greenhouse gas emissions (see also paragraphs 26-28 below).

The Association accepts, of course, that it is reasonable to conduct reviews of the electricity industry, but it urges the government to be cautious about hastily introducing changes as a result of any particular review. It must recognise that each of the various matters under review has a relationship with the others and it is therefore essential that there should be an opportunity to reflect on the effects of any changes which are proposed. This is vital in an industry whose standards of performance have encouraged customers to have high expectations of it, where so much capital has been invested; and where the need to maintain investors' confidence for the future is so important.

Furthermore, the announcement of so many reviews could suggest to some observers that there are fundamental problems with the electricity industry. If such a perception were allowed to develop, it could not only have a detrimental effect on inward investment in the UK electricity industry but undermine the efforts of British companies who are seeking to invest abroad on the basis of the success of the UK market and their contribution to it. For the avoidance of doubt, the Association's assessment of the electricity industry is that, in virtually every respect, it has performed extremely well since privatisation and it is capable of meeting the rising expectations of its customers in the challenging years ahead.

The response went on to say a great deal about security of supply, including:

The commercial reality is that electricity producers cannot secure the revenue which they require to stay in business without access to fuel from which to generate. Neither can they expect to sell their product if the system itself is not secure. In this sense, their interest in maintaining security of supply and an efficient and secure system matches exactly that of the industry's customers.

One key question arising from the debate about security is how judgements about such security matters should be made and also what effect such judgements have on the paying customer. Security can never be absolute. No fuel supply is completely secure and no system can be completely secure, either. So, debates about security are apt to become debates about the extent of risk and then the extent to which steps should be taken to cover such risks, including that of catastrophic failure. The Association would be pleased to provide further comments and advice on this issue if the government wishes to explore it further.

As for security where it relates to the availability of fuel supplies, the Association, whose membership includes producers using the full range of fuels and technologies, has always been well disposed towards diversity and it understands concerns expressed about undue dependence on one fuel. The Association has, however, encouraged the development of a market where generators are largely free to choose the fuels and generating technologies which enable them to produce electricity successfully in a competitive environment. To date, the competitive market has introduced more diversity via the use of gas. The Association recognises that, from now on, the same competitive market will begin to reduce that diversity. If the government is inclined to recommend that, in the interests of diversity, fuel choice should be curtailed in some way, it will also wish to take account of the impact of such an intervention on prices. Indeed, induced diversity and measures to reduce risks associated with security of the system invariably involve extra costs which, in due course, have to be accounted for.

On environmental issues, it read:

The Association is an active participant in the debate about the response to potential change to the world's climates. In recent months, it has been involved in important discussions about the scope for trading emissions on the basis of permits. It favours the adoption of measures which would be most compatible with an open and competitive electricity market and is not attracted to taxation measures as an influence over emissions, if there is a risk that they could add to the costs of the electricity industry and its customers, without achieving proportionate environmental benefits. With those issues in mind, the Association is concerned that the government should not commit the United Kingdom to targets which are unrealistic or which exceed international agreements.

I cannot help but reflect that many of these comments, which were committed to paper early in 1998, could have been cut and pasted and with very little change, used in response to the reviews during the period of uncertainty from 2010-2014.

Also, in 1998, National Power and PowerGen were given consent to buy the supply businesses of two regional electricity companies (Midlands and East Midlands, respectively). They were allowed to do so without a reference to the Competition Commission on the understanding that they would further divest some more coal-fired capacity, which they did. This led the way, of course, to more vertical integration in the industry and in later years, to a great deal of controversy about the impact of that integration on competition in the market. I could see both sides of that argument, but could never understand why, if there was to be vertical integration, its challenges could not be addressed effectively by the growing forces of regulation.

Nevertheless, in 1998, in the midst of that tangle of policy – a desire to increase competition, matched by a desire to intervene in the generating mix – a reference to the Competition Commission was creeping closer.

In November 1998, Callum McCarthy entered the industry as a new regulator, taking the post of Director General of Gas Supply, then, in January 1999, Director General of Electricity Supply and in June of that year, becoming the Chief Executive of the merged gas and electricity bodies – the Gas and Electricity Markets Authority, or 'Ofgem'.

When the news broke that Callum McCarthy was to become

the new regulator, Michael Spicer told me that he knew Callum, who had been a senior civil servant from the days of the Conservative government, when Michael had been a Minister. He spoke of him in glowing terms and I was pleased to hear what he had to say. That should have made for a good start, but alas, it did not. In an early encounter, Callum approached me at a lunchtime reception, when I was in conversation with Yvonne Constance, who chaired the Electricity Consumers' Committees, and having said that he was pleased to see me, proceeded to complain to me that I was 'dumbing down the debate' at a time when there were serious issues to be addressed. He went on to say that if I persisted in doing that, he 'would not be able to deal with me.' I took this to mean that he would choose not to. Somewhat taken aback, at first I gave him puzzled look and then said 'I can only think that you are referring to things that I say to the press and if so, I have to say that, if I use technical and highfalutin language, they won't report anything I say.' That was exactly what he meant and afterwards, I had mixed feelings about this grumpy encounter. On the one hand, I was not a great fan of simplifying things to the extent that their meaning was lost, so I was embarrassed. On the other hand, perhaps we had been winning more arguments than I gave AEP and myself credit for and regulatory nerves had been touched. I am pleased to say that this relationship became a good one before Callum ended his term of office, but not before we had gone through a couple of battles over a serious issue.

It was not long before Callum picked up where his predecessor, Stephen Littlechild, had left off – with reports on prices in the Pool. OFFER's work and later that of Ofgem – criticism of pool prices and concern about the small number of companies setting prices in the Pool – led to the publication in December 1999 of a consultation proposing a licence amendment which became known as the 'Market Abuse Licence Condition' (MALC).

Having a dominant position in a market is not, in itself, illegal, although the abuse of such a dominant position is. But the potential penalty for contravening the legislation was severe – a fine of up to 10% of a company's worldwide turnover and the possibility of damages claims against the company by third parties and the risk of fines and imprisonment for individuals convicted of offences. Competition law was taken seriously by the companies in the industry and indeed, by the Association, where there was a compliance procedure, which included, among other things, an instruction to staff that they should close any meeting where the discussion appeared to stray off-limits. This ruling never had to be invoked, of course, because the members had no inclination to break the rules.

Ofgem's argument for a Market Abuse Licence Condition acknowledged the importance of competition law, but suggested that the electricity market is different from other commodity markets and needed special attention – in Ofgem's view, a different test of competitiveness, namely 'substantial market power'. That was despite the fact that it was preparing to introduce new electricity trading arrangements, to replace the Pool, on the grounds that the electricity was just like any other commodity and the arrangements for trading electricity should reflect that.

The licensed generating companies were invited to accept the proposed change to their licences. Within AEP, there was serious discussion about this issue. It concerned the membership deeply, because there was no definition of what might constitute 'abuse' and it appeared to put Ofgem in a position where it could decide, after the event, that abuse had taken place. This looked like too much power going to a court that had too little law on which to make judgements. The members concerned felt that Ofgem wanted to avoid the obvious route – a reference to the Competition

Commission – because it wanted to be able to influence the way the generating companies behaved, whether they were in breach of competition law or not. Worse still, although Ofgem acknowledged its powerful 'judge and jury' status in this proposal and suggested that it would put, to a specially-appointed panel, cases where it thought that abuse had taken place, that panel would be no more than advisory and there would be no formal appeal process, other than judicial review. Generating companies, of course, have to be able to tell those staff who bid to trade a plant's output what they may and may not do. Ofgem offered some guidance, but it was inadequate and at meetings to discuss the issue, its managers seemed to know that.

Eventually, six companies said, albeit most of them reluctantly, that they would accept the change in their licence conditions. They will each have had their own reasons for doing that – a quiet life, an intention to fight on this later, case by case, or, even the hope that acquiescence would be helpful to them on other regulatory issues may have swayed them. They also knew that two companies felt very strongly about the proposal and were unlikely to accept it, and if they fought and won the battle, those who had been prepared to sign on the dotted line would also be excused from the MALC regime, having first earned points for accepting the proposal.

Two companies did, indeed, hold out – AES and Nuclear Electric. This gave the rest something of an each-way bet and battle commenced. The deadline passed and Callum McCarthy referred the matter to the Competition Commission, which would have to decide whether the dissenting generators' refusal to accept the change to their licence would be against the public interest. The AEP prepared concise but powerful written evidence. In an 18-paragraph submission, it referred to the uncertainty that the condition would create; the wider impact of the proposal; the discrepancy between Ofgem's view (introducing NETA) that the electricity market is a commodity market like any other and (proposing this condition) that it is different and therefore requires its own test for competitiveness; the market where 'abuse' was alleged (but not proven) was being abolished; the risk that the development of the new market would be hampered by Ofgem's ability to interpret behaviour after the event and the risk that lobby groups would take advantage of the licence condition and try to use regulatory power, in addition to commercial influence, concerning prices.

The conclusion of AEP's short paper read:

The licence condition is unnecessary in a competitive market governed by stringent competition legislation. It amounts to an extra layer of regulation in a sector of the electricity market where regulation really ought to be declining. The way in which it might be applied is far from clear and there is a serious risk that it could be used, unwittingly or even politically, to penalise perfectly healthy market behaviour. It will add to the risks and costs faced by the licensees and in that respect, it is, in fact, Ofgem's licence condition which could operate against the public interest.

The Association, of course, was an interested party, but not a licensee. So, although AEP provided the forum where the affected members could meet to discuss the case, it was the two dissenting licence holders that were in the line of fire. They conducted themselves very well and the rest of the industry will have felt that it owed them a debt of gratitude.

In due course, the spotlight did fall on the Association. The Competition Commission announced a day of oral evidence, which took place at the Royal Society of Arts on Monday 26 June 2000.

I was invited to give evidence. I was, however, due to be on holiday in the period leading up to the hearing and the drafting was done by our then part-time Head of Electricity Trading, Steve Johnson, who had joined AEP from PowerGen. Steve was top quality; with years of electricity industry experience, he knew the people and how the business worked and people, myself included, found him very easy to work with. Nicola was very sharp, very diligent and knew how to use the written word, having worked on heavyweight material in her previous role at Chatham House. Between them, they did a marvellous job weighing up what I ought to say. I, however, was on holiday in a small hotel in Panzano-in-Chianti and commenting on their early drafts by fax. The Competition Commission hearing was to be held on my first day back at the office and on the flight home, a few days before the event, I felt that one or two of my comments could have been a bit more robust. I went into the office in the evening and changed the draft. When Steve and Nicola came in the next morning to do a final run-through, they were surprised.

'We didn't think you would go that far' said Nicola.

'Until yesterday, you would have been absolutely right' I replied. 'It must have been the holiday.'

The hearing was chaired by Mrs Denise Kingsmill and I recall that Professor Martin Cave[72] was on the panel. A statement from Dr Eileen Marshall of Ofgem addressed the impact that NETA would have:

'To summarise, we consider that NETA will provide a much more competitive wholesale trading environment, but we consider that the threat to the public interest from the abuse of market power is likely to remain. NETA will make it less extreme, but NETA cannot actually solve all the problems and that is why we firmly believe that, for the new trading

[72] From January 2012, Deputy Chair of the Competition Commission.

arrangements to be the success that we all want them to be, there needs to be a market abuse licence condition even under NETA.'

Ofgem clearly wanted to get its retaliation in first. From the consultation meetings and from our written evidence, they knew that we would point to the huge changes to the trading arrangements, that Ofgem itself was leading, to deliver a more competitive market.

My turn at the lectern arrived and with Callum McCarthy and Eileen Marshall listening from the front row, I delivered the messages that we had prepared. I knew exactly where, in the notes, the key sentences lay.

The transcript showed that, after some introductory comments, I said:

'NETA is a massive change in the arrangements for trading electricity, and it is being implemented to deal with the problems arising from the Pool, some of which are real, and some are merely perceived. Not only will the impact of NETA be huge, but the cost of putting it into effect will also be considerable, and the Association expects NETA to work.

'Ofgem has always put faith in NETA as well. After all, it was Ofgem's idea and Ofgem's project, and it is Ofgem that told us from the outset of the review of electricity trading arrangements, and right through the NETA process, that electricity is just like any other commodity.

'So, to read at this stage of the doubts expressed by Ofgem is somewhat surprising, and I would like to give you a short quote from their NETA proposals which were published last summer:

"The new trading arrangements will help promote competition by replacing restrictive characteristics of the Pool that have served to facilitate the exercise of market power. The proposed trading arrangements detailed in this document promise significant advantages over the present

arrangements. They will deliver more efficient and more competitive trading, greater choice of markets, and more scope for demand management. These advantages suggest the new arrangements offer the prospect of relatively large and rapidly achieved reductions in wholesale electricity prices, and lower prices for both industrial and domestic consumers."

'Now we hear that the trading arrangements, the Competition Act and the financial services legislation are between them inadequate, and that special licence conditions are needed to ensure that the market is not abused.

'I said earlier something to the effect that Ofgem's apparent doubts were surprising, but to hear that NETA with its new rules, and the ability to change those rules quickly, and that the Competition Commission, backed by the toughest competition legislation we have ever known, plus the stringent rules of the Financial Services Authority, are between them incapable of governing a competitive electricity market, I suggest is barely credible.'

At that point, you could have heard a pin drop.

The statement went on:

'I would like to turn to a little more of the detail more specifically related to the question of NETA and market power. The Association considers that continuing without modification the licences referred to would not operate against the public interest. We made that comment in our formal initial submission to the Commission. On the contrary, there is actually a risk that the modification could act against the public interest.

'NETA takes away the Pool and at this point I must disagree to some extent with Dr Marshall, it also takes away the opportunities for the behaviour that has been criticised by Ofgem and which forms the basis of its licence modification. Any opportunities that may remain for the exercise of market power can be adequately dealt with by existing competition legislation.

'NETA, of course focuses on bilateral trading and physical energy. Imbalances in bilateral trading will be managed by an imbalance mechanism. The mechanism quite intentionally places strong incentives on parties to balance, by specifying potentially penal consequences for failure to do so. Regulatory interference in this, or even the suggestion that there might be regulatory interference in the price signals generated by the imbalance mechanism, will weaken the incentive to balance and inhibit the development of liquid bilateral markets, and this would be against the public interest.

'The demand side which was admittedly very weak in the Pool will become a significant feature in NETA. So a licence condition of the kind proposed by Ofgem is open to very wide interpretation and I was interested to note that when the question was put by Professor Cave, he could not really get from this audience a clear answer to the distinction between what is normal commercial activity and what constitutes abuse.

'What we have before us at the moment does not make clear to licence holders what behaviour is acceptable and what is not. This is especially difficult to manage in the context of a massive change like NETA and Ofgem's insistence on the licence modification shows a surprising lack of faith in the NETA design.

'There is potential for misuse of the licence condition itself, which would inhibit innovation and proper development of the new market. I think this is what AES were alluding to earlier this morning when they talked about indirect price control.

'All this will be conducted as it always has been over the last ten years in a very public atmosphere where lobby groups and the press play an enormous part. The Association recognises that this is life in a liberalised commercial electricity market. We have lived with it for ten years but we have to draw your attention to the fact that lobbying is occasionally used as an alternative and a supplement to normal effective bilateral price negotiation and market risk management.

'People in this room buy their desks, their stationery, their paperclips from an office supply company – the deal is pretty straightforward, they do not expect to go to the press if they do not like the price on any particular day of the week. That does not apply to electricity. There is always a risk that the regulatory body will be unduly susceptible to lobbying, and that there will be political pressure put on it as well.

'The ability of the body to differentiate between normal economic behaviour and market abuse depends critically on a detailed understanding of the issues facing the producer. There has been a certain amount of loss of real electricity expertise from the Regulator's office, and I notice in the debate so far this morning there has been very little discussion about anything connected with the real day to day running of a power station, which is not something that financiers and bankers, and traders and speculators get involved in. It operates in a real world of dirt, noise, emissions, spanners, oil, fuel and so on.

'I was going to conclude my comments with a remark to the effect that the proposal for the licence condition is one akin to slaying dragons that either died a long time ago or will be dead by November. But one or two comments were made from the floor this morning, Madam Chairman, to the effect that people regretted not owning generating plant.

'I would like to point out to them that there is a vast amount of it on the market at the moment. This is a serious comment, it may sound flippant. There is a vast amount of generating plant on the market at the moment and anyone that is seriously interested in buying plant can come to me at the end of the morning and I will be very pleased indeed to put them in touch with those of our members who are very keen to get rid of it. Thank you.'

I returned to my seat, near Nick Baldwin and Simon Skillings, of PowerGen, to listen to the rest of the day's evidence. Good oral evidence was presented that day by Nuclear Electric and by AES – the latter from Vic Danks, who ran their small plant at Indian

Queens in Cornwall, which was used infrequently, but was important to the system in the south west. It was a plant of a type that – in our view – could easily have fallen foul of the proposed condition.

Some six months would pass before the Competition Commission announced its decision and during that time, the issue was occasionally in the press. The AEP's President, Sir Michael Spicer MP, made reference to it in his speech to the members' AGM on 3 November 2000. This was reported by the *Daily Telegraph*:

Electricity producers yesterday accused Callum McCarthy, the gas and electricity industry regulator, of being too interventionist and trying to stifle competition. Sir Michael Spicer, a former Tory energy minister and president of the Association of Electricity Producers, said the regulator was providing confusing signals to the market and was guilty of "very intrusive regulation". The attack comes after growing unease among energy generators about Mr McCarthy's complaints about the abuse of market power and against the background of delays in launching electricity market reforms that hold the prospect of reducing electricity bills by up to 10pc.

The new trading system, which replaces the existing electricity pool, was due to be launched later this month but Mr McCarthy has pushed back the launch until March 27 because of continuing technical problems. Stringent tests of the new wholesale trading system in January will determine whether there are further slippages in the revised timetable.

Producers are worried that the Competition Commission's investigation into the "market abuse" clause in their operating licence could lead to further restrictions. Sir Michael, speaking at the association's annual lunch in London, said that the regulator was obsessed with market abuse licence conditions.

He said: "This shows either an astonishing lack of faith in competition law or that Ofgem simply will not give up the scope to control a competitive market." Sir Michael argued that the divestment of generating plant by National Power and PowerGen had helped liberate the market and reduce the risk of market abuse by the big power players.

In December 2000, the Competition Commission announced its decision. It concluded that the Market Abuse Licence Condition was not justified for the companies that had refused to accept it. Ofgem was then obliged to withdraw the controversial condition from the licences of those companies that had accepted it, for various reasons. The regulator seemed to take the Competition Commission's decision very badly and continued to argue that it was right to demand such a condition. Already looking like a bad loser, Ofgem not only criticised the Competition Commission's analysis of the case, but took the extraordinary step of asking the government to use powers in the Utilities Act 2000, granted to the Secretary of State, to implement a Market Abuse Licence Condition.

BBC News reporting the Competition Commission decision on 11 December 2000 said:

The Competition Commission probe followed a refusal by two generators, British Energy and AES, to accept clauses curbing their ability to alter their electricity output. The rules, which the firms said deterred "normal competitive behaviour", had been accepted by seven rival firms. The high demand for power is such that in July a decision by Edison Mission Energy, which produces about 10% of UK electricity, to close down part of capacity for two months led to price increases of £100m. Although Edison has maintained it was not attempting to manipulate the market, by prompting a rise in the price of the rest of the electricity it was producing, this undertaking has not been accepted by Mr McCarthy. "He has gone on the record as saying he would have fined the company if he had had the powers," an Ofgem spokesman told BBC News Online.

That last statement from the Ofgem spokesman showed just how aggrieved the regulator was, which helps to explain why, in this regulatory horror movie, the corpse of MALC would soon exhibit strong signs of life.

Events elsewhere seemed to play into the hands of those who wanted to eliminate 'market abuse', however ill-defined the alleged activity may have been. In California, where the electricity system is roughly similar in size to that of England and Wales, the electricity market had been partially de-regulated in 1998-2000. 'Partially', because some generating plant was divested from existing utilities to independent producers; wholesale prices, although capped for Californian electricity production, were derived from competitive markets, but retail prices were capped by regulation.

Professor James Sweeney of Stanford University wrote later[73]:

The markets, however, were run as two separate organizations rather than as an integrated system, creating market inefficiencies and opportunities for market manipulation. In addition, retail price controls were established and these served to isolate the consumer economically from the producer of electricity. California had created at the wholesale level a volatile commodity market but had fixed sales prices for the investor-owned utilities at the retail level, a potentially untenable combination.

In California, electricity demand rose, not particularly dramatically – but certainly faster than an industry plagued with slow consent processes could respond to – and in the spring of 2000, wholesale electricity prices rose sharply, with retail customers blissfully protected by a price cap. For various reasons, imports from neighbouring states were limited and the outcome, in June 2000, was rolling blackouts in San Francisco – at the heart of one of the

[73] Professor of management science and engineering, Stanford University. The California Electricity Crisis: Lessons for the Future. http://www.stanford.edu/~jsweeney/paper/Lessons%20for%20the%20Future.pdf

world's most advanced economies. There were damaging consequences for some of the energy companies, too – two major utilities were plunged into financial crisis when their rising expenditure on wholesale energy[74] exceeded their income from capped retail sales. For a liberalised power market, the headlines got worse when the inquest began. Energy traders, most prominently at Enron, were accused of manipulating the market. Just as some regimes like to blame 'speculators' for currency perturbation when creditors lose faith in a government's management of the economy, market manipulation seemed to be a very useful scapegoat for the failings of a flawed system. Nevertheless, some of the actions of the Enron traders – for instance, deliberately creating transmission congestion and then being paid to relieve it – seemed perfect examples of 'market abuse'.

In London, despite the ruling of the Competition Commission, Ofgem remained committed to introducing some form of market abuse licence condition. With the events in California still playing out, the climate in the news media and in politics could hardly have been better for a proponent of MALC.

Callum McCarthy was asked about this on 28 November 2000 at a hearing of the House of Commons Trade and Industry Committee.

Chairman: 'You have been quoted as saying you are ready to withdraw this licence condition from the six generators should the Competition Commission find against you. I imagine that is quite a logical position but have you got a fall-back position? You may not wish, for tactical reasons, to offer it to us at the moment but if you find this market abuse condition is not acceptable to the Competition Commission, will you be trying again to get it right?'

[74] From within the state, this was capped by regulation, but imported power was not.

Mr McCarthy: '*Absolutely, because under the law as it stands there are direct responsibilities, and under the law as it will stand once the Utilities Act is implemented the Authority will have direct responsibility, to promote the interests of consumers. Generating costs account for 50 per cent of domestic bills, 65 per cent of heavy industrial users' bills, it is a sector which has manifestly not been showing the signs of competitive behaviour over an extended period where there have been repeated instances of abuse and where there is scope for continuing abuse in the future. If we cannot use this instrument, which we believe is the most appropriate instrument, we will have to use other means because we have a direct legal responsibility to promote this and it happens to be absolutely central to everything that Ofgem does.*'

The regulator was true to his word. He asked the government to use powers in the Utilities Act 2000 which were available to the Secretary of State for Trade and Industry to impose a licence amendment on a company, without the company's consent and without a reference to the Competition Commission. These were powers made available on a time-limited, precautionary basis and we understood that, strictly speaking, they were there in the event of problems arising with NETA. The Secretary of State, Stephen Byers MP, issued a consultation on the proposal.

AEP led the challenge to this, on behalf of the generators. It was some challenge. That the generating companies manipulated the power market was conventional wisdom; there had been numerous regulatory investigations and regardless of the outcome of them, the investigations alone implied guilt. Large industrial customers were critical of the generating industry, there had been power cuts in California, with market manipulation blamed and the Chairman of the House of Commons Trade and Industry Committee had referred to the generating companies publicly as 'rascals'. Then, as if to underline how tough it would be to persuade the Department not to introduce the MALC powers, on 19 July 2001, the *Financial Times* reported that the recently-appointed Energy Minister, Brian Wilson MP, had visited California to check for himself what had happened in the Californian market and he had commented afterwards that the main lesson was that the generators 'needed to be controlled'. That newspaper report prompted a fax to the Minister, from me, expressing concern and asking for a meeting.

The detail of the AEP's response to the consultation was expertly managed by its new Head of Electricity Trading, Dr Malcolm Taylor. Malcolm had joined us in September 2000 from National Power, after his excellent predecessor, Steve Johnson, had resigned to give more time to his leisure, family and community interests. When he announced his departure, Steve said that much as he had enjoyed the job, there was one thing he needed to tell me about it – that it was in no sense a part-time job. He was right, of course, and for the AEP, having that key role filled on a part-time basis may have been acceptable in the days when the Association was finding its feet in the industry, but it was now an inadequate response to the challenges it faced. Malcolm brought to the Association immense experience in the industry, including some gained abroad, and the invaluable ability when facing problems to break them down so that they became more digestible. Many of the working days at Waterloo Place started with Malcolm coming into my office with a take-away coffee in one hand and a less than delicate-looking pastry in the other, to dismantle whatever issue we were working on. We worked well together and having left behind the culture of a big company, he soon adapted to working in a tiny organisation which could not afford to become bureaucratic, even if it had wanted to. The change of style must have been a shock at first. He loved to tell people, in front of me, that if a candidate had a job interview at AEP, it would take the form of a lunch with David Porter. Very amusing, but not true for all prospective staff members. Sensitive HR professionals should probably overlook the rest of this paragraph, but in Malcolm's case, I had his CV, which looked very good; he came highly recommended by two members of AEP who knew how the Association functioned, Dr Keith Miller and the late Peter Clubb, who had worked with him closely and whom I knew well and trusted. All I needed to know was whether I could work with Malcolm and that assessment, indeed, was made over a pleasant lunch at Shepherd's in Marsham Street, Westminster, where I was always well looked after. I enjoyed the restaurant's fish cakes, the liver and the attentive service, but the place was usually packed with politicians and lobbyists making it a hotbed of intrigue. That always demanded caution as far as the eyes and ears at nearby tables were concerned.

The battle against the MALC II proposal was intense, but conducted almost entirely in private. I always felt that the majority of people – from the informed man or woman in the street to politicians and journalists – would think that a Market Abuse Licence Condition was perfectly reasonable. Worse still was the perception that if one was 'against' a MALC, then surely one was 'for' market abuse? We had nothing to gain from fighting this battle in the open and probably a great deal to lose.

I was not granted the audience I had requested with the Energy Minister, Brian Wilson, but I did secure a one-to-one meeting with Anna Walker, Director General, Energy at the DTI and I was grateful for that. AEP set up a working group to deal with the issue and the members, Malcolm Taylor and I had various meetings with DTI officials, including one with an Ofgem representative present.

Mike Bowden of Innogy, David Love of British Energy, Melanie Wedgbury of Entergy and Peter Bedson of Barking Power were prominent among the member companies in the Group.

We also picked up signals that Treasury officials were uncomfortable with the Ofgem proposal, so Malcolm Taylor and I arranged a lunch with one of their senior people, to make our case and seek support. It was an encouraging and pleasant encounter and we were satisfied that we had explained our position, albeit, the usual civil service caution prevailed and we could not be sure how strongly, if at all, the Treasury would back us. There are, inevitably, disagreements between government departments, of course, but most remain out of the public gaze and for a department to become associated publicly with the position of a particular interest group is not likely to be helpful to either party.

At the DTI, the civil servants whose task it was to work through the consultation and make a recommendation on the issue were Ian Fletcher and Nicola Pitts. They understood the pros and cons and importantly, the politics, and they were utterly professional. This allowed a high degree of trust to develop between the Department and the AEP. Between us, we explored what the Department's misgivings were about not adopting the MALC. The officials made clear how much at risk, politically, their Minister would be if 'misbehaviour' occurred after any decision not to impose the Condition. We understood that and we did our level best to reassure them – it was most unlikely, for example, that plant would be withdrawn when capacity was in great demand in the winter ahead. It was also of some comfort that there had been no allegations of 'misbehaviour' in the first six months that NETA had been operating. But we also made clear that we had good reason to doubt the legality of what was being proposed (a punchy opinion from a QC) and we demonstrated this, warning of the risk of a judicial review if the Minister decided to adopt Ofgem's proposal. Of great importance, of course, was what we, AEP, might say if the Minister did decide to rule against Ofgem. I undertook to ensure that, if that were the case, we should say as little as possible to the press – however happy we might have been with the outcome, there would be no real advantage to the Association in making a big story of it. So, if we won, there would be no 'victory' declared. No trumpets would be blown. Any celebration would be strictly private.

One morning in December 2001, I took a telephone call from Nicola Pitts at the DTI. There was to be no 'MALC II'. I asked my PA, Sam Inns to get Malcom Taylor to look in. Just outside my office Malcolm and I leapt about like a couple of football fans who had witnessed their team score a cup-winning goal in the last minute of stoppage time. Sam looked on, delighted at the news, but failing to conceal her doubts about the way grown men are apt to behave at times. Later, the government announced, with none of that exuberance, that it did not believe it was necessary to use the Secretary of State's powers in the manner that had been proposed. The reporting of the decision was low key.

My long experience of working for the Association of Electricity Producers and its predecessor, demonstrated to me that big, set-piece battles with a clear victory or defeat are rare. There were many – usually short – periods of excitement when the Association was in the news and when, as a spokesman, I was in the thick of it. But looking back, trade association life tended to be more about long periods of attrition and issues that are important, but not necessarily headline-grabbing. This issue, however, had been far from routine, albeit without headlines when it was resolved.

Early one morning in the latter part of 2007, Malcolm Taylor came in with his usual cardboard cup of coffee and Danish pastry, but also bringing news that he had accepted an offer of a senior job with a gas-fired power project in Nigeria. He had always said that he was very happy at AEP and that, having worked abroad before, only an interesting job in another part of the world would be likely to tempt him away. I was pleased for him and said so, although he must have seen from my face that Nigeria – which, rightly or wrongly, was known at the time for its lawlessness – would probably not have been my first choice.

Malcolm did well there and later moved on to work in Tanzania. Before leaving AEP, he helped me find his successor. To the surprise of some people, I appointed, as Head of Electricity Trading, Barbara Vest, who had plenty of experience of the industry, including the wholesale market - although not on the 'generation' side, having worked for regional electricity companies and then on regulatory and commercial matters for Gaz de France in the UK. I had known her in the days of the Electricity Pool and although very different in style from her predecessor, Barbara made a great success of the job.

CHAPTER FOURTEEN

SOME ENCOUNTERS OF
THE FOREIGN KIND

Trade associations like AEP must have a clear focus on what they want to achieve, but inevitably and often inadvertently, they also acquire other responsibilities. When a member of the public writes with a question about the industry, they must respond. My experience of such enquiries was that it was actually a pleasure to respond to them – they usually prompted a bit of thinking that was often more meaningful than the sometimes turgid day-to-day agenda. But it was not just letters like that which demanded attention. Quite often, we would receive requests from foreign delegations to visit AEP, so that they could hear how the British electricity industry worked, or, to discuss the pros and cons of a particular issue.

A visit by a delegation from the energy trade association for the Netherlands was amusing. At precisely the time when the British industry was thinking of changing its support mechanism for renewable energy, to move from an 'obligation' to 'feed-in tariffs', our visitors opened their discussion in the AEP meeting room by informing us that they had come to talk to us because the government in The Netherlands was contemplating abandoning its feed-in tariff in favour of a British-style obligation. An opportunity simply to swap two rule books?

In my last few years at AEP, the majority of the delegations seemed to come from the People's Republic of China and setting up the visits was a lengthy process. Not only did a visit need to be synchronised with meetings at several other organisations – typically including Ofgem and National Grid – but having been asked if we would meet them, we then had to send to China, via an agency, a formal invitation for a delegation to come and talk to us – as if AEP had initiated everything. Su-Yen Foong, my marvellous PA, who had succeeded Sam Inns, became particularly adept at dealing with that, albeit she was often driven to distraction by the agency abruptly changing dates and times.

The delegations may have come from different regions and different parts of the Chinese electricity industry, but a pattern developed for these visits and only rarely did my PowerPoint presentation need very much adaptation, beyond incorporating the latest changes in UK energy policy. The discussions were always conducted through a young, female, highly westernised Chinese interpreter whose grasp of electricity terminology was surprisingly good. It was clear, however, that some of the delegates – usually younger ones – actually understood English. I would be relating something and before the interpreter had provided the translation, as I looked around the room, I would see one or two heads already nodding to indicate their understanding of the issue. I could see them doing so when I expressed the personal view that if and when electric cars became commonplace, lots of pedestrians would be killed because the vehicles are so quiet – accustomed to hearing the internal combustion engine, they would do as so many do today and step off the pavement before looking for oncoming traffic. There was one thing, however, that nearly always prompted questions via the interpreter. When we got to the subject of competition between generators in the wholesale market, they would ask 'How is the price agreed?' I would then explain that the price was determined through supply and demand. Result? Puzzled looks. I would try again, perhaps making a comparison with markets for fruit, vegetables or fish. This time, glimmers of understanding, but still far too many puzzled looks. On the last such occasion, exasperation got the better of me and I said to the interpreter 'Please tell them that I think that the Chinese know at least as much about markets as we do.' Outcome? Smiles all round.

Many years before the visits by the Chinese – shortly after privatisation – I was asked by Her Majesty's Government to go to Warsaw, to speak at an electricity event run by the liberalising Polish government's Anti-Monopoly Office. Many other countries were fascinated by the reforms that had been achieved in Britain. The Warsaw conference was interesting and not a little illuminating. My presentation seemed to go well and it was followed by a lengthy question and answer session. That also went well until I was asked a question about how companies investing in the privatised industry in Britain were able to secure a return for their investment. I described the sequence of events, from investors putting up money, through the wholesale trading and the network costs all the way to the end customer receiving the electricity and paying the bill. A plain language description, although merely having to explain it was a reminder of how far removed life had been in the former Soviet states, from what we took for granted in the West. In fact, the difference was even bigger. When I gave what was, for me, a perfectly simple answer, there was a buzz in the audience. The delegates had found something to question in an answer that I had explained carefully and simply. I asked the interpreter to find out what the issue was. She challenged them and then said 'Mr Porter, you explained the process very clearly and at the end, you said "The customer pays the bill."

'That's right. What did they not understand?'

'They understood everything, thank you, but the problem is that in Poland, people do not pay the electricity bill.'

Clearly, I should have done more research before I left for Warsaw.

In early 1995, the UK government asked me to respond to a request from the USA to give evidence to the California Energy Commission, the Energy Research, Development and Demonstration Committee of which was to hold an inquiry into support for renewable energy technologies and in particular, the impact of liberalisation on research and development work. At the time, the Non-Fossil Fuel Obligation ('NFFO') was the British mechanism for renewable energy support. It had its flaws, among them the intermittent nature of the tendering timetable and the limiting of support only as far as December 1998, but compared with the terms of the Energy Act 1983, it was a big step forward for renewables. It was also too small in scale to have any serious impact on the competitive wholesale market, to which the Association of Independent Electricity Producers attached great importance. Having submitted written evidence and had a briefing on the telephone from officials in California, I found myself in a hotel in the state capital, Sacramento, where that night I was woken by the sound of something being forced under the door of my room. Not an 'express check-out' hotel bill, but an envelope containing a last-minute note from officials at the Energy Commission, with suggestions about how I might present my evidence at the hearing in the morning. But the oral evidence had to conform with my written evidence, which had been submitted well in advance and as I had already planned what I was going to say, it was hard to change very much of it. I wondered later if my hosts were unhappy about that. Sam Inns, my wonderful Personal

Assistant, who, at the time, also did the day-to-day work on the AIEP's finances, was particularly good at chasing up unpaid bills. Even so, it took her about two years to get from the Californian Energy Commission the travelling expenses they had promised to reimburse.

There was quite a lengthy period when other countries wanted to hear how the liberalisation of the British electricity market had been achieved; how it was working and in many cases, how support for renewable energy could be delivered in a liberalised and competitive market. It was the British approach to the renewables issue that attracted an invitation to speak at one such conference in Kuala Lumpur, Malaysia. I recall, after a lengthy but pleasant flight to Singapore and then a short flight up to Kuala Lumpur, I arrived at the conference venue, the Hyatt Regency Saujana Hotel, for some reason, feeling much fresher than colleagues with more long-haul travelling experience had warned me that I should feel. I checked in to my room and still feeling wide awake, I went for a meal in the hotel restaurant. After declining, with rather laboured politeness, an invitation from the waitress to help her with her English – 'Just talking, in your room' she had explained to this surprised visitor to anything-but-liberal Malaysia – I went back to the room and was so overcome with fatigue that it was all I could do to get undressed. I managed that, but things lay where they fell. Something as demanding as setting an alarm was way beyond me, however, and in any case, probably unnecessary – I seldom sleep well when travelling. That night was an exception.

I woke at 08.45, refreshed, but with a sudden feeling of anxiety. What time was I due to on the conference platform? The papers were on the dressing table. The answer was 09.00. I shaved, showered and dressed in little more than 10 minutes, grabbed my bundle of overhead transparencies and left the room intent on running to the conference centre, which was at the opposite end of the hotel complex. Coming out of the air-conditioned bedroom, I was hit head-on by a wall of heat and humidity. OK, I would walk. As I approached the conference centre, I could see the organiser, clipboard in hand, looking around anxiously for her missing speaker. I put on my very best calm and collected, playing it cool look. At the doorway, I smiled and said 'Good morning' and glancing in, I saw a large audience and on the stage, three chairs occupied and one, of course, empty.

The presentation went smoothly and in the morning coffee break, I was asked to do an interview with a young journalist. No problem, except that she wanted to find a quiet corner, where she 'would not be watched.' I never did understand exactly what the implication of being watched was – except, of course, this was Malaysia and it had to have been political – but I recall that she spent much of the interview impressing upon me the importance to the region of the Crown Princess of neighbouring Thailand's personal interest in renewable energy. The whole thing was bizarre.

I travelled home the next day via Singapore, where the schedule allowed me just enough time to go into the city and to see a few sights. Brits like to have tea at Raffles. It was a quick cup of tea, because I also went to the hairdresser at the hotel, to be told that my hair was in very poor condition[75]. Almost certainly, it was, but probably not so bad as to require treatment quite *that* expensive, so I asked the young woman simply to cut it. This commercial pushiness was matched elsewhere in the city by old-fashioned kindness. In the shopping district, in Orchard Road, I emerged from a shop in my Liberty cotton suit, to walk to the next store and suddenly, it began to pour with rain. In fact, it came down with a ferocity that would probably have warranted a mention in the

---

[75] When I next visited my regular hairdresser – Toni, an Italian – in London, he took a look at my hair and declared with an undisguised measure of disgust, 'Meester Porter, a woman 'as cut your 'air.' So, I confessed readily to the error of my ways.

news if had happened in the UK. A woman passing by saw that I was about to be soaked and she asked if I would like to share her umbrella. I accepted gratefully. There are aspects of life in Singapore that those of us accustomed to fewer restrictions and less order would not find attractive, but I could not imagine anyone – a complete stranger – doing that in Oxford Street.

Although renewable energy issues represented only part of the Association's brief, I was often asked to talk about the place of renewables in a liberalised electricity market. I did so every year in response to an invitation from Professor Ali Sayigh[76], who ran the World Renewable Energy Network. Every year, he arranged an international congress in the UK and attracted members of his network from the four corners of the world. Ali's event covered issues from high-level policy to the detailed application of renewables, but it seemed to focus more on detail. The delegates were invariably appreciative of my presentation, but in the audience were always a number of people from countries where energy supplies were either limited, or, far from secure and for them, improving on that situation by one means or another, must have seemed more important than the pros and cons of NFFO, a Renewables Obligation or a feed-in tariff. In April 2008, Professor Sayigh invited me to deliver some lectures to staff and students at the University of Bahrain, where they were beginning to think of a future beyond oil. The welcome was warm and the hospitality was generous and in 2011, when the disorder broke out in Bahrain, the suffering there surprised and saddened me.

In May 1992, I was invited by the McGraw Hill publishing business to speak in New York, about the British privatisation. This was to be my first visit to New York, but there would be very little time for sight-seeing. No more than an afternoon, in fact, so I spoke to John Macadam, who knew the city, about how to get the best

---

[76] Chairman and Founder of the World Renewable Energy Congress and Network. Former Professor at Saudi Arabia, Kuwait, Reading and Hertfordshire Universities.

value out of the few hours available. As always, John was very helpful, but I had my priorities and going up tall buildings was definitely among them. In fact, the conference was in one such building. Setting off from the Holiday Inn in Manhattan for the event, I stopped at the desk of the concierge to ask which was the McGraw Hill building. 'It's the tall one, sir' he replied. Not the clearest description for an office block in Manhattan, but fortunately, I managed to find the right one. The presentation was a success and the questions, from a well-informed audience, were interesting. The failings of the UK's Energy Act 1983 intrigued them, not least because in the United States in 1978, the Public Utility Regulatory Policies Act ('PURPA') had been introduced and some of its requirements were similar to those of the Energy Act. PURPA required the regulated electricity utilities to buy power from other producers if the cost was less than the utility's own 'avoided cost' of producing extra power. As in the UK, there were disagreements about what that avoided cost amounted to, but PURPA stimulated development of combined heat and power (the Americans call it 'co-generation') and some renewable energy technologies, albeit with different outcomes in different states.

With the Non-Fossil Fuel Obligation then under way in England and Wales, the last question from the audience was about renewable energy. I was asked which technologies were attracting support and I ran through the early NFFO programme, where generation from landfill gas, sewage gas and small hydro-electricity schemes was dominant.

'You didn't say anything about solar power' someone said. I was about to respond when another delegate chipped in. 'I had a vacation in England once' he said. 'I can tell you why they don't do solar power.' The laughter told him that neither he nor I needed to explain. Surprisingly – in the context of early 1990s thinking –

there would be considerable support for solar power in the UK when the feed-in tariffs were introduced.

After lunch, before heading for the airport for the overnight flight to London, I was free to be a tourist for a few hours. With the help of subway rides, I saw many of the usual sights before going up a couple of famous skyscrapers. I spent more time than I should have at the top of the World Trade Centre, knowing that I still had to visit the Empire State Building – a must for someone who had enjoyed 'Superman' serials on Saturday mornings in the early 1950s at the Sudbury Town Odeon. The view from the observation area of the Empire State Building, of course, was wonderful. I spent a lot of time trying to pick out landmarks and taking photographs. Far too much time. I needed to get back to the hotel to pick up my suitcase and then on to Kennedy Airport for the flight, so the fun had to end. I looked for the lift and at first, could not see it. That was down to the huge number of people queuing to use it. Movement of the queue was virtually imperceptible and I decided that I could not wait[77]. I was reasonably fit and healthy and well used to walking, so I took the stairs.

After a while, it began to dawn on me that the pace of my descent was not what I had expected it to be. By timing my progress between floors, I calculated how long it would take me to get to the ground. The arithmetic alarmed me. Go back and wait for the lift? No, that would waste time and there might still be a long queue. Clearly, the right thing to do was to keep going and get down those stairs rather more briskly. I did that, but despite all my efforts, progress was still not good enough. I became more anxious, until, on the next landing, I was relieved to come face to face with the doors of a lift and this time, there was no queue – in fact, there was no one else in sight. I pressed the 'down' button. The lift arrived. I entered and although a bit puzzled by the array of buttons, I pressed the one that I felt sure meant 'Ground'.

[77] Online reviews suggest that, even today, there can still be very long queues at the top of that building.

I could feel how rapidly the lift was descending and I began to feel pleased with myself. Then it stopped and the doors opened. With my sunglasses on my forehead and my camera slung round my neck, I stepped out and found myself not where I had hoped to be, but in the office of a law firm – a 'Mr Bean' moment, the like of which I sensed that the receptionist had witnessed before. With an intensely bored look, she pointed towards another lift a few feet away. Embarrassed, but conscious that it could have turned out much worse, I thanked her and was soon striding purposefully along Fifth Avenue towards my hotel and the left luggage desk.

Perhaps interestingly, invitations to talk about the British electricity market fell away when NETA replaced the Pool. Whereas other countries could grasp the notion of pooling for the wholesale electricity market and were interested enough to discuss it, they appeared to be uninterested in the model which succeeded it.

CHAPTER FIFTEEN

GETTING TOGETHER FOR LUNCH

If there was one thing that I could be confident AEP was known for in the industry, it was its Annual Lunch. So popular was it that in my worst moments, I was inclined to think that members valued the AEP more for their early November get-together than for the Association's year-round efforts to advance the interests of the electricity generating industry. The event, of course, had an attraction that was at times much greater than the Association's day-to-day work – it was almost guaranteed to promote happiness, whereas the work of responding to consultations, lobbying the government and defending the industry in the news media, however well managed, could not always do that.

The Annual Lunch began as no more than a practical measure – refreshments after the members' Annual General Meeting. It was a tradition in the Association that the AGM should serve properly the interests of the wide range of members, who came to it from all over Britain. That meant, instead of trying to conclude the proceedings as quickly as possible, one and a half hours were allowed, not just for the necessary governance formalities, but to give members an opportunity to air their views on how the Association was performing.

Members who had travelled from the four corners of the country had to be fed and watered. Initially, with the event being held at the Institution of Electrical Engineers, the catering was limited to sandwiches and coffee, but as the Association grew and began to be recognised, it seemed natural that the annual event should have more status and be held somewhere interesting – not just for the members, but for the Association's guests. In 1991, it was held in HMS *Belfast,* near Tower Bridge. Other early venues included the Hop Cellars in Southwark and HMS *President,* alongside Victoria Embankment on the north bank of the Thames, Trinity House, the Stationers' Hall and then Claridges, where after-lunch entertainment was introduced for the first time – on that occasion, an amusing speech from writer and journalist Frances Edmonds.

From 1993, a great deal of the responsibility for the event rested on the shoulders of my newly-appointed Personal Assistant, Sam Inns. Sam enjoyed it and the event was in very capable hands. Each year, of course, the lunch had to be as good as, and ideally better than, the previous year. For many years, the home of the AGM and Lunch became the Café Royal, in Regent Street – a venue dedicated to events of that kind and one that was run with the utmost professionalism. It was also close to the office, which made the arrangements easier for Sam and her colleagues. When the Café Royal closed for a major rebuild in December 2008, we moved the event to The Brewery in Chiswell Street close to the City.

A formula developed. The AGM, followed by a reception for members and guests, a short speech from a guest of honour, then lunch, followed by entertainment. For many of those present, what little was left of the afternoon and then the evening was spent in a nearby pub. Was this 'networking' or 'notworking'? Definitely the former. I confess that I never did understand fully why the Annual

Lunch was quite such a success. Huge efforts went into making it work well, of course, but something made it more than the sum of its parts. This may have been because, unlike some annual lunches and dinners, it was run with a light touch – with the least possible formality. [78] Not only that, but many of the members and guests knew each other from their involvement in the industry and some relied on the Lunch as an annual point of contact. The entertainment was carefully chosen, but a mixed audience of 450 people aged from teens to eighties, from young professionals to journalists, politicians and peers of the realm, is not easy to satisfy. That challenge was very clear when we engaged not only the immensely talented young musician Alex Prior[79], who sang before lunch, but also the then little-known comedian Jimmy Carr. I had seen Jimmy Carr on a late night TV programme and we tracked him down through an agency. But my confidence that he would amuse our very mixed audience was shaken when I told the AEP staff that I had booked him. One or two looked blank, but three of the younger ones, mostly in their first jobs since leaving university and still free enough to enjoy a night out at the *Comedy Store*, were clearly absolutely delighted. In fact, so delighted that I became concerned. If they thought Jimmy Carr was that funny, wasn't there was a fair chance that a great many people in our mixed audience would not understand him? Worse still, they might not approve of him.

The answer, surely, was to explain to Mr Carr the composition and likely tastes of his audience. His agent arranged for him to call me. When the call came, I delivered the rather boring explanation

---

[78] In fact, what may have looked like a very lightly-scripted event, became, after a few years, the subject of detailed background planning and implementation. The Association took on 'Professional Conference and Project Management Ltd', whose Director, Sharon Moncur managed the details meticulously and on the day, the vital relationship with the catering staff, the audio-visual team and the venue managers.

[79] A composer from his early childhood and usually referred to as a prodigy (a description which, apparently, he disliked) Alex joined the conductors at the Seattle Symphony Orchestra at 17 and went on to become an internationally-renowned composer and conductor. He is the son of Peter Prior, whose company, Summerleaze, was a member of the Association for many years.

about the nature of his audience and how they were not accustomed to hearing anything rude at the AEP Lunch. At first, I began silently congratulating myself for the practical way in which the problem was going to be resolved. Jimmy Carr replied, more than once 'Yes, I understand.' Each time he said that, it was a great relief to me. Then finally, he said 'I'll just "try one" early on, to see how it goes'. Oh dear. Instead of feeling reassured, I was now more nervous than before. I also felt a bit stupid, having realised that I had been advising a professional on how to do his work.

The result? Success. After a difficulty with the setting up, during which time I was told by an anxious Sam Inns that Alex Prior might not perform because of the inadequate arrangements for rehearsal, the immensely talented young man delighted the audience. But I watched that audience much more anxiously when Jimmy Carr was on stage. He sent them away happy, of course. But it is fair to say that the humour did not strike a chord with everyone. At least half of the audience, however, seemed to like it. So, did that mean that nearly half did not? My totally unscientific research afterwards led me to conclude that, of those that did not laugh, some definitely did not like it, but others who may have appeared not to like it actually did – I think the problem could have been that they did not want to be seen doing so.

Twenty minutes of stand-up comedy was not the only way to please the guests. Over the years we used singers, a magician, a hypnotist, ventriloquists and illusionists. The singers include The Three Waiters – opera singers, between jobs, who were dressed as waiters and worked with the waiting staff, before bursting into song. So secret was the arrangement and so convincing were they that it was only after they had broken cover that Philip Jackson, a former Chairman of the AEP Board, finally realised why his repeated requests to one of them to adjust the air conditioning had not been complied with. That was a minor problem compared with the one presented by a ventriloquist a few years later. He had asked, in advance, for us to nominate someone in the audience – a 'good sport' – to be invited by him to come on to the stage and help with the act. 'Help' in such situations could sometimes mean putting the victim through a certain amount of humiliation. In fact, nearly always.

Poring over the guest list, I chose Tony Dicicco, who was then working for RWE npower. Tony was experienced in the industry, well-known, a good supporter of AEP's work and above all, a strong and confident character. The moment came. The ventriloquist looked in the direction of his table and asked for Tony Dicicco to come forward. Nothing happened. He asked again and Tony did not appear. I looked across at the RWE npower table and someone called out that Tony had had to leave early. I needed a Plan B urgently and I concluded that I would have to volunteer. Too late. The ventriloquist was pointing at someone at the table nearest the stage and inviting him to step forward. I did not recognise him, but to a huge round of applause, he stepped on to the stage. He was soon fitted with a grotesque mask and found himself 'answering' the ventriloquist's questions and obeying his commands – a ventriloquist's dummy, in human form, with a downright ugly mask. The audience loved it. But the table near the stage, from which the guest had been chosen, was that of the event's biggest sponsor – the consultancy Pöyry. Not only that, but the victim on the stage was a guest of Pöyry, from an important client, in Denmark. We had always promoted the event as one which was good for networking and a great opportunity for member companies to entertain their clients. Humiliating clients in front of 450 people, however, was not one of the selling points. Afterwards, I was greatly relieved to be reassured by Pöyry that their Danish client had enjoyed enormously his experience at this most interesting British lunch. All's well that ends well.

It was not just the entertainers that made the AEP Annual Lunch so popular. Each year there would be a guest of honour, who, before lunch, would speak briefly on the serious issues affecting the industry. I recall in 1999, on the only occasion that the Lunch was held at Claridge's, a stirring speech delivered without the aid of notes, from Lord Ezra, which prompted these comments in the 'Disconnector' column in the following week's issue of *Utility Week:*

Guest speaker Frances Edmonds cracked some good jokes. But Disconnector's award for best contribution in unlikely surroundings must go to Lord Ezra, former chairman of British Coal, who savaged the Climate Change Levy and laid into Ofgem's plans for reforming electricity trading. Lord Ezra said the initiative was flawed and wouldn't lead to cheaper power. One of the guests was energy regulator Callum (or should that be, er, Malcolm McCarthy). It must have made him choke on his entrée. Or wish that life peers had become as endangered as the hereditary variety.

It was customary to try to get the Energy Minister of the day (they tended, however, to be replaced with astonishing frequency) to be the guest of honour and speak before the Lunch. Politicians, however – especially Ministers – could not always be relied upon to fulfil the engagement, although they were always more likely to if the event provided a timely opportunity for an important announcement to a large and interested audience. Once or twice, we were let down. On the last occasion when that happened I resolved privately never again to succumb to the temptation to invite the Minister and instead to find another prominent figure who would be less likely to cry off at the last minute. I was surprised to find that my resolve was put to the test. When Charles Hendry MP became Energy Minister in 2010, I went to see him at his office in Whitehall Place to talk through the some of the big issues that concerned the Association. I already knew him because he had been the Shadow Minister since 2008. I had met Charles in that capacity and he had also accepted an invitation from the Association to discuss with the Board of AEP the then Opposition's thoughts on energy issues.

We were winding up our discussion in his office when Charles said to me 'You have a rather good annual lunch, don't you?'

'Yes', I replied, I think you were there as a guest once or twice when you were in Opposition.'

'Do you invite the Minister to speak?' said Charles.

'No' I replied. 'We were let down, so I decided not to invite the Minister in future.'

'Would you invite me?' he said. I was delighted to confirm that I would and in November 2010 he gave an important and highly entertaining speech. What was more surprising perhaps was that he spoke at the event again in 2011, when he amused the large audience by reminding them how extraordinary it was for an Energy Minister to survive long enough in the job to speak at two successive annual lunches of AEP. He did not manage a third one though. To the disappointment of the many people in the industry who appreciated his grasp of the brief and also valued the stability and consistency that seemed finally to have come to the office, he was the victim of a reshuffle in September 2012. Charles Hendry's successor, incidentally, was in the job for barely eight months before himself being replaced.

Between 1987 and my retirement in 2012, I must have met all the Energy Ministers. They were changed far too frequently. Without a great deal of research, I should be hard put to list them all, so I shall not attempt to.

CHAPTER SIXTEEN

PUTTING THE HEAT ON ENERGY POLICY

In Europe, from about 1991, public policy for the energy industry became increasingly influenced by politicians' response to the issue of what was called, at first, 'global warming', then 'climate change' and eventually – by those who thought people were not taking their message sufficiently seriously – 'dangerous climate change'. For the electricity supply industry, this would mean the penalising of fossil-fuelled electricity production and the encouragement of – at the time – more expensive, 'low carbon' technologies. It should have been perfectly possible for the UK, and the EU, to make policy on this issue compatible with the other two drivers – that is, reducing emissions whilst keeping the lights on and delivering prices that, although higher, were as low as possible in the circumstances. But with misplaced confidence in their ability, the policy makers made the task more complicated and, of course, more expensive.

When they decided to make the climate change issue the main ingredient of their energy agenda, the politicians in the UK had acknowledged openly that the way that they wanted to respond to this threat – that is, by reducing carbon emissions in an attempt to control the warming – would mean that customers faced bigger bills. This, of course, was during a period of relative contentment, before the financial crisis, which began to bite in 2008. When energy bills did go up – partly because of fuel price increases and partly because of various social and environmental obligations that government imposed on the electricity and gas suppliers – the politicians changed the emphasis of the message. Customers were already feeling the pinch and as the people who would have to pay for efforts to 'save the planet', they had to be reassured that climate change policy would not, after all, prove to be expensive. So the government suggested that by 2030 – because fossil fuel prices could be expected to rise, or, at least would prove to be volatile – a policy-driven switch to electricity production which would result in lower emissions of CO_2, would, in fact, prove to be cheaper for customers. In 2013, when the Coalition Government announced its deal with EDF Energy for a long-term strike price for output from the proposed new nuclear power station at Hinkley, voters were told that government policy meant that in 2030, their bills would be about £77 lower than they otherwise would have been. Perhaps they will be, but governments have never been good at forecasting energy prices, so to be able to look ahead 17 years and make a prediction as precise was the sort of thing Sir Humphrey Appleby[80] might have told his Minister would be 'courageous'. But the government wanted to calm the nerves of people who pay the bills. Those people also vote, of course. The problem for those who were already struggling to pay their energy bills was much more immediate, however, and they were far from reassured. Jam tomorrow might have had some appeal, but waiting 17 years for it was hardly compelling.

The new nuclear power project at Hinkley was at least as much about maintaining the reliable supply of electricity that underpins modern life as the reduction of carbon emissions, but we should

---

[80] Permanent Secretary in the Department of Administrative Affairs, played by Nigel Hawthorne, in the TV comedy 'Yes Minister' (BBC).

remind ourselves of what is at the heart of the carbon reduction policy. The 'duvet' around the earth which keeps the planet warm enough to be habitable comprises mostly water vapour. The issue in question, however, relates not to that, but to the increase in the amount of carbon dioxide in the earth's atmosphere, which the scientists and the many other interested parties whose work is considered by the Inter-governmental Panel on Climate Change (IPCC) judge to have come from gases emitted largely as a result of human activity – the burning of fossil fuels for energy. The safe limit is deemed to be 0.0350 per cent (350 parts per million) of the earth's atmosphere. By 2014, it had reached about 0.0400 per cent (400 parts per million) and the IPCC argued that at 0.0550 per cent (550 parts per million) there would be an average temperature increase of over two degrees Celsius, with serious consequences for the earth's inhabitants.

The principle that the earth will warm as a result of this additional amount of carbon dioxide being in the atmosphere is widely accepted by the experts; much more so, probably, than the predictions of the actual impact of this warming, to say nothing about what, if anything, should be done in response. Though the scientific arguments are said to be overwhelming, they nevertheless attract a great deal of scepticism. The policies to control the predicted changes to climate are also the subject of scepticism, some of which is overt and expressed strongly. I sense that it may be the less overt scepticism, however, which is lurking in the minds of those who argue publicly in favour of action, but who exercise caution when it comes to making the tough decisions that follow from the logic of their argument.

I can understand, however, some of the concerns of the sceptics and would feel better if we were all a little more open-minded, not least because of the hazard of using hugely complex computer models to predict long-term outcomes in a field where there is so much uncertainty – the discrepancy between the predicted and the observed warming rates makes that risk clear. Not only that, but for centuries, science has progressed by responding to challenge. Without the benefit of that we might still be following science of the kind that owed more to religion than to research, experiment and analysis. So, let us be a little more polite to people who ask sensible questions about all this. They tend to be labelled 'deniers', a word which is more usually employed to describe people who question a religious belief; but the use of that term is not worthy of the serious people that study climate change. Nor, incidentally, can be the way in which carbon dioxide – the gas which sustains plant life on the planet – is so frequently referred to, by journalists and politicians, as 'pollution'.

I am not a climate scientist and when questioned on the detail of the issue in question, let me make it clear that I defer to the judgement of those who are. So, there is no need to call me a 'denier', nor to send the unmarked van to my house. Not only that, but frustratingly, before sufficient time has elapsed to see the theory proved or disproved, I shall be in the earth rather than on it. This reminds me that many years ago, over drinks at a reception in the House of Commons, I had a conversation with an ardent environmental lobbyist that went something like this:

David Porter: 'I am exhaling CO_2 as I breathe and talk to you. It seems to me that you would prefer me to stop talking, stop breathing and die.'

The environmentalist: 'Not at all. You would then decompose and begin to emit methane, which is far more damaging than CO_2.'

Very few of us are climate scientists of course, and the pronouncements of that profession seem to divide us – into those who are predisposed to believe the theories and those who are predisposed to question them. But I am not seeking here a debate about climate science. My concern is with the policy response to it and the impact of that on the electricity industry and more importantly, upon its customers. So the focus here is on the relationship between climate change science and energy policy. By and large, that is how things were at AEP - I recall that the AEP's policy position was not greatly different from that of Prime Minister Tony Blair's in 2003, namely that mitigation measures by the UK should go no farther than those implemented by other countries and should not disadvantage the electricity industry's customers. I do not recall the Association ever agreeing formally to change that position. Looking back, however, what happened over a period of time seemed to amount to tacit acceptance of a shifting political stance.

When the question of reducing CO_2 emissions first found a place on the AEP's agenda, we became deeply involved in helping to determine the process by which mitigation might be managed. One possibility was a carbon tax to influence energy users' behaviour and energy companies' investments. At the Parliamentary Group for Energy Studies, I had heard Dr Dieter Helm speak on the policy response to global warming and recalled thinking that the level of tax that he warned might be required to induce change in investors' decisions about power generation seemed very high. Not only that, but if we were serious about reducing emissions, there was a risk that taxation might prove to be rather imprecise – tax might be collected, but that does not guarantee a change in behaviour. Tax income could, of course, be hypothecated to subsidise change to more expensive forms of electricity production, but governments have a rather strong appetite for taxes and they might become dependent on the tax income and lose sight of the emissions reductions. So having considered and rejected a carbon tax, the Association's favoured solution was a 'cap and trade' scheme. The cap would limit the emissions and the trading of permits to emit – made available in the market by those businesses that had worked within their allocation – would deliver efficiency. The entire process would allow the principles of a competitive market to prevail and by creating a 'carbon price' it would leave to the companies competing in that market the choice of fuels and technologies to make electricity. That approach, focused on limiting emissions cost-effectively was eventually adopted – first by the UK government, then, more significantly by the EU.

The Association did not devise single-handedly this approach to policy, but I know that it had a very great influence on it. For me, it started one evening when Nicola Steen came into my office on the First Floor at 41 Whitehall, to point out how big the issue of emissions was becoming for the Association's members. With so much on the agenda of our small organisation, I was still hoping that the issue would go away, but it interested Nicola very much and it certainly would not go away that evening. As we talked, I can recall chalking thoughts on to the blackboard on the wall of my office. My first reaction was that although governments love taxes, it would be surely unusual for an industry to propose, in effect, that its product should be taxed. Furthermore, taxation to change behaviour could not deliver tax *and* behaviour change. Success in one of those things would imply failure in the other.

Nicola explained that the 'cap and trade' approach had been used successfully in the USA to reduce sulphur emissions and she referred enthusiastically to discussions about this with her former colleague at Chatham House, Dr Michael Grubb and similar conversations with Dr Bill Kyte of PowerGen, who chaired the Association's Environment Committee. Before long, the Association found itself ahead of the game. So much so that when I headed up a team of members to discuss this at a joint meeting with senior Department of Trade and Industry and Department of the Environment officials, we were effectively asked to pipe down for a while. The civil servants were beginning to get worried about the impact of the issue on coal-fired electricity production and more particularly on the mining industry, which was already feeling sore about the trend towards gas-fired power production. They explained that the government would need time to address that problem. In fact, quite a bit of time – they were talking about years. For the Association, that meeting in the bowels of the DTI at 1 Victoria Street was not the only important one on the question of reducing carbon emissions. In 1998, the government had asked Lord Marshall (formerly Sir Colin Marshall), the Chairman of British Airways, to report on how best the issue should be addressed where British industry was concerned[81]. With the members now in favour of the cap and trade approach, we needed to talk to him. Nicola managed to find a 30-minute landing slot in his diary and we met him at the Mayfair offices of British Airways, in Berkeley Square. He listened sympathetically and asked a few questions. But time was soon up. When Nicola and I strolled back in the direction of the AEP, after leaving Lord Marshall's office, we reflected that neither we nor he had mentioned CO_2 emissions from aircraft. I suspect that this was for the good. It was a considerable time before that difficult question found its way on to the politicians' agenda.

But the first question for policy-makers, noting carefully that any meaningful answer must allow for the global nature of the warming and climate change issue, is whether there is anything that we can do about it.

'Doing something' means that we try to reduce substantially the carbon emissions from the planet, or, adapt to climate change as and when we need to. Or, perhaps, as the IPCC reports[82] at the

[81] Economic Instruments and the Business Use of Energy, Lord Marshall, November 1998.
[82] Climate Change 2014: Impacts, Adaptation, and Vulnerability. IPCC. 31 March 2014.

end of March 2014 suggested, do both of those things. The first option must be global. The second need not be. Indeed, whereas in some parts of the world, the priority might involve measures to protect low-lying property from a rising sea level, in others it could mean taking advantage of new opportunities to irrigate land, grow food or secure other economic benefits.

This reminds me of another conversation about the issue. It was with my friend Martin Alder. Martin, the long-standing Chairman of the AEP's Renewable Energy Committee, was a developer of and passionate advocate for renewable energy and he had a good grasp of the bigger picture in which the industry operated. One day, he came in to my office at Waterloo Place brandishing a report and asked 'I wonder if you would like to endorse this, on behalf of AEP?'

The document was a report by a regional body for the south west of England, which had looked at the impact of climate change on the region. Martin was a member of the committee behind the report. He knew that I was rather cautious about the climate change agenda and also that, like him, I lived in the region which was the subject of the report; he was in Gloucestershire and I, at that time, was much farther west, in Cornwall. I said that I ought to read what the report had to say before adding the AEP's name to it. I promised to read it on the train journey back to Liskeard and talk to him about it when he came in to the AEP office the following week. I did that. When Martin came back, the conversation went something like this:

'Did you read the report?'

'Yes, it was really interesting. If I have understood correctly, in Cornwall we shall have warmer, drier summers, which would be good for the holiday industry; the winters will be wetter, which will fill the reservoirs and reduce the risk of water shortages in the summer and we shall be able to grow things that it is not possible to grow in the south west at the moment. Can I get this straight? We are trying to stop this?'

Martin smiled and replied 'You won't like the mosquitoes.'

I am not sure that the arrival of mosquitoes had actually been predicted, but I conceded that I should not like them much. We both chuckled and I found some words to enable me to associate AEP with the report.

Much more serious than that is whether or not we have any reason to believe that 'mitigation' could ever be made effective through political agreement. Nation states, industries, companies and individuals have achieved a great deal. Men have gone to the moon, devastating diseases have been conquered, people now travel widely and encounter new cultures, and information technology has expanded communications to an extent that would have been almost unimaginable throughout most of the twentieth century. The list is endless. But do we have much of a record of co-operating successfully to address global issues such as this one? Not really. The record is a bit mixed, because economic self-interest prevails. Yes, self-interest may be judged over a shorter term than some thinkers might wish, but people and governments will make their own judgement about how far ahead to look. They will weigh up the pros and cons of any issue and they will apply their own discount to pay-offs.

The climate change policies of the EU and the UK seemed to make little sense unless they were underpinned by a global accord in which countries did indeed take steps that appeared to be against their individual economic interest. As far as the UK government was concerned, although reducing the country's man-made CO_2 emissions – they amount to less than two per cent of the global total – could have no discernible effect globally, it wanted to show leadership on this issue and from its experience expected the country to benefit economically when a global accord finally led to universal action. We were given little information about what those economic benefits might have been and I wonder whether they were mooted because the cost of simply taking the moral high ground might have attracted even more questions from those who were at risk of having to pay for the policies. However questionable they may have been, those are the foundations upon which, eventually, the UK's climate change policies for energy were built. The Department of Energy and Climate Change liked to describe its climate change role as 'Encouraging the EU to demonstrate leadership on climate change'[83]. But its efforts went farther than simply trying to put forward persuasive arguments across the conference table. Despite making a huge national commitment to the climate change agenda, the UK did not deter China, India nor even Germany from building lots of coal-fired power stations, but its policies had a considerable impact on the UK electricity industry and its customers. It appears to me that that was partly because it seemed to lose faith in the EU Emissions Trading Scheme (EU-ETS) – the flagship cap and trade scheme that it had pioneered.

Numerous policy measures to address the climate change issue were implemented by the Westminster government, but two of them were particularly forceful – the Climate Change Act 2008 and the introduction of the 'Carbon Price Floor'.

The Climate Change Act 2008 was remarkable. It set a target for the year 2050 for the reduction of greenhouse gas emissions; provided for a system of carbon budgeting; established the Committee on Climate Change and introduced many other things including provisions for adapting to climate change. It also introduced reserve powers to make provision about shops charging for single use carrier bags. That made front page news. But however

[83] https://www.gov.uk/government/policies/taking-international-action-to-mitigate-climate-change/supporting-pages/encouraging-the-eu-to-demonstrate-leadership-on-climate-change

important the legislation about plastic bags might have been and however large the headlines about it, it was the legal obligation on the government to reduce the UK's greenhouse gas emissions that should have been the big story. It was remarkably uncontroversial and had an astonishingly comfortable ride through the House of Commons. The Conservative Party in opposition, of course, was anxious to develop an image that would appeal to a wider range of voters, and it wanted the UK electorate to know that a vote for the Party in the general election of 2010 would also mean a vote for green policies. I suspect that the consensual political mood (on this issue) which led to the Climate Change Act had also been responsible for encouraging the Labour government's negative attitude towards companies that had plans to replace some ageing coal-fired power stations with modern, more efficient ones. Those plans, of course, were most important to the other two parts of the energy policy agenda – security of supply and competitive prices.

In 2012, the Coalition Government went a step farther in trying to put the UK in a position of leadership on the issue of climate change, when it proposed a carbon price floor. This measure, implemented in April 2013, required the power industry and other major emitters to pay a carbon price which was no longer simply the market price of allowances in the EU Emissions Trading Scheme. The price floor was a response to EU carbon prices being considered to be too low and it meant that, as long as the EU carbon price was deemed too low, the price in the UK would be propped up at a higher level.

This was somewhat more controversial. It was warmly welcomed by the nuclear power interests on the grounds that all it did was pitch the carbon price where it 'ought to be' and strongly criticised by some of the generating businesses that used fossil fuels, on the grounds that it presented their nuclear-powered rivals with a commercial advantage long before any new nuclear power station had been built and that it would push up customers' bills in the process. It also provided the Treasury – a government department that otherwise would surely have had more concern about it – with a precious additional income stream. But by the time that the price floor – in effect, a tax – had been introduced, energy bills had become a major issue – not just for domestic customers, but also for energy-intensive industries, who were not squeamish about blaming the government for increasing their costs and putting employment at risk.

The government was soon looking for ways of not just mitigating global warming, but reassuring those whose energy bills were going up. So in the budget of April 2014, it was announced that in 2015, the carbon price floor would be frozen at that year's level, instead of maintaining a rising trajectory year-by-year until 2020 – confirmation, as if it were needed, that the politicians would trim their environmental agenda to safeguard votes in a forthcoming election. It was also further evidence to potential investors in electricity production that policy can be changed as rapidly as it is made. Perhaps more rapidly, in fact.

The government was certainly worried about the effect of its policies upon household energy bills. Energy prices were constantly in the news and under pressure from a hostile press and public, energy companies regularly pointed out that a proportion of the bill was attributable to things that government required them to do. Government could hardly deny this. At the end of 2013, the Coalition decided to help the largest energy companies trim their costs by reducing some of the obligations on them to fund measures which had been introduced to improve energy efficiency and reduce CO_2 emissions. Easing this pressure on the companies was expected to reduce customers' bills by an average of £50. The promise of a reduction in bills grabbed headlines. It was, at least, more meaningful to the customers than the earlier policy announcement suggesting that bills would be lower than they might have been in 2030 - although the customers' response to the short-term saving was hardly ecstatic. There were also unintended consequences. Andrew Warren of the Association for the Conservation of Energy complained[84] *'It is completely perverse logic, to help cut fuel bills, to cut the one programme that helps householders cut fuel bills.'* There was expected to be a loss of jobs in the businesses that serve the energy efficiency sector and the confidence of those businesses must have been shaken. It is, of course, not just in the energy efficiency sector that confidence is liable to be wobbled when governments change their minds about things, or, send out mixed messages.

What seems to be incontrovertible is that if man-made carbon dioxide emissions are to be reduced in any meaningful way, then not even concerted European action will solve the problem - the challenge is a global one. Only global action can make a difference and other countries will surely be less likely to participate if the experience of the early movers is that it is an expensive process. In the UK, we paid very little attention to the cost-effectiveness of the various mitigation measures that were deployed. Governments were unwilling to let the EU-ETS carbon price steer decisions by the market. Instead, they promoted a range of different measures, with little apparent concern for the value for money they offered. For a given quantity of CO_2 reduction, was the best buy roof-top photo-voltaic systems, loft insulation, wind farms, carbon capture and storage or new nuclear power stations? That was never made clear and those who pay the bills – particularly those who struggled to pay their bills – deserved better than that.

So, if we continue with mitigation measures, spending should

<hr>

[84] http://www.ukace.org/2013/11/statement-on-the-50-reduction-in-the-energy-company-obligations/

surely be deployed where it is most cost-effective. The policy framework for the energy industry should steer it in that direction. But that cannot happen without the credible pricing of carbon emissions. The most credible mechanism to control and price carbon emissions was the EU Emissions Trading Scheme – a measure that emerged in the UK and one for which the UK deserved a great deal of credit. The introduction of the scheme was a remarkable achievement. Unfortunately, it fell into disrepute. At first, emissions allowances, which were later auctioned, were allocated free of charge. That attracted a steady stream of criticism from those who had no sympathy for energy companies. The critics seemed to be concerned very little about the impact of a more penal approach upon security of supply and I clashed with them from time to time in the press and on radio and television. It was argued that, with free allowances, companies were able to secure revenue from selling them. Yes, and of course they were meant to be able to do that. But when UK energy companies needed to exceed their allowances in order to keep plant operating, they had to buy permits. That pushed up power prices. It was meant to, but in the eyes of the critics it was unacceptable.

Then, with the financial crisis and recession reducing energy use, the demand for permits fell and so, of course, did the carbon price. As far as new electricity production was concerned, the price was clearly too low to induce any significant change in investment decisions. From that angle, the nuclear power interests that were in favour of topping up the carbon price had a point. But behavioural change of great magnitude had not been expected to occur until the gradual tightening of the cap on emissions led more naturally to a much higher carbon price. The process was too slow for the industry's critics, though. They wanted a cut in emissions not as a result of a reduction in economic activity (financial crisis and recession), but because entirely new power-generating technologies had been introduced. Looking back, I am sure that, at the beginning of the scheme, it was right to avoid an overnight economic shock to the viability of the fossil-fuelled power stations upon which so much of Europe depended. From the point of view of the enduring credibility of the Scheme, however, it might have been better to have charged for all allowances at the outset, even if the charging had been introduced gently.

The EU, which was looking not just to combat climate change, but to reduce Europe's energy imports, had what it must have thought would be good news for those who considered that the market-orientated cap and trade scheme was not fast enough in bringing about change. In 2008, the EU Renewable Energy Directive introduced for each country in the EU a mandatory target under which, by 2020, a percentage of its energy would have to be secured from renewable sources. In the UK, 15 per cent of energy would have to come from renewables and with little prospect – in that timescale – of significant change in transport technology or domestic heating, the target would have to be achieved by the electricity industry delivering at least 30 per cent of the country's electricity from renewables by 2020. From a starting point of barely five per cent of electricity coming from renewables (2007), that was a tall order, but it was mandatory and it would prove to have an enormous impact on the electricity supply industry in Britain. Just as in the rest of Europe, that impact would not be entirely helpful with regard to security of supply or prices. The Directive promoted vigorously the growth of renewable energy, but perhaps because of the degree of Euro-scepticism in the UK, the fact that the growth came as a result of legislation from Brussels was rarely mentioned in Westminster. When the Coalition Government wanted credit for renewables – clean, modern, sexy technology etc – it tended to take that credit itself. Faced with criticism about visual amenity or the impact on bills, however, it was unlikely ever to say 'Sorry, but we have to do this to meet an EU legal requirement.'

The UK government is not alone in devising conflicting policies and sending out mixed messages. The Renewable Energy Directive, of course, was seriously at odds with the EU's flagship policy to reduce CO_2 emissions. Instead of a price for the emission of carbon forcing up the cost of running fossil-fuelled plant and gradually bringing a new direction to investment in electricity production without hampering progress towards a single electricity market, the mandatory forced growth of renewable energy would reduce demand for EU-ETS allowances and therefore depress the carbon price. Instead of carbon pricing leaving energy companies free to choose the most efficient technology to reduce emissions commensurate with keeping customers' prices competitive, their choice of technology was almost dictated to them, regardless of its cost-effectiveness. In the UK, where there was a huge target to achieve and onshore wind power was so often controversial because of its visual impact, an absence of mature alternatives meant that the emphasis had to be on building offshore wind farms – one of the most expensive of the renewable energy technologies and one which demanded additional investment; to bring power networks to remote places and also to ensure that other on-demand capacity was always available to provide electricity when the wind was not blowing.

If investors became hesitant about putting their funds into electricity production in the UK, it was hardly surprising. Before the global financial crisis, public policy was reasonably clear and it was assumed that the price of the low-carbon agenda would be paid. After the crisis, the policy remained in place, but it seemed far less credible, especially in the light of complaints from customers and concessions from policy-makers. Energy companies and their investors could see only too well that there would be a need for new production – apart from anything else, to replace power stations that would close before the end of 2015 – to comply with the air quality legislation of the Large Combustion Plant Directive[85]. To meet the government's objectives regarding security of supply and prices, companies would have built new combined cycle, gas-fired stations. One or two, looking to ensure that they were not over-dependent on gas, would also have been building modern, coal-fired plant. But by 2014 - in the face of a dramatic narrowing of the gap between peak demand and available capacity – only one gas-fired station was under construction, no coal-fired stations were being built and even new nuclear plant, upon which the Labour government, and later the Coalition, had pinned great hopes, was unlikely to be operational until 2023 and perhaps only then if an EU inquiry into the role of the UK government in its funding gave the go-ahead.

Renewable energy schemes were being built, albeit perhaps not quite quickly enough to meet the 2020 target. Those investments, however, were raising serious questions for potential developers of other technologies – the very technologies that were required to provide the security of electricity supply that customers wanted, regardless of whether the wind was rotating the blades of wind turbines or sunlight was powering photo-voltaic arrays. The imponderables for new gas-fired stations, for example, included how often they would be called upon to produce electricity, what they would earn when they did and how they would be able to procure their gas for an unreliable running regime – for, if those EU requirements were to be met, such stations would become operational at a time when some 30 per cent of the UK's electricity

[85] Large Combustion Plant Directive 2001/80/EC

was coming from renewables, most of which would be wind-powered and claiming pole position on the grid.

The business of power generation in a liberalised marketplace was never meant to be risk-free. Even before the forced growth of renewables, developers of gas-fired power stations had serious questions to ask themselves before committing hundreds of millions of pounds – sometimes as much as a billion pounds – to a new plant. Serious though those questions may have been, however, they were capable of being answered in the context of judgements about fuel and technology, customers' demand, competitors' behaviour, the challenges of a competitive market and clear and stable regulation.

In the world post 2020, however, it would all look very different. So much so that the Coalition Government (and until 2010, its Labour predecessor) had been reviewing how the market should work. What the politicians of Brussels and Westminster wanted was for the energy companies to build power generating capacity that was known to be a great deal more expensive than that which they would normally have chosen to provide the most competitively-priced electricity. Not only that, but it was production that could not deliver electricity on demand. Nor was it always technology that was tried and tested in the same way that a coal- or gas-fired power station would have been. So there were greater investment risks that had to be taken account of. If such risks are accepted by investors, those investors are likely to want a higher return for the money that they have put in to a project and that pushes up the price for the customer. But too much risk may drive investment away – to other sectors or to other countries.

The 'Electricity Market Reform' (EMR) embodied in the Energy Act 2013 was the Coalition Government's explicit attempt to address that problem; to give investors confidence to build, or keep available, the 'low carbon' plant that would not normally have proved competitive. A range of measures included providing long-term revenue certainty for electricity producers, through the use of feed-in tariffs with contracts for difference. The government's decision to set tariffs to encourage investment and as a means of protecting the interests of consumers was, of course, entirely different in its approach to that when the electricity supply industry had been privatised. Then, it was not government decisions about tariffs that were expected to protect consumers. Government was to have played its part largely by keeping out of the way and letting competition meet the requirements of customers. The new thinking, however, looked like this:

The Government's energy and climate change goals are to deliver secure energy on the way to a sustainable low carbon future and drive ambitious action on climate change at home and abroad. To achieve this it is critical that we address both security of supply and climate change challenges while maximising the benefits and minimising costs for consumers and taxpayers. Nowhere in our energy policy are these challenges more evident than in the electricity sector.[86]

Electricity Market Reform seemed to me to confirm that the issues arising from the global warming/climate change agenda and our politicians' muddled response to them, were the cause of much of the uncertainty that energy companies faced in making decisions about investment in the UK electricity supply industry. Some of those that make policy so conscientiously will find that hard to understand. They might argue, as I have heard a representative of the European Commission argue[87], that they had given the industry

[86] https://www.gov.uk/government/uploads/system/uploads/attachment_data/file/48371/5349-electricity-market-reform-policy-overview.pdf

[87] Eurelectric workshop on investment, 6 December 2012

all the certainty that it needed with regard to what was expected of it for the long term. For example:

- the published trajectory for the reduction of greenhouse gas emissions of 1.74 per cent per annum, rising to a 2.2 per cent per annum from 2021 to 2030;

- the binding renewable energy targets for 2020;

- in the EU Emissions Trading Scheme, the progressively rising share of allowances that were to be auctioned;

- proposals to reform the carbon market, with the introduction of a market stability reserve in 2021 and

- more generally, the road map for a low carbon economy in the EU in 2050.

But companies contemplating investment know that, although politicians hate to admit it, priorities change and political decisions can be changed, and they have seen those things happen. External events can trigger the drafting of new policy - the politics of gas supply, for example. But internal decisions by individual member states can have huge a huge effect, too. Decisions caused pain in Spain, for example - radical cuts in renewable energy tariffs; retroactive taxation of energy companies and a massive payments deficit in the energy companies' accounts, where the law prevented them from charging their customers as much as fuel prices and their previous investment decisions dictated that they should. In Germany, energy-intensive industries challenged the government's policies, which were forcing up companies' costs at much the same time as North American industry was beginning to enjoy lower energy bills as a result of the successful exploitation of shale gas in the USA. German households were not immune, either. Fuel poverty, which had usually been associated with the UK, became an issue in Germany too. The impact on domestic customers' electricity bills of large subsidies for renewable energy led to a proposal to change the country's renewable energy law, to include a tax on 'own consumption' by households that have their own photo-voltaic electricity supply. In the same country, the vast amounts of renewable energy that subsidised tariffs had brought on to the system, forced the closure of some gas-fired plant that was unable to earn its keep. With German nuclear power stations closing as a result of the government's decision following the impact of a tidal wave on the Japanese nuclear power station at Fukushima and numerous new coal-fired power stations being built, the German policy of *Energiewende* began to look – even to those who respected the way that the German economy had been managed – somewhat less coherent than it had been.

In April 2014, the IPCC published a further report on climate change which noted that global carbon emissions had actually increased between 2000 and 2010, despite policies to reduce them. It also reiterated its view that governments should oversee a switch from fossil fuels to renewable energy and nuclear power and revealed that, in most of the scenarios that the Panel had considered, a reduction to near-zero emissions from electricity production was a common feature. The report suggested that the cost of the proposed mitigation would be manageable, involving the limiting of global growth by 0.06 per cent. But even if that figure had been correct, as a global average (and averages can mask the difference in the effect on rich and poor countries), just how meaningful was it for countries already mired in debt, that were trying to deliver economic growth in order to ease pressure on their voters and keep their creditors happy? At the time of that IPCC announcement, despite its efforts to reduce expenditure, the UK government was spending on behalf of its already indebted voters much more than its revenue and incurring some £2 billion per week of extra borrowing. At almost the same time as the IPCC announcement, incidentally, the same government had reported that its decision to freeze duty on fuels for transport had been shown to stimulate economic growth. It is no wonder that policies that looked likely to increase energy costs had caused the UK's Chancellor of the Exchequer to say in his speech to the Conservative Party Conference in October 2011:

We're not going to save the planet by putting our country out of business. So let's at the very least resolve that we're going to cut our carbon emissions no slower but also no faster than our fellow countries in Europe.

The significance of energy prices to the economy would have come as no surprise to businesses in the United States, of course, where the successful exploitation of shale gas had reduced energy bills and led to some industrial production being re-patriated from countries where previously the economic conditions had been more favourable.

Policies to reduce carbon emissions are riddled with difficult challenges. They extend well beyond the high-profile questions emerging from the closure of coal- and gas-fired power stations and their replacement with wind turbines and photo-voltaic panels. Most UK households now have central heating and most of that is gas-fired. Low carbon scenarios envisage that being replaced with electric heating. But for decades, 'gas-fired central heating' has been highlighted by estate agents as an attractive feature of a UK property. 'Electric central heating' has not. At home, in 2013, when our gas-fired central heating boiler became too unreliable, we replaced it with a new gas-fired boiler – 'condensing', more reliable, more efficient, but gas-fired. What would have induced us to convert the entire system to electricity? What would happen to the gas network in the unlikely event of households, *en masse*, deserting gas in favour of electricity? How much more electricity generating capacity would have to be built? What changes to the electricity networks would be required?

The questions do not begin and end with the impact of changes to domestic heating. About a quarter of the UK's man-made CO_2 emissions come from transport. Massive changes to personal transport are expected. In 2009, when Eurelectric launched its report[88] about achieving a carbon-neutral future by 2050, a switch to electric vehicles featured prominently. An electric car was on loan to Eurelectric at the time. I drove it in Brussels and had an official photograph taken alongside it afterwards. It was pleasant to drive, of course, but if this transport revolution were to come about, how much more electricity production – more power stations – would be required to power our electric cars? What would be the implications for the electricity networks – charging points and greatly increased electricity demand in areas where the network had not been designed for it? And exactly how would the switch from petrol- and diesel-powered vehicles be managed? Would those who wanted to get the maximum working life out of their fossil-fuelled car, or who simply could not afford to replace their vehicle, be priced off the road by taxation, or, would they be immobilised because of the gradual disappearance of petrol stations in their area? Taxation itself is an interesting and not unrelated issue. Fuel duty raised over £26 billion for the UK government in 2012-2013. That is a significant sum in the income column of the government's accounts. Something would have to replace it.

These are issues that would challenge a deeply-rooted dictatorship, let alone a democratically-elected government with a deficit to reduce, a huge debt to manage and a five-year term of office in which to impress an electorate which may, or may not, be

[88] Power Choices: Pathways to carbon-neutral electricity in Europe by 2050. Eurelectric. 2009.

sceptical about climate change, but is certainly sceptical about politicians and energy companies.

Fossil fuels are finite, of course, so some of these challenges are heading towards us, anyway. But when? Who knows? We are forever being surprised by the availability of new resources. The headline example was the impact of the exploitation of unconventional oil and gas in the United States – sufficient not only to reduce energy prices just when an economic boost was required, but probably sufficient to end that country's dependence on imports and perhaps reduce even its intense interest in the politics of the Middle East. But closer to home, in 2014, it was announced that under the North Sea, as well as the oil and gas yet to be exploited, there were vast coal reserves, sufficient for perhaps 200 years of energy supply – no surprise to geologists, nor to the area's oil and gas pioneers, but probably of great significance if those coal reserves could be turned into gas, via underground gasification. The scope for extracting oil and gas from deep-lying shale under parts of England was also being explored as I wrote this.

It was interesting that the IPCC report in March 2014 seemed to put so much emphasis on adaptation to the effects of climate change, although the later report, in April 2014, urged action on mitigation. If the climatic effects of global warming are as predicted, then voters will indeed display more interest in having concrete poured, rivers dredged or air-conditioning installed than in funding measures to reduce emissions. But none of this can come cheaply. Adaptation, however, has one or two advantages over attempts at mitigation. It is understandable to the people that must eventually foot the bill for it. It can be phased in to deal with problems as and when they arise. It may also be more meaningful politically. Consider whether a Minister facing voters in an area that was liable to flood would be more convincing if he or she said to the local people 'We are taking steps to reduce emissions, so as to avoid climatic changes which might threaten your houses' or 'We shall be building a flood barrier to protect your houses'.

Few people can doubt that, for government, the 'correct' order of priority for the three energy policy objectives is first security of supply, in second place (but behind security by only the tiniest margin) prices, and third, reducing emissions. Anyone who has any doubts about that order should imagine themselves in the shoes of an Energy Minister facing the consequences of failing to achieve one of them. The failure of which one has the potential to cause a Minister most pain? Being insufficiently green can lose votes; presiding over price increases can lose far more votes, but presiding over power shortages could see a Minister fired or a government lose office.

I remember going to see the late Malcolm Wicks MP, shortly after he was made Energy Minister. Malcolm was certainly one of the best Energy Ministers I encountered, not only understanding the policy conflicts but deeply concerned about the problem faced by poorer people who struggled to pay their energy bills. I had about five bullet points to discuss with him. He was politely interested in four of them but showed keen interest in the fifth. In the presence of his civil servant, the excellent Nicola Kirkup, he probed me about the risk of power shortages in the coming winter – something that the press was already making a fuss about. I described the steps the industry was taking to maintain supply (including increasing stocks of coal and arranging influenza vaccinations for key staff), talked about wholesale price rises triggering the return to the system of moth-balled plant and gave all the re-assurances that I could. We ended with a brief discussion about the acute discomfort I would feel at having to go on television to explain why power cuts had happened. He said 'I think I would get invited to go on TV before you were, David, wouldn't I?'

'Yes, I am afraid you would' I replied.

In the final analysis, within the present framework, policy will be whatever secures votes, and the implementation of it will be through whatever measures can be afforded. On the winding road that policy for the electricity supply industry has followed, mixed messages, changing priorities and even changes of tone have increased investors' risks. Customers are paying for that. Adaptation measures will have to be paid for when they are required. But if we continue with mitigation measures, it should surely be only on the basis that other countries are following suit and if we are sure that they are, then we owe it to all of those who foot the bill to ensure that we do it cost-effectively.

CHAPTER SEVENTEEN

THE TURMOIL OF 2008

In 1997, the incoming Labour government implemented its pre-election pledge to impose on the privatised utilities a 'windfall tax' which, it argued, was justified because the Conservative administration had privatised the companies too cheaply, allowing them to gain excessively from the increase in their value. The income from that tax was earmarked for a scheme to reduce youth unemployment. In his budget speech in July 1997, the Chancellor of the Exchequer, Gordon Brown MP, told the House of Commons '…Our reform of the welfare state — and the programme to move the unemployed from welfare to work — is funded by a new and one-off tax on the excess profits of the privatised utilities.'

Measures like this tend to be popular – they are seen to affect 'only' companies, not people, and in any case, government spending is apt to be seen as 'good' and business wealth as 'bad' – and only a minority are likely to make a connection between business success and their own financial well-being. The proponents of the tax in Parliament might have agreed privately that a tax imposed via retrospective legislation was far from ideal, but would reassure critics by underlining the fact that it was, of course, a one-off measure.

The tax took £5.2 billion from the books of the privatised utilities. The reach of this extended beyond energy businesses to include water and sewerage companies and BT and BAA. £1.45

billion came from the Regional Electricity Companies and £0.65 billion from the privatised generating companies. It is, of course, difficult to argue against the aim of bringing work to young, unemployed people. But how successful this measure was in achieving that, I have no idea. Nor any idea of what a cost-benefit analysis of the impact of this tax would have shown. What is clearer is that the utilities lost the argument and among the losers were the major companies in the electricity supply industry. But neither am I sure how vigorously the electricity companies made their case. At the time, I sensed that somewhere a conscious decision had been made to appease the incoming government. Whatever the industry had said, the last word, of course, would always have rested with the legislators, but when you pay off hostage-takers, they may be encouraged to try again. Fortunately, this was not a group of terrorists, but the government of the United Kingdom.

The incoming Labour government also pledged to eliminate fuel poverty and it made its intentions clearer with its Fuel Poverty Strategy, introduced in 2001. A household was defined as being in 'Fuel poverty' if it needed to spend more than 10 per cent of its income on fuel to heat the home. Eliminating the problem may have been a desirable aim, but it was one that was rather difficult to deliver, not least because the government controlled neither people's incomes, nor, their electricity and gas bills. Winter fuel allowances, cold weather payments and home insulation schemes seemed to offer some hope, but after fuel poverty numbers had fallen by about 1.5 million between 1996 and 2000, the prospect of energy price increases as a result of rising fossil fuel costs meant that it remained a tough challenge. For some lobby groups, progress was never rapid enough. On 27 August 2008, by which time the debate had been simmering for months, Zoe Gannon wrote in *The Guardian*:

The arguments for a windfall tax are obvious; from individuals and households to small businesses, the prices charged by the energy companies have hit everyone hard. Since 2000 we have faced gas price rises now in excess of 100% and electricity price rises in excess of 61%, both of which are set to increase. At the same time the six big energy providers – British Gas, npower, Scottish and Southern Energy, EDF, E.ON UK, and Scottish Power – have seen their profits rise from £557 million in 2003 to in excess of £3bn. While wholesale gas and electricity prices have increased for the energy companies, this has been more than compensated for by the exponential growth in the cost to the consumer. This boom in profits is unearned and is costing society heavily, pushing thousands more into fuel poverty. We believe that this cannot be allowed to continue, and we are not the only ones. A raft of social and environmental campaigners, political figures and 80 Labour MPs back the campaign – but perhaps more importantly, a Compass/Observer/YouGov poll – has shown overwhelming public support across the classes and the country.

Compass began to put pressure on the government through a campaign in Westminster and in the news media. It called for a windfall tax to fund an attack on fuel poverty and it had in its sights the electricity generating industry. Among other things, it alleged that generating companies had made windfall gains through the EU Emissions Trading Scheme (EUETS). The argument (also made by other organisations) was that, because, under the EUETS, the first allowances to emit CO_2 were granted to generating companies free of charge, those companies had acquired free assets; they were able legitimately to sell their emission rights in the trading scheme and that, to their advantage, the Scheme had forced up the wholesale price of electricity. This had some 'official' credibility because the regulator, Ofgem, had mooted a windfall tax in 2006 and on 17 January 2008, the *Financial Times* reported:

Ofgem first raised the possibility of a raid on the windfall profits of electricity companies in April 2006. Now, says Alistair Buchanan, the regulator's Chief Executive, "maybe it is an idea whose time has come". Alistair Darling indicated his reluctance yesterday to levy another windfall tax on electricity companies but the idea has some logic and considerable political appeal. The proposal, put to the chancellor when he met Mr Buchanan and Sir John Mogg, Ofgem's chairman, on Tuesday, has put the ball back in the Treasury's court.

The report went on to talk of hitting the profits of energy companies when they were unpopular because of price rises and quoted Elliot Morley, the former Environment Minister, who alleged that generating companies made 'obscene profits' from the free allocation of allowances under the EU Emissions Trading Scheme.

AEP soon found itself at odds with Ofgem on this issue. My comments in the press ranged from 'Windfall taxes are a bad idea...' (*The Times* 28 February 2008) to 'Every pound you take away is a pound that is lost for investment...' (*Daily Telegraph* 3 March 2008), but an invitation from *Utility Week* at the end of January to write an opinion piece on the issue gave me the chance to let off some steam and my keyboard must have been almost over-heating, that day:

My concern is not with the painful issue of the impact of energy bills on poor people, but with the way that Ofgem has added to the confusion surrounding the generation industry's role in the climate change agenda ... The subject is complicated, but that is no reason for Ofgem to oversimplify it so crudely ... Ofgem appears to have advocated an act of legalised piracy. That is not a good signal to be sending to investors who have included assumptions about the ETS in plans to spend, in the next 12 years, about £30 billion on new power stations in the UK. Nor is it a good signal about the way that we regulate business in the UK. Although the disagreement was real, the day-to-day relations between the Association and the various parts of Ofgem continued, more or less unaffected. But a public spat with the regulator was not something that we ever went looking for. From time to time, however, such things are unavoidable. One of the staff at Ofgem, though, was kind enough to tell me privately how amused they were at the reference to 'legalised piracy'. Understandably, the Chief Executive, Alistair Buchanan, was not. *Utility Week* published a letter from him the following week, which, of course, attacked my opinion piece vigorously.

The EU emissions allowances had, indeed, been issued free of charge. This was part of the phasing of the EUETS and it was designed to ensure that the first steps towards restricting the emission of carbon from fossil-fuelled power stations were not so severe as to make coal-fired electricity production – upon which much of Europe depended – suddenly too expensive. Later stages of the scheme would both tighten the emissions limits and require emitters to buy their allowances via auctioning. The Association of Electricity Producers had encouraged the introduction of the EUETS – 'cap and trade' - as a means by which the industry's carbon emissions could be reduced, as the politicians wanted, and by which a transition could be made to 'low carbon' electricity production, via investment incentivised through avoiding the rising cost of emissions.

Unfortunately, it became 'fact' that the British generating companies were making a killing and the energy journalists made the most of it. I made numerous statements and gave many interviews to press, radio and television. I explained that our companies had become net buyers of allowances, but it had little effect. I accepted that the scheme put upward pressure on electricity prices, but explained that that was what it was expected to do –

charging companies for emitting a gas (CO_2) which until recently, they had been able to emit free of charge, would have precisely that effect. One way or another, restricting carbon emissions had to be paid for. The latter point was one that I took every opportunity to make. I was astonished at the number of otherwise well-informed people who needed to have that simple message explained to them. The greater exposure of the energy industry had made everyone at the metropolitan supper tables an energy expert and there the economics of fairyland are liable to take root and flourish.

Through the spring and summer of 2008, the issue of energy bills, fuel poverty and the role of the largest energy companies built up a great head of steam. The bosses of the largest energy companies were summoned to Downing Street to be told that they faced retribution – either a windfall tax, or a requirement to contribute to a scheme to address fuel poverty.

Even Drax Power, which operated Europe's largest coal-fired power station and sold power only into the wholesale market (it had no domestic retail role), seemed to be in the frame, prompting its Chief Executive, Dorothy Thompson, to say to the *Daily Telegraph* on 4 March 2008 that 'To do something so destabilising at a time when the industry is being asked to make long-term investments would be unwise, and we have been clear to the Government on that.'

I continued to comment to the news media and thought I made the situation clear in a recorded interview with Michael Crick on BBC2 *'Newsnight'* on 31 July 2008:

The risks are that you scare investors and this can make them more reluctant to invest, or it can make it more expensive to invest. If it makes it more expensive that means the cost of new power stations goes up and in the end, customers pay for that. If you scare them off altogether – and this is a global investment market – they can go somewhere else. But if you scare them off, then you'll end up doing interviews about a different subject, which is why we don't have electricity, why the lights have gone out.

There were months of uncertainty for the industry, with the government doing little to dispel the view that the imposition of a windfall tax was imminent. Until the summer of 2008, that is, when some reports suggested that it was considering imposing other measures on the companies. It seemed that, as happens rather frequently, there were divisions within the government regarding the advisability of inflicting the tax on the industry. As a spokesman, I had been a consistent opponent of a windfall tax, but I had not been involved in discussion of any alternative. The UK Business Council for Sustainable Energy (UKBCSE), which was a grouping of the six vertically-integrated companies, was much closer to the action, and its Chief Executive, David Green, briefed me from time to time on the state of play regarding the threat to the companies. I remember taking one of those calls on my mobile phone as my wife and I were on holiday, enjoying a walk one June morning, through the sunny vineyards of Chianti and heading for Montefiorale and Greve. David was closer to the politics of this than I was, but unlike AEP, UKBCSE tended to keep itself away from the news media. To this day, I am not certain whether the members of UKBCSE met to agree with government any alternative to the threatened windfall tax, although I heard nothing to suggest that there was ever any form of joint agreement. I was to learn later that although there may not have been a meeting, there had been some high-level discussions between government and the companies.

On 31 August 2008, *The Observer* reported that the windfall tax was 'being blown off course' and journalist Tim Webb wrote:

On Friday, Shriti Vadera, the business minister and baroness, did not mince her words when she spoke to the senior executive of one of the Big Six energy suppliers. "If you don't sign up to the package, we will do something you won't like," was her terse warning before she hung up.

The article went to quote E.ON as saying 'We can't do it all' (invest in new plant and pay a windfall tax); me (on the investment programme) 'This must be the biggest investment programme the industry has ever seen'; Chris Sanger of Ernst and Young 'Capital is mobile and will go where the best investment is' and Jenny Saunders, Chief Executive of the charity National Energy Action 'Wherever the resources come from, the government needs to do much more to tackle fuel poverty. Voluntary payments by companies are only scratching the surface of the problem.'

In May, there had been an entirely different concern about the state of the British electricity industry. On Tuesday 27 May, late in the morning, a fault at Longannet power station in Scotland and within two minutes, a shut-down at Sizewell 'B' in Suffolk, caused a drop in the system frequency, which triggered automatic cut-offs and black-outs affecting 500,000 people. The press, radio and television journalists were soon on to the story. *The Times* reported: 'Operations were cancelled, people were stuck in lifts, traffic lights failed and fire engines were sent out on false alarms. Householders were unable to use any appliances or make phone calls as the blackouts hit areas including Cleveland, Cheshire, Lincolnshire and London.' I was quoted as saying 'A lot of plant is getting old and is scheduled to close. More plant will be forced to close because of environmental pressure. The more clarity we can get from Government to help build new power stations, the better.' On the BBC TV News Channel, however, I almost stumbled into saying something rather dismissive of the impact of the power shortages.

I was explaining that it been an 'amazing coincidence' that two power stations had failed within minutes of each other at a time when other plant was off the system for maintenance when the presenter interrupted:

'Why though? Sorry to interrupt, why did they suffer failures?'

'I can't tell you that and I dare say they are still investigating what went wrong, but what is important is that very quickly, the system was tripped to protect the customers. A few had to be… in fact a great many had to be… cut off, in order to protect the supplies of the great majority, and very soon afterwards, in fact about 40 minutes, power was restored, because the power stations that were working stepped up their production and we got back to normal.'

'Is this an example, then, of the fragility of Britain's infrastructure, power infrastructure, now?'

'No, I think it was just a very unfortunate coincidence and I think an apology has to go out to the customers who were affected. If it's any consolation to them, those that were affected by being switched off were actually helping the rest of the country stay in power when that happened. But this isn't a fragile system, this is a system that actually worked very well after the breakdown and it's the sort of event that we see only rarely in the UK and actually that's why it's become so newsworthy, I think.'

I had been, of course, about to say that 'a few' people had been cut off, but in the nick of time, reflecting that 500,000 people could hardly be described as 'a few', managed to say 'a great many'.

The fuel poverty/windfall tax issue began to come to a head in September, the same month in which the credit crisis – the first signs of which had become apparent in the spring – saw Lehman Brothers, the fourth-largest US investment bank, file for bankruptcy protection.

It emerged that there was to be a government announcement about the fuel poverty and windfall tax issues on Thursday 11 September 2008. My message, from AEP, continued to be that a windfall tax would be unwise and would have unintended consequences. I began to get requests from radio and TV channels to be interviewed about the windfall tax on the day of the expected government announcement. The six vertically-integrated companies – members of AEP, but on this occasion, with the issue extending well beyond power generation, planning their response through UKBCSE – recognised that it was important that I should be aware of their considered position on the issue and David Green invited me to telephone him on the Wednesday evening – the eve of the announcement. They were preparing a statement, but like everyone else outside the government, were doing so without knowing the detail of what was to be announced.

I rang UKBCSE a couple of times to be up-dated and heard the gist of the organisation's draft statement. At about 10pm I told them that, as I had an interview arranged with the BBC TV 'Breakfast' programme early the next morning and a number of other interviews that day, I needed to go home to my flat and get some sleep. I took with me what was then the latest draft of their position. It had been a long day. I was tired and when I left the office in Waterloo Place and dashed across Pall Mall to get a taxi, I tripped over the kerbstone at the base of a bollard and fell on to the road. Fortunately, the damage was limited to grazing on my hands and the toecap of one of my black Oxford shoes. My nose, which had caressed the tarmac, would look no worse than it usually did in front of the BBC's cameras, so I was fit enough to walk into what would prove to be a huge controversy the next day.

At around 5 am, a BBC car came to collect me from my flat in Dolphin Square and whisk me off to an interview involving the

BBC's Declan Curry and a young woman, Zoe McLeod, representing the charity National Energy Action[89] (NEA) – an organisation for which I had a lot of respect. Zoe McLeod spoke well about households in fuel poverty on whose behalf NEA worked and argued that there was 'some justification' for 'clawing back' money from the energy companies to help people who were struggling with their bills. I said my piece about the proposal for a windfall tax, including the statement 'A windfall tax is a daft idea, first of all because there is no windfall'. It was neither my best interview, nor my worst. It passed and I began to think about the interviews scheduled later in the day, including BBC Radio Five Live, which would be on air after the Prime Minister's announcement.

As expected, later that morning, the Prime Minister, Gordon Brown MP, held a press conference to announce the government's proposals. He told the expectant journalists that the government's objective was '…nothing less than a sea change in energy efficiency and consumption. At the same time as helping the most vulnerable families this winter. This is the right approach, giving priority to permanent, not just one-off changes, with the offer of lasting benefits and fairness for all families, cutting bills permanently every year.'

The measures which Gordon Brown announced included extending a scheme to provide free cavity wall and loft insulation to older people and those on certain benefits, incentives to all households to install insulation and an increase in the government's 'cold weather' payments to vulnerable households. Deemed preferable to a windfall tax, these proposals were to be implemented through legislation requiring the energy companies[90] to contribute some £910 million to put the measures into effect. But wouldn't this mean that the cost of the scheme would end up on customers'

---

[89] In 2013, I became a Vice President of NEA and a member of its Advisory Committee.

[90] It became apparent that this was to include more than the six vertically-integrated major energy retailers and that the proposal would draw in some of the larger 'generation-only' companies, such as Drax Power, whose business was with the electricity wholesale market, rather than supplying to domestic customers.

bills? The Prime Minister was at pains to emphasise that the cost would not be passed on to customers and in his statement to the press he said 'I do not expect the £910 million we raise to be passed on to the consumer by the energy companies.' That was soon questioned by sceptical journalists at the session at 10 Downing Street and in his response, Gordon Brown re-emphasised his earlier message.

This was not a normal energy issue. It was becoming highly political, not just because of the months of attacks on the energy companies, but because the Prime Minister headed a government which was itself the subject of a great deal of criticism and his own approval ratings were at a low ebb. The highly political nature of this issue and the way I responded to it would later have important ramifications for the Association.

Later that morning, I took part in a studio discussion on BBC Radio Five Live, with Roger Gale MP phoning in to welcome the energy efficiency measures and show at least some sympathy with the need for energy companies to be able to invest in new plant. He did, however, launch an attack on companies' billing practices, specifically related to his own recent experience of challenging his supplier's intention to increase his monthly direct debit for gas and electricity. He had felt that what he was paying was adequate and the company finally conceded that it was, so he suggested on air, '…if the power companies are doing this to a lot of subscribers, you don't need to be a genius to work out they're actually making a lot of money on the interest on our money.'

I was challenged by Radio Five's Victoria Derbyshire. 'David Porter, that's true, isn't it?'

I replied: 'Well, as a customer, I would do exactly what Roger suggested.'

But it was to get tougher later that day – a day that was already very busy, with a huge number of calls for me to field and more interviews, of course.

I did a recorded interview with Martha Kearney for BBC Radio Four *World at One*, by which time the issue of who would really pay for the newly-announced proposals was beginning to show itself as 'the story'. 'What' was to be displaced by 'How'. Martha Kearney set the scene and then played her interview with me, when I said:

'We see that it's not just energy retailers that are being dragged in to this, but some companies that simply run power stations and sell electricity into the wholesale market are now suddenly discovering the government wants them to get connected with community energy efficiency schemes. This is a very unusual situation where the government is coming to an industry that is being asked to stump up and do a lot more, just at the time when the government also wants it to raise a great deal of money – I'm talking of possibly as much as £160 billion – to build new power stations in order to avoid the 'generation gap' putting the lights out in the UK.'

'How will you be funding the £910 million? Is it inevitable that consumers are going to be asked to pay more?'

'Well, whenever people impose costs on an industry like ours, or indeed just about any other industry, the bill, to some extent always ends up with the customer. But the energy retailing business and indeed the energy wholesaling, which I represent, is competitive, so you can't simply pass through the entire cost.'

'Not the entire cost, but you will be passing on some of it?'

'Well, companies will have to decide whether they can risk passing on some of those costs or whether they will lose customers to other businesses. There are competitive pressures there, but in the end, somebody's got to pay for this, just as somebody's got to pay for the green agenda, which is already costing a great deal of money.'

'Gordon Brown said this morning that he expected the companies not to pass on any costs to the consumers.'

'Well, I think that's a little bit too sweeping. They will try to contain this because they have to, but it remains to be seen just how much of it ends upon the customer's bill in the longer run.'

The Secretary of State for Business, Enterprise and Regulatory Reform[91], John Hutton MP, was then interviewed live and in that interview, he concurred with my comments about the extent to which the costs might be passed on. In his 15 months in the job, Mr Hutton had shown signs of having balanced views about energy policy, including making comments about the importance of coal-fired electricity production. Three weeks after the major announcement about energy efficiency, he was moved out of the Department to become Secretary of State for Defence.

Unknown to me, at least initially, the interest in this story was growing in a way that today, we might call 'viral'. The Association's Communications Executive, Laura Schmidt, was fielding calls in the office and my mobile phone was ringing constantly. It was my comments on *The World at One* that were the focus of attention. They had been picked up by the Press Association, which apparently had fired off a report about them to the UK's press. I was called by Dr Garry Felgate, the recently-appointed Chief Executive of the Energy Retail Association (ERA) to be told that his phone was also hot and that he had traced the surge of interest to the Press Association, whose statement must have been all the more appealing to reporters because the regurgitation of my remarks appeared to have omitted any of the 'qualifying' comments about the impact of competition and implied that the whole of the cost of the proposed scheme would simply be passed on to

---

[91] The Department of Business, Enterprise and Regulatory Reform (BERR) was created in June 2007 (replacing the Department of Trade and Industry) and disbanded in June 2009, when it was replaced by the Department for Business, Innovation and Skills. In October 2008, energy policy responsibilities were moved to the newly-formed Department of Energy and Climate Change.

customers. Garry had been with the ERA for no more than two months, but to his great credit he had telephoned the Press Association to ask them to issue a more accurate report. Persuading an agency to change a statement of that kind is quite a challenge, but Garry succeeded and I was enormously grateful for that, although some misleading headlines had already been written. I was also grateful for the way Garry very quickly briefed me on the reaction he was getting from members – his six members were also among 'my' members, but his contacts were with the retail side of the companies – namely growing concern, not least because calls were coming to them from someone senior in the government. Someone close to No 10 was decidedly unhappy with what I had been saying.

I reflected on what I had said and concluded that it was exactly the sort of comment that AEP would always have made in response to government proposals that threatened to impose costs on members' businesses. That was no comfort, however. I had a deep sense of unease and there were two more major interviews to come that day.

The next was a recording for ITN. They were late getting in their bid to talk to me and I had been reluctant to accept the interview. I had already arranged to appear on the BBC TV national news at 17.00 and time was running short, not least because I wanted to get back to my flat to freshen up before the BBC car came for me. So I asked my PA, Su-Yen Foong, to tell ITN that there was only a very brief window of opportunity to do the interview and that they could interview me very quickly at my flat, at Dolphin Square at 16.00, or not at all. They were keen to do it, so they accepted the conditions – an implicit warning to me, as if it were needed, that I had to be on full alert. The interview was with ITN's Political Editor, Tom Bradby. That was even more reason to be wary. It signalled that this was more than an energy story. Tom Bradby knew Dolphin Square and he suggested an interview in the rose gardens in the central area of the Square. I was all for a quick 'take', but it was not possible. I was careful to stick closely to the line I had taken on *The World at One*. After all, the Secretary of State, no less, had endorsed what I had said. But Tom Bradby clearly wanted more. I messed up one recording and asked to do it again, but whenever I felt that my comments were just right, it seemed that they were not right for him. He tried again, each time putting the questions slightly differently, but I kept repeating more or less the same statement. In the end, with both of us concerned about the time – he because he needed to get the story back to ITN and I because I was due at its rival, the BBC at the Television Centre in White City – it had to do. I was relieved and grateful that the next interview looked likely to be the last of the day. Thankfully, there had been no call from *Newsnight*.

The BBC car collected me and we set off for White City. As the car approached the Television Centre, my mobile phone rang. I knew the person at the other end - a senior press officer from a large energy company which I need not name.

'David, there is some concern about what you have been saying today. It is all true and honest, of course, but I wonder if you could find a different way of saying it?'

'Bloody hell! I'm just going in to the BBC to do a live interview with Huw Edwards, but... I'll try, of course.'

When I arrived at the studio desk where Huw Edwards sat, a recorded item was being broadcast and he began a perfectly friendly conversation, which turned to a particular aspect of the electricity industry.

'What your industry needs to do is get its billing right' he said. I agreed readily, but thought privately 'If only it were as simple as that.' We were about to go live.

I was asked about the package that had been announced that morning and was able to enthuse about the advantages of its focus on energy efficiency and also to begin explaining that it was rather odd to impose the energy efficiency measures on power companies that had no relationship with domestic customers, until I realised that, whereas this was an important issue for AEP, it would mean nothing to the BBC's viewers. But it got worse. With my mind still wrestling with the last-minute message to try to find a new way of explaining the issue of who would pay for the government's good intentions, I found myself practically saying that customers would have to pay and would not have to pay in the course of the same interview. Surprisingly, Huw Edwards seemed to think that things were clear, but I felt when I left the studio that the interview had been a mess – in fact, probably the worst interview I had ever done. I should have stuck to precisely the same explanation as I had used on *The World at One* at lunchtime, but it occurred to me that what some people *thought* I had said on *The World at One* was the incomplete and headline-making comments the Press Association had attributed to me that afternoon, before Garry Felgate had asked them to publish a clarification. But even if that had been the case, my effort to address the problem that had been presented to me on the way into the BBC had done nothing to help. It marked a highly unsatisfactory ending to a busy, high-pressure day.

At 6.30 pm, the Prime Minister's announcement was the top story and my interview with Tom Bradby had spiced it up. Within seconds of ITN showing a recording of Gordon Brown telling the press that the energy companies would not be passing on the cost of his scheme, they showed me saying that some of the costs would probably find their way to customers' bills.

At least the evening went according to plan. With two or three directors from the Board of AEP, I had a dinner at the Sofitel hotel, opposite the office, discussing industry issues with senior people from National Grid – always a productive and enjoyable occasion, not least because National Grid's Executive Director, Nick Winser, and I had known each other for many years and despite the unavoidable commercial tensions between the system owner and the companies I represented, trust and respect had developed between us.

The next day, the newspapers reported not just the Prime Minister's announcement but the controversy over where the cost of the measures would fall. A government trying to win support from the electors and a Prime Minister struggling with poor personal ratings were looking to this package to help change their fortunes. It failed to do that.

In the *Daily Mail*, Secretary of State John Hutton was quoted as saying that the government could not stop energy companies increasing their tariffs (to pay for the energy efficiency measures) – 'Of course they are able to. The question is whether they are going to. We don't have powers to fix prices.' In the same newspaper, Labour MP Frank Field said: 'The government has spent all summer roaring about the package it will produce and now out pops a mouse of a proposal that will probably do very little for many of the poorest pensioners.'

In *The Times*, Dr Dieter Helm, Professor of Energy Policy at New College, Oxford, was quoted as saying that it was '"completely naïve" to believe that the money raised for the scheme from the Big Six power companies would not be passed on to consumers in the form of higher bills. In the *Daily Telegraph*, trade unions and Labour MPs were reported saying that they would continue to press for a windfall tax.

Eventually, the dust settled and I was left to wonder what had gone on between Downing Street and the big companies, both before the announcement and on the afternoon of Thursday 11 September. It was hard to imagine that there had been any prior agreement that the companies would meet the cost of the government's scheme. If there had been, I had certainly not been acquainted with it. More likely, I concluded, was that one party thought that something had been agreed.

The following week, I had a visit from the Communications Director of one of the big companies. I knew, of course, what he wanted to talk about and I welcomed the chance to discuss it. He thought that, on 11 September, I had been 'hung out to dry'. That wasn't quite how I saw it. I felt that I had been scorched by getting too close to some red-hot politics. But I could certainly see the need to do things differently in future. So, I felt, did the industry's biggest companies.

The windfall tax and the energy savings measures were the big electricity story of 2008; bigger than the brief power cuts in August of that year and even bigger than the 'climate camp' protests at Kingsnorth Power Station. But after the windfall tax issue had come to a head in September, another issue followed close behind. In early October, Ofgem published the findings of a detailed investigation that it had carried out into increases in gas and electricity prices earlier in the year. That triggered a flurry of interest by the press and led to me being interviewed on BBC Radio Five. Unsurprisingly, as far as I was concerned, Ofgem found that there had been no 'fixing' of prices so it gave me an opportunity to mention that uncertainty arising from the investigation had been hanging over the industry for a long time and that we needed to get on with investing for the future.

CHAPTER EIGHTEEN

A STRONGER VOICE

With the Electricity Association having left the stage in September 2003, the industry's representative bodies were not well placed to deal with the big issues that cut across the work of the three sectors – those bodies being the Association of Electricity Producers (AEP), the Energy Networks Association (ENA) and the Energy Retail Association (ERA). Issues such as investment and prices, for example, affected all parts of the industry, even though some members of AEP might have wished otherwise. A small generator, using renewable energy subsidised through customers' bills, for example, was part of the answer to questions about retail prices, albeit a small part. The associations were each capable of facing up to the news media to deal with the issues on their own agenda, but many journalists and politicians either did not see the industry as quite as segregated as it was, or they did not want to see it that way. Government departments also tended to claim that they liked to deal with one strong voice for an industry[92], although, undoubtedly it suited them from time to time to use in a debate a view favoured by one sector, rather than another – they could 'divide and rule'. But there was also the challenge of the type of radio or TV interview that began with a sector-specific matter and then led into issues concerning another sector. I might have accepted an interview on an investment problem and then found – perfectly

---

[92] Note, in particular, the attempts of Michael Heseltine MP, as President of the Board of Trade at DTI, to persuade trade associations that only those above a certain size and turnover deserved to be taken seriously by government.

understandably from the point of view of the journalist – that it veered into questions about retail prices and the impact on customers. It would have sounded unhelpful and even evasive, if I had responded 'That's not really my area of responsibility.'

I always felt that it was the events of 11 September 2008[93] and their aftermath which brought this challenge to a head.

I became aware that the need for a clear, stronger voice had been discussed by the Chief Executives meeting under the auspices of the UK Business Council for Sustainable Energy, which comprised the six large, vertically-integrated companies, plus National Grid and one or two other businesses, including certain AEP members, which appeared to have some kind of secondary status in the organisation. A merger of the associations had been mooted. Even if they had wanted to, of course, the UKBCSE members could not dictate a solution against other participants' wishes – we were all independent associations, even though there was some overlap in our membership. It would be, admittedly, a little easier – at least, on paper – to influence the Energy Retail Association, as its members comprised the six vertically-integrated companies. The Association of Electricity Producers (AEP), however, had around 70 members and a constitution which was based on 'one member, one vote', so any relationship that it had with other associations would have to be by consent only. And, bearing in mind the different interests represented, that consent could not be taken for granted.

Over a period of a few months, when there were discussions about our activities and our resources, the idea of a fully-fledged merger fell away and instead, a way of working more closely together was drawn up. The outcome was reasonably predictable and it suited me rather well. It was agreed that we should co-operate in the areas where big issues suggested that it would be

[93] Chapter Seventeen.

worthwhile and that this would include the attendance of the heads of the trade associations at meetings of some of the groups, including the UKBCSE-hosted meetings of the Chief Executives of the biggest companies and also the meetings for the communications heads and the strategic policy people. UKBCSE did some good work in mapping out the issues that lay ahead and logging up who was doing what. This increased our chances of working harmoniously and effectively. The Board at AEP accepted my involvement in this, although, understandably, they were wary – they reminded me to be careful what I agreed to.

I welcomed this liaison role, but was always conscious of the risk of getting out of step with what the broader membership of AEP wanted. For most of the time, that particular problem did not arise – the matters being discussed were almost entirely about the issues of the retail end of the industry. Rising bills, incorrect bills, helplines, energy efficiency, doorstep selling… and so on.

There was, however, a surprise in store, which was revealed when I was at a meeting of the major companies' communications directors. Unknown to me, and as far as I knew the heads of the other associations, the six major companies had decided to recruit and employ between them an experienced communications professional, and the search for this person was already at an advanced stage. The companies clearly wanted a much stronger presence in the news media, where the industry had been given a hard time for so long. I had a great deal of sympathy with what they wanted to do, although I was less comfortable with the way the issue had been handled. As the industry's longest-serving spokesman, I felt that I might have had something to contribute to the discussion about how the problem should be addressed. In fairness to those who had made the decision, however, they were only too aware that my constituency of members extended far beyond theirs and they may well have thought that I would have been uncomfortable, even compromised, if I had been taken into their confidence at that stage. Having had a grumble about this, I received, face-to-face, a number of assurances that the decision was not a reflection on what I had been doing. My morale was restored, but I harboured some concern that having spoken, apparently effectively, for so long for a generating sector which included the interests of the six vertically-integrated companies, I might now find myself competing for air time with another spokesman representing only the six biggest companies. Competition of that kind would have been counter-productive and could not be allowed to occur. A way of working would have to be agreed. With the need to keep things under wraps until terms had been settled and the contract signed, it was a little while before I became aware of the identity of this person.

Eventually, the appointment became public. Christine McGourty, a highly experienced newspaper journalist and former Science Correspondent of the BBC, had been appointed. The announcement about an appointment of this kind is an interesting challenge. It can hardly be kept under wraps. It must be publicised, but there is a risk of it drawing more attention to the organisation's deficiencies than to its brighter future. I remember British Rail when it advertised 'We're getting there' – cheering itself on, but admitting that it was not 'there' yet.

On 11 October 2009, in the *Sunday Times* under the headline 'Lobbying for support: Spin doctor for worried energy chiefs', Danny Fortson reported:

Britain's utilities have formed a lobby group fronted by a former BBC journalist to lead the under-fire industry's fightback amid public fury over high household energy bills. The new organisation, Energy UK, will bring communications of the sector's four trade bodies under one umbrella and provide a "united voice" for an industry that has become a whipping post for the public and consumer groups. It is expected to play a bigger role in explaining the immense costs of cleaning up the highly-polluting sector and the need for us all to share the burden. Christine McGourty, the former BBC science correspondent, who travelled to Antarctica to cover the effects of climate change, has been hired to lead the effort. She said "The industry realises that it has to do better because it has often been caught on the back foot. That is the main reason for my appointment."

Not surprisingly, the report prompted questions from my staff and calls from members. I had to explain that the appointment did not mean that communications for AEP members would be handled by Christine McGourty, nor that I would be seeking her approval to any comments that I made on behalf of the generating sector - in fact, to have done so would have implied that comments by the smaller generators were somehow subject to approval by the larger ones, which would have been not only unacceptable to the smaller players but damaging to the reputation of the six big ones. I stressed, however, that there was a need for co-operation and liaison, so that the messages we all wanted to convey were delivered as effectively as possible. I also had to underline that 'Energy UK' was simply a brand for the big companies and not an organisation of the kind AEP members belonged to. In fact, at first, it was barely an organisation at all. It was supported initially by very limited staff secondment and located in the offices of the UK Business Council for Sustainable Energy, in Victoria, London SW1. Later, it would move to the premises of the Energy Retail Association, where it would of course, be closer to the staff involved in the issues that attracted – at that time – most of the industry's hostile press reports.

The concerns that members and staff of AEP had expressed

had been echoed in the Energy Networks Association, where the membership was so different from that of AEP and where the commercial and regulatory environment was different, too.

On paper, the setting up of 'Energy UK' and the appointment of Christine McGourty may have made sense, but with the interests of four independent associations at stake, it might also have looked like an accident waiting to happen. That there was no such accident where AEP was concerned is a tribute to the way Christine worked and between us, a commitment to making sure that both operations – hers and mine – functioned well, albeit independently. Christine and I got on well from the start. It goes without saying that she was highly professional, but there was more to it than that. She was fun to work with and also a good listener, who grasped quickly the key issues. As I waded through the industry's problems as perceived from my desk, we seemed to be of one accord on many of them. In fact, for me, instead of her presence being a threat, it was encouraging. After friendly discussion, without having to draw up a treaty, we soon developed a way of working where we would keep each other briefed, but journalists' questions permitting, we would not get in each other's way. There was an added benefit for me. I had someone at hand who could give me a quick appraisal of how I was doing in front of cameras and microphones. That was very helpful, especially as she was apt to communicate her thoughts on such things without holding back.

However imperfect these arrangements may have been, they were a step forward. But we should have paid attention much earlier to the way the big industry-wide issues were addressed. The AEP's stubborn resistance to the proposal by the Electricity Association that upon the EA's demise and replacement by three sectoral associations there should be an 'Energy Association' at the top of the trade association structure, had left a void to which my members and I were too busy to pay much attention. We recognised that there was a need for a central body to address the 'cross-cutting' issues that faced the industry, but our counter proposal then was that it should sit below the three associations on the organisation diagram and that what it should be responsible for should be determined jointly by the sectoral associations. That seemed logical to us and it avoided the possibility of independent associations being dictated to from above, but it did not win the approval of the disintegrating EA. So, content that the EA would break up, leaving the three associations to focus on their sectoral work, we allowed the matter to drop from the agenda. This was understandable at the time, but it was a mistake. A void was created and AEP would not influence how it was filled. The void was filled. The UK Business Council for Sustainable Energy was never intended to be a high-profile body as far as the press spotlight was concerned, but it provided a home for the Chief Executives and senior staff of the six vertically-integrated companies, plus National Grid, to meet legitimately to discuss the big issues of the day, in the context of sustainability. It was a powerful group that would command the attention of Ministers. So discreet was it initially that it had been functioning for months without my being aware of it. Only when it was mentioned at an AEP Board meeting that UKBCSE was also preparing views on an issue that we were discussing at AEP, did I grasp the significance of what had happened.

But looking back too often at what might have been is distracting and unrewarding. Not only that, but in an energy trade association, when one finds time to look up from the matter at hand, it is usually to focus on the road immediately ahead and seldom further than the next corner. To my surprise, it was not long before the road took an unexpected turn.

The efforts of AEP, ENA, ERA and UKBCSE to co-operate

effectively seemed to me to be working. So did the engagement of Christine McGourty as Director of Energy UK. She performed well in the hostile environment of the radio and TV studios and her messages and mine were generally in harmony. At least as important as that was that Christine began planning communications strategically. Sad to say, at AEP, that was something we did less frequently than we should have. One part of the approach was to engage Ernst and Young to produce a study on the importance of the electricity and gas supply industries to the UK economy – an impressive piece of work, which embraced, among other things, employment, skills and investment figures – that was to be carried forward later by Energy UK.

Despite her efforts, it was far too soon for the reputation of the industry to be transformed by better communications. In any case, that was not enough. The 'product' had to be right before good communications work could have any lasting effect. To put it more plainly, the activity of one dodgy doorstep salesman could lead to damaging headlines which, virtually within hours, could destroy months of carefully-planned communications work. Nevertheless, the right processes were being put in place – assembling a good communications team, giving journalists reliable facts and figures, anticipating the future news agenda, having robust responses ready for issues that would prove controversial and trying to get positive stories about the industry into the news. But this was high profile snakes and ladders, and going down the snake would always be faster than going up the ladder.

In June 2010, at a meeting with the Chief Executives of the six vertically-integrated companies and National Grid, I was asked if I could stay behind at the end for a discussion with one of them. In fact, we went to a pub just off Trafalgar Square, where I was asked if I thought it would be possible to achieve a fully-fledged merger between the four associations, setting up a new body that would be properly representative of the way the industry was evolving and would embrace large, medium and small players.

Why me? There were several reasons. I was the longest-serving of the heads of the four associations; the success of AEP had demonstrated that the large, medium-sized and small companies could work together constructively; AEP had more members than the other associations put together; I was known and trusted; and I was of an age at which AEP might have been starting to think about my successor. The justification for the merger proposal was that the industry had to have a strong and properly representative voice to deal with the huge questions that it was facing and the massive investment issues that were emerging. A secondary consideration was the prospect of financial savings from having one office instead of four. It was not the first time such questions of 'efficiency' had been raised and I had had to explain that some of the expected savings were probably more apparent than real – at least, initially. Real savings would not be seen for some time, because the organisations each had commitments that could not be broken without incurring costs. Not only that, but these organisations were already quite lean and a new, larger organisation would find itself with costs that the smaller bodies did not face – for example, requiring expertise that the smaller organisations were able to manage without. Bigger organisations tend to require more staff to look after other staff. But the big prize was something much more valuable than any money saved by reducing overheads. An industry that is vital to the economy and the general well-being of every person in the country was suffering from a dreadful reputation and had to do something about it. A strong and representative voice was vital if the relationship between government and the industry was ever to be stable and constructive, rather than dysfunctional. For the avoidance of doubt, a 'stable and constructive' relationship is not just 'nice to have'. Without it, investments are harder to deliver, the cost of capital is likely to be higher and customers pay more than they need to. There really was a big prize to be won.

I pointed out the scale of the challenge of bringing together four constitutionally separate bodies, but said I would be pleased to try. To avoid the risk of any misunderstanding about what the big company Chief Executives had in mind and no less importantly, to ensure that I could explain the proposal clearly to my own employer, AEP, I also asked for the idea to be confirmed in writing.

When the brief finally arrived, I was on holiday at our house near Cahors, in the Lot in south-west France. Michael and Ann Spicer were staying with us for a few days and on the terrace under a sunshade, Michael and I picked over the attachment to the email. We had long faces when we finished reading it. The principles underlying what should be done were on the lines that had been described to me, but there were also indications of *how* some things ought to be done. The principles had always seemed a reasonable starting point, but in order for the idea to have any chance of success, I knew that the much wider range of interests that would make up the new organisation would want to contribute to the thinking about how it should all work. To secure 'buy-in' to the project, all concerned would need to agree terms of reference and start with a blank sheet of paper. Thankfully, that became the approach that was adopted.

Two of the bodies concerned were composed of roughly similar, although not identical, memberships – the ERA and the UKBCSE. Provided that their work could continue in the new organisation, their coming together promised to be least problematic. My association, AEP, with its large and diverse membership and 'one member, one vote' constitution was another matter. So was the ENA, where the vertically-integrated companies were very much in a minority and the association's culture reflected the different regulatory regime and absence of competition.

I quickly approached David Smith, the Chief Executive of the Energy Networks Association. He agreed to put the proposal to his members, but indicated that it was unlikely that they would want to go ahead. To his credit, David had the proposal discussed by ENA very rapidly and the formal response was just as he had predicted. I could not afford to dwell on that and instead, I concluded that at least we had established quickly where we stood. In that sense, the negative response was helpful. ENA also offered to sit on any steering group that we might set up – to keep a watching brief and contribute expertise where it could be helpful.

The response of AEP would not be as straightforward, of course. I felt that it was important to air the issue first with some of the medium-sized member companies – not the six largest, but the big businesses in, by size, the 'second rank' of AEP members. Initially, they showed little enthusiasm and could envisage agreeing only if a number of conditions were met. They were wary of the way the UKBCSE, representing only the largest companies[94], had established a relationship with government and more particularly, what it might be saying in Westminster and Whitehall. But for them, probably the most important condition was that the governance of the new organisation should be such that there was no possibility of it being dominated by the six well-known vertically-integrated companies. Constitutionally, the six would have to be in the minority on the Board of the new body. AEP, of course, had functioned successfully on that basis for years. The AEP Board of about 16 people included representatives of the six vertically-integrated businesses, but they would have been out-numbered in

[94] One or two of the companies in the 'second rank' of the AEP membership had accepted some kind of associate status at UKBCSE, entailing a reduced level of subscription, but also, of course, fewer benefits. They were apt to express to me their concern about that. In the lead-up to the eventual merger of the associations, however, they were to become more fully engaged.

the event of a formal vote being called. Running the Board of the AEP by voting, of course, would have been a last resort and a sign of failure and in my view, the same thing would apply to the Board of a merged organisation.

I reported back to the Chief Executives who had instigated this move to the effect that, although ENA had said 'no', there was a possibility that a merger between the remaining associations could be achieved, albeit there would be many difficult issues to overcome.

With the blessing of the Boards of the three associations, a steering group comprising a balance of interests was set up and below that, a working group, which addressed some of the issues in more detail. Keith Maclean of SSE chaired the Steering Group with my support and I chaired the working group. The heads of the three bodies – Lawrence Slade, Chief Operating Officer of ERA, David Green, Chief Executive of UKBCSE[95] (later Clare Dudeney for UKBCSE) and I, plus Christine McGourty for 'Energy UK', also began meeting regularly under my chairmanship from the end of 2010. This work became intense in 2011 and it presented a huge challenge for the heads of the associations, who also had the unrelenting pressure of their day jobs to cope with. It was, of course, a very unsettling period for the staff of the three organisations, whose questions about how things would shape up were invariably one step ahead of even the provisional decisions that we had reached. Those who have been through mergers and takeovers in their working lives will understand the stresses and strains that we all went through. I cannot say that it was something I enjoyed, but I can say that I would not have got through it without the brainpower and immense effort put in by Clare, Christine and Lawrence. Nor without the patience and understanding of my AEP staff – a wonderful team comprising

[95] David left UKBCSE and in 2012 became Chief Executive of the Clean Energy Council in Australia.

Barbara Vest (later in 2012 I appointed Barbara as Director of Generation at Energy UK), Gwyn Dolben, consultant Andy Limbrick, Julie Cox, Alastair Tolley, Rachel Hunter, Brendan Murphy, Stephen O'Neill, Su-Yen Foong, Judy Panayi and Whestly Dio. Many very good people had worked for AEP over the years, but as a team, this one was as good as any. I was also encouraged by Martin Lawrence[96], who as Chairman of AEP's Board of Directors at this difficult time was hugely supportive and understood the challenges that I and my colleagues faced. Steve Holliday, the Chief Executive of National Grid, who chaired the CEOs' group of the UKBCSE, was similarly helpful and seemed to appreciate that, although many people in the industry had gone through mergers and acquisitions, this one was different – it was not focused simply on a financial bottom line and it involved bringing together three businesses, rather than the usual two.

The AEP Board recognised that the wider membership of the Association had to be engaged in the decision about the proposed merger and well-attended members' meetings were held to air the issues frankly. Those were tough meetings. But if I had ever harboured any doubts about the value that members attached to the AEP, they would have been dispelled at those two gatherings. Not surprisingly, their concerns were that the 'generation' issues should not become secondary to other things in a merged organisation – they saw little point in giving up AEP to find themselves in a more broadly-based association if their views might be frustrated by a Board which included 'retail' interests – and that the governance of the organisation should ensure that the six vertically-integrated companies could be outvoted in the event of the Board finding it hard to reach a decision. I understood fully that wish, although I think I reminded them that, as often as not, the greatest obstacle to reaching a position in AEP was, in fact, the

---

[96] Managing Director Energy Sourcing and Customer Supply at EDF Energy.

difficulty that I had in securing agreement among the six vertically-integrated companies. The assets, ownership and culture of those companies were different and so were the personalities that led them – contrary to popular opinion, however similar they may have looked, those companies were not out of one mould. As work progressed, the proposed structure of the merged organisation allowed for a generation team of staff and a generation committee reporting directly to the Board. There would be similar arrangements for the retail interests.

Eventually, there was a clear proposition to be put to the Board of AEP and then to the other two organisations. On 15 September 2011, the AEP Board agreed to recommend the merger to the members of the Association. It was not quite unanimous. Unfortunately, Peter Prior of Summerleaze, who had been involved with the Association since 1987 and had never been a believer in the merger proposal, resigned from the Board. Peter had been an active Board member for a number of years and had provided challenge to the Board on a number of issues, which included questioning the eventual effectiveness of the EUETS and proposing instead – but unsuccessfully – switching policy to the support of a carbon tax. It was a resignation on an issue of principle and it was conducted with dignity.

On Thursday 3 November 2011, the merger proposition was put to the Annual General Meeting of the AEP at The Brewery in London EC1. The formal process was that of seeking agreement to new Articles of Association for AEP, which would include setting up a new Board of Directors, embracing interests from well beyond the generating sector. The expectation was that the revamped association would then adopt a name more suited to the more widely representative body. 'Energy UK' had always looked the likely choice, of course, and although I invited ideas about alternative names, the suggestions were never as attractive. From the chair of the AGM, the Association's President, Lord Spicer, called for a ballot – the first time that voting papers had ever been used at an AEP AGM. For a few minutes, there was a great deal of tension in the air. I had been asked on a number of occasions in advance of the event what I thought the outcome would be and I told people I could not be sure. I don't think many of them believed me, but I meant it. For months, I had worked hard to explain to members what I saw as the advantages of a merger and had discussed the pros and cons frankly with some of those whom I knew were sceptical. I was reasonably sure where the 'pro' votes rested, but what I could not be sure of was the extent to which those that were opposed or unenthusiastic might gather support to vote down the proposition. I took the view that if there were to be a concerted effort to defeat the motion, then no one involved in that effort would be likely to tell me.

Tension grew as my staff collected and counted the votes. Finally, Rachel Hunter came to the top table and handed Michael Spicer a note of the figures. Michael, Martin Lawrence and I then went quickly into a huddle around Rachel's note. The announcement that followed must have reminded our President of the occasions when, as Chairman of the Conservative Party's 1922 Committee, he declared to the news media the result of a ballot for the leadership of the Party. This declaration had a much smaller audience, but it was about an outcome that left no one in any doubt – in favour 44, against 4. There was no emotion shown, but a great many mobile phones were suddenly put to use.

It had been hard work getting to this position, but the challenge would now become harder and more intense. For months, the associations had been preparing for a merger. Huge amounts of work had been undertaken on the staffing, legal and financial issues

– with stresses and strains for all concerned – but no commitments could be made without formal resolutions by the associations and the AEP decision was always destined to be the crucial one. The ERA and the UKBCSE boards later passed their enabling resolutions and we entered the home straight. It was not a question of coasting home, however. It was more akin to battling up the hill to the finishing post in the mud at Cheltenham.

The merged organisation went 'live' on Monday 2 April 2012, albeit, at that time, with the staff operating from their former offices. For weeks there had been no chance of a good night's sleep. The notepad on the bedside table, in my flat at Dolphin Square, was scrawled on every night. Whatever high ideals we had for the new organisation, the day-to-day practicalities took over the agenda – not least, ensuring that employment laws were conformed with and that the staff were paid when they expected to be. These things were quite a challenge because the three organisations concerned were small and simply not resourced for the task that they were undertaking. AEP's lawyers, Morgan Cole, kept us firmly on track as far as company law was concerned. AEP's long-standing relationship with its accountants, Wenn Townsend, was important too. We also had some help from the associations' member companies of which the HR advice from Stephen Duffy, Head of Reward at RWE npower was invaluable to me. It was good, as well, to have been loaned the project management skills of Ian Jackson of E.ON UK. But it was the management team of Clare Dudeney, Christine McGourty and Lawrence Slade who had to make everything happen. We shared out tasks, set up working groups with staff and met frequently to monitor progress. We were heading in the right direction, but I think we were all alive to the possibility that we might overlook something critical. Lawrence came to me and spelled out that risk. He suggested that we ought to engage, for a short time, some professional help from people who specialised in mergers and acquisitions. I agreed immediately and a small team from Grant Thornton was soon alongside us, probing, questioning, cajoling and producing lists and charts that would steer us to our destination. They were more familiar with M&A work for listed companies and we must have seemed like a cottage industry in comparison, but it was the right thing to do and not for the first time, I was grateful for Lawrence's thoughtful input and the progress-chasing role he allocated to Kerry Le Van. I leaned heavily on Lawrence throughout the exercise and was impressed by the way he and indeed the other members of the team were able to cope with the huge burden of merging the associations and continuing to manage the work that each of them had been appointed to do – government, regulators and journalists, of course, did not take a break to allow us to get our trade association act together.

Sadly, the decision at the AEP AGM led to the resignation from the Association of Dr D C 'Spike' Pike. One of the first members of AIEP and in the early years a most influential Chairman, he had given the matter considerable thought and had concluded that he did not want to be part of the new organisation. This was not entirely a surprise and in a break in the formal proceedings, I had noticed Spike engaged in a conversation with the then Chairman, Martin Lawrence. It emerged that the two were having a civilised discussion about the matter. As far as Spike's business style was concerned, nothing had changed since we had first met in 1987. He did everything correctly and with all due courtesy.

At a meeting of industry Chief Executives with the Secretary of State for Energy and Climate Change, the Energy Minister and the Chief Executive of Ofgem in Westminster on 27 March 2012, I was invited by Steve Holliday, Chief Executive of National Grid, who was chairing the meeting, to update everyone on what we were trying to achieve and how we were progressing. Steve, of course, was well aware that we were almost there. I explained to the politicians and regulator what was happening and was able to say that we expected the merger to take effect on Friday 30 March 2012 with 'Day One' for 'Energy UK' being Monday 2 April 2012. In the event, I was a few hours out regarding the legal completion – it took place on the Saturday morning.

On 23 April 2012, the staff of Energy UK, who had suffered from months of uncertainty and even then were still working in their previous associations' offices, had an afternoon out. Not quite an 'away day' but an afternoon get-together with work attached. Christine McGourty's team had arranged a boat trip, with tea, on the Thames. It poured with rain, but that was barely noticed as Christine had asked a branding specialist to join us and we were all engrossed in discussing various 'Energy UK' logo designs[97] – a useful step towards everyone acquiring the necessary sense of belonging to the new organisation. It definitely helped, but I felt that for the sake of everyone involved, the sooner all the staff of Energy UK were under one roof, the better. Their offices were within walking distance of each other, so with a little effort, staff could work together in the manner that was now expected. I underestimated, however, the extent to which that would hold back change. Real team spirit would not come until they shared an office.

But that was not the only outstanding issue. I had to begin the work to find my successor – a new Chief Executive who would bring leadership and fresh thinking to the organisation and deliver what it was set up to achieve. Keith Maclean of SSE and I chose Odgers Berndtson as head-hunters, and when we had sieved through a long list of candidates, I set up and chaired a working group, representative of the wide range of interests in Energy UK,

[97] I could not help but reflect that this was a far cry from the day in 1987 when I had, in effect, 'doodled' a logo for the Association of Independent Electricity Producers.

to interview the chosen shortlist. From an impressive list emerged Angela Knight CBE. Angela's credentials were all that we might have wished for and more. She had run her own business, had worked in industry, had later become an MP and risen to the rank of Economic Secretary to the Treasury and after her political career, had run trade bodies, including most recently the British Bankers' Association.[98]

On 12 September 2012, with Angela in the audience, I found myself making a farewell speech to some 150 guests in the Institute of Directors at 116 Pall Mall, just a short distance from the offices where I had spent so many happy years at work. Michael Spicer, who hosted the reception, had arranged it with style, hand-in-hand with my PA, Su-Yen. It was wonderful to see so many friends and colleagues there and I was particularly pleased to see Lord Parkinson who, as Secretary of State for Energy with Michael Spicer as his Energy Minister, had privatised the electricity industry. Not only that, but 25 years earlier, he had been the first Secretary of State I had faced as part of a lobbying team from AIEP. Also among the guests were Willy Rickett, a senior civil servant at that meeting in 1987 and Stephen Littlechild, the first regulator of the industry, who had done so much to encourage a competitive electricity market to develop.

When given the microphone, I talked for far too long, but there was so much to tell. It was a happy occasion and that is how I wanted it and expected it to be. A day or two earlier, Christine McGourty had asked me 'Do you think you'll cry?' I knew that emotions could take over on such occasions, but I replied confidently 'No' and I didn't. I was, however, showered with presents on that evening and one of them was a book of good wishes signed by many of the people that I had worked with in the previous 25 years. I read through it later and saw an entry from

[98] On 11 September 2014, Angela Knight announced her resignation as Chief Executive of Energy UK, to pursue, at the end of the year, her 'interests in non-executive roles'.

Janet Foster, whose family's small hydro-power business on the west coast of Scotland had been a member from the time when the AIEP had been formed. Janet and her son, Roy, were at the reception. Her husband Chris had died of cancer a year or two after I had first met him, leaving Janet and her sons Roy and Martin to run their farm, their holiday business and the hydro scheme Chris had developed. I had admired Chris, who was gritty, down to earth and probably not one for the frothier aspects of trade association work. I got on well with him, but told myself that in truth, he probably had little time for Westminster public affairs, silk ties and wine-fuelled networking. That may or may not have been the right assessment, but later when I read what Janet had added to my book of fond farewells, I did feel emotion taking over. In her very generous comments, she wrote '…Chris always said stick with you.'

CHAPTER NINETEEN

SOME TICKS AND CROSSES

Looking back at energy policy under Conservative, Labour and Coalition governments, it soon becomes clear that politicians have had a lack of regard for the principles that underpinned the privatisation of 1990-1991. All three administrations stressed the importance of the market, but time and again, their interventions shifted the balance of power away from reliance on competitive solutions. To be fair, I suspect that very few of them appreciated the effect of their good intentions and certainly not the cumulative impact.

But despite policy-makers' desire to play more of a part than had been envisaged for them, there is much about the electricity supply industry that has worked in the way that the architects of the privatisation must have imagined it would. Without attempting to apply the rigour that would be expected if this were a text book, I offer a brief review of what has worked and what has been less successful.

Networks

The regulation of the networks, via 'RPI-x' price controls, was a success. In an area where competition was always hard to envisage, regulation delivered valuable efficiencies. In fact it worked so effectively that when changes to renewable energy policy looked likely to require major investment in the networks, a different measure of control had to be devised to allow that investment to go ahead. From the point of view of the generating sector, although the cost may sometimes be disputed – and, in some areas, the time it takes to get connected can be an issue – access to the network is more or less assured. Of some further help to electricity generating businesses was the introduction of competition for the physical provision of a connection – a measure that enjoyed encouragement from AEP. Not only can generators have more confidence in being able to secure connection to the network, but at the level of the transmission system (the high voltage wires) the services which generators provide in support of the system are delivered to National Grid on a commercial basis. These relationships are not problem-free and there will always be some tension between the owners of the networks and those who have to pay to use them - one party wants to charge as much as possible, the other wishes to pay as little as possible. So the 'success' box for the networks can be ticked. But the environment in which they operate has changed. It was one dominated by economic regulation to achieve efficiency through price controls. That still plays a big part, but the role of the networks now attracts far more political attention than it used to. There has to be more infrastructure to accommodate renewable energy, whose accelerated arrival was prescribed by policy-makers; new power lines have to be built in locations where they had previously been few and far between or even non-existent, and politicians and industry commentators have become attracted to the idea of 'smart' grids to cope with different types of power production – especially those that respond to wind or the sun – and the management of demand, which was usually considered to have played too small a part in the competitive market.

Interestingly, the generating and retailing sectors chose to draw attention to the rising cost of using the networks when they themselves came under political pressure because of rising prices. Penetrating questions also began to be asked about whether the networks performed well enough when power had to be restored after outages in difficult weather conditions – expectations of something that had once been taken almost for granted. The summing up of the Chairman of the Energy and Climate Change Committee of the House of Commons, Tim Yeo MP, when – following the winter storms – the networks interests appeared before the Committee on 21 January 2014, will have reminded the witnesses of the kind of dressing-down that used to be the preserve of the headmaster and with which it would always have been unwise to argue: 'I have to conclude that you are exploiting your privileged monopoly position and you have displayed a neglect of your customers which I personally find absolutely astonishing.' This statement was that of an experienced politician and was carefully calculated to grab headlines, but it also signified that the regulated part of the industry which had usually done its job successfully and had kept its head down was no longer immune from criticism.

Supply competition and customers

Industrial and commercial customers enjoyed plenty of choice between competing suppliers. Popular thinking was that this did not apply to the domestic market, which had been dominated by six large, vertically-integrated companies. But although they could claim most of the market, those companies did face competition from vigorous and innovative smaller companies. Those smaller companies could choose whether to compete on the same territory, or, occupy a niche - they are able, for example, to offer a supply entirely from renewables for those customers who want that. It is usually argued that vertical integration gave the bigger companies an advantage; access to this market is harder than it needs to be and the wholesale market, in which participants have to procure their power, had not been sufficiently liquid. Energy retailing is certainly a tough place to be in business. Margins are small and scale is important, but compared with the situation we were in under the state industry and before the opening of the domestic market in 1999, there is now a huge amount of choice. The doors to the retail market are definitely open. Not only that, but the largest suppliers are disliked; their competitors are warmly approved of; the politicians want to see more choice; the smaller players are excused from the social obligations that are imposed on the larger ones (an interesting disincentive to growing a business) and the regulator, politicians and journalists are constantly encouraging customers to switch supplier. Specialist 'price comparison' websites make that reasonably easy and – this seems not to be noticed by many commentators – they earn a living from doing so.

Despite all this, the political pressure on energy retailers was to get prices down at a time when it was far from clear that there was very much fat to be cut from their businesses and when the vast amount of new investment needed – usually pitched at up to £200 billion – could be expected to force up wholesale prices and then do the same at the retail level. Before the global financial crisis and the government's response to it hit customers' budgets, Ministers were prepared to say openly that their policies to reduce carbon emissions from the industry would push up energy bills. Though they had had little in the way of a conversation with voters about that, the politicians assumed that those voters would be happy to pay for the green vision which their elected representatives wanted to pursue. The tone of the politics changed, of course, when those who have to pay began to say that they were fed up with seeing bigger bills. It was also argued that the bills were too complicated. But at least one part of the bill – in bold figures at the bottom – must have been only too clear.

Prices and fuel poverty

Privatisation, the introduction of competition and the regulation of the charges by monopoly network assets, was meant to drive down electricity prices for customers. It did, but although 'downward pressure' (on prices) could always have been maintained through vigorous competition and careful regulation, falling prices could never have been a permanent state of affairs. Price rises invariably attracted critical headlines and sometimes that was hardly surprising. Between 2005 and 2008, for example, prices of electricity and gas together went up by about 55 per cent.[99] This led to investigations by Ofgem and select committees and to the industry finding itself in the dock for trial by media. Its reputation, which had never been particularly strong, began to plumb new depths.

But if competition and regulation could not ensure that prices would always be falling or stable, nor, of course, could it guarantee that all customers would be able to pay for what they had consumed – incomes matter, too. 'Fuel poverty' became an issue. First defined clearly by Brenda Boardman in 1991[100], it drew attention to the millions of people in households that had to spend at least 10 per cent of their income on domestic energy costs. From time to time, academics, lobby groups and government use different definitions of fuel poverty[101], but the differences matter little when considering, in principle, how the issue should be addressed. The

[99] The British Electric Industry 1990-2010. The Rise and Demise of Competition. Alex Henney. EEE. 2011.

[100] B. Boardman, Fuel poverty: from cold homes to affordable warmth, Belhaven Press, London 1991

[101] In the government's updated Fuel Poverty Report of August 2013, a previously-announced re-definition was used, employing the 'Low Income, High Costs' framework recommended in the report of a review by Professor Sir John Hills. The Secretary of State for Energy and Climate Change wrote that the government was not 'moving the goalposts', but a report by the House of Commons Environmental Audit Committee later accused the government of doing exactly that.

great challenge presented by fuel poverty had led to an ambitious commitment to eradicating the phenomenon 'as far as reasonably practicable' by 2016, with a focus on more vulnerable customers much earlier than that. This was promised at a time when there was still a degree of attachment to the electricity market and despite grumbles in the press about energy bills, there was some evidence of a 'feel-good' factor in the economy. So the commitment took little account of the risk of that energy company costs might push prices up – still less that some of the growing costs might have their roots in government policy. It led to a succession of measures being applied to the largest retailers of energy. These were domestic energy efficiency measures (to which savings in carbon emissions were also attributed[102]) which began in 1994 with the Energy Efficiency Commitment, implemented through the Energy Efficiency Standards of Performance (EESoP). Note that EESoPs, which concentrated on disadvantaged households, were funded through an allowance per customer in the Public Electricity Suppliers' regulated pricing. These had been known as 'franchise' customers – they had no competitive market from which to choose a supplier until 1999. In those circumstances, the provision by suppliers of measures to deliver the prospect of reduced energy use (and also the prospect, if not guarantee, of lower bills) of disadvantaged customers was not particularly remarkable. It was just the kind of thing that might have made sense elsewhere in vertically-integrated monopoly energy businesses. But would such measures 'fit' in a market where, from 1999, there was competition between suppliers, customers had the right to choose a new provider and economic growth would push up demand? This question did not seem to be subjected to very much scrutiny.

In 2002, the 'Energy Efficiency Commitment' (EEC) took effect. By that time, the Labour government of Tony Blair had been

[102] Policy makers are apt to assume that energy efficiency measures will also reduce carbon emissions. They may, but there can be no guarantee of that, of course.

in power for five years and although it referred often enough to the importance of markets – and in 2001, had reformed the electricity wholesale market entirely in the interests of achieving greater competition – it was through legislation governing the behaviour of the largest electricity and gas companies that it tried to address the fuel poverty issue. In 2008, EEC was replaced by the Carbon Emissions Reduction Target (CERT) (2008-2012) and - as an alternative to a further Windfall Tax - the Community Energy Savings Programme (CESP) was introduced. An official note in the House of Commons Library records that 'Overall CESP was targeted on income-deprived homes in defined areas and concentrated on a community street-by-street approach led by the major energy suppliers/generators and local authorities. The scheme was better at incentivising suppliers to deal with hard-to-treat homes (especially with solid wall insulation) than the Carbon Emissions Reduction Target scheme (that concentrated on individual households).'

The reference to 'generators' in the note above was important to AEP and to me. In Chapter Seventeen I describe the period in 2008 when, under pressure from back-benchers and lobbyists, the government seemed very likely to impose a second windfall tax on the industry and how the battle to avert this led to the announcement of CESP. When that became law, it imposed obligations, not only on the six well-known, vertically-integrated retailers, but also on a number of companies that were simply electricity-generating businesses, selling power competitively into the wholesale market. In the first meeting between those companies and government officials to discuss how CESP might be implemented, I chatted during the coffee break to a civil servant from the Cabinet Office. To my astonishment, he told me that he did not realise that the power companies affected had no involvement in the retail market and no direct contact with the customers. Although I had spoken out against the windfall tax proposal on TV and in the press, AEP had not been a party to the negotiations. With the spotlight on the six vertically-integrated companies, it was through the UKBCSE that, for months, companies had been in talks with the government. I concluded that the inclusion in the obligation of the likes of International Power and Drax Power had been a cock-up on the part of civil servants. Much later, however, in a conversation with the Chief Executive of one of the six largest companies, he intimated that it had resulted from a suggestion by one of his rival companies – presumably, they had wanted the burden to be shared as widely as possible. I could understand why they may have argued for that, but it was frustrating that we had not had an opportunity to explain, to the officials concerned, who did what and how the industry worked.

The outcome was that generating businesses that had no contact with, nor any experience of, supply to domestic customers found themselves having to make arrangements to provide home insulation services on a large scale. In early November 2008, between the time of the government's announcement and the implementation of CESP, I led a group of the Chief Executives of the affected AEP members to raise concerns about this with the Secretary of State for Energy & Climate Change, Ed Miliband MP, and two of his energy ministers, Mike O'Brien MP and Joan Ruddock MP – an impressive line-up. One of our concerns was that with energy efficiency obligations having been in place for many years, the 'low-hanging fruit' might already have been picked, meaning that these generating companies could find themselves having to deal with the more costly, more complicated and perhaps less cost-effective measures. I put that point to the Secretary of State. Briefly, he went into a huddle with his officials and then replied 'But David, I understand there are still thousands of houses without cavity wall insulation.' I am afraid that it brought out the cheeky schoolboy in me and I said 'Yes, but have they got cavity walls?' The answer was not entirely clear.

It should concern all of us that millions of people on low incomes have to spend a large proportion of their budget on their energy bills, but in dealing with that, as with so many political issues, it is easier to get agreement on what the problem is than on how to fix it. On just about the only occasion I can recall when the AEP[103] replied to a government consultation that included a question about those issues, our official response suggested that these were not matters for energy policy, rather they were matters that should be addressed by the welfare system. The generating divisions of the big companies that were affected signed up to the understandably robust AEP position. I always wondered, though, whether their colleagues in the retail divisions of those companies were already looking at ways of working with, rather than against, the proposal. That thought may have been too cynical. Some time later, it seemed that at least one of the companies might have been sympathetic to the AEP line. On 11 February 2009, when giving oral evidence to the House of Commons Committee on Energy and Climate Change, the Chief Executive of SSE, Ian Marchant, told the Committee:

I fundamentally believe that our industry will never be as good at dealing with social justice issues as the tax and benefits system and, whilst we have the most active social programme of any industry in this country in dealing with the consequences of the prices we have to charge, I query whether the burden is too great on our industry because we do not know who these vulnerable customers are. We do not know their tax and benefits.

---

[103] The Energy Retail Association would also have been responding.

The concept of fuel poverty found its way from Westminster to Brussels. At the pan-European trade body, Eurelectric, a draft EU Directive was being discussed by the organisation's Markets Committee, of which I was then a member, and within the draft were references to 'fuel poverty' – the issue having been added to the vocabulary of the European Parliament by Eluned Morgan[104], a bright and hard-working British Labour MEP that I had met through AEP's work in Brussels. As the Committee waded through the draft, paragraph by paragraph, we came eventually to the words 'fuel poverty'. At this point, the representative from Finland asked a question. 'Mr Chairman, what is fuel poverty?' Virtually everyone in the room looked in my direction and the Chairman, Gunnar Lundberg, invited me to explain. I acknowledged that the expression had originated in the UK and I explained how it was defined. The Finnish representative listened carefully, raised his eyebrows and briefly shook his head and we moved on to the next issue in the draft Directive. At lunchtime I spoke to him about it, saying 'I think you understood my comments about fuel poverty, but you still looked puzzled. It must be because everyone in Finland is wealthy, or energy is cheap, or, perhaps you have much better insulated houses than we have in the UK.' He replied, 'No, we just have a good welfare system.'

I know nothing about the Finnish welfare system, but I do know that in the political climate in Britain in 2008 – and, in recent times even more so – it would have been a brave move for the energy companies to have argued that the welfare system should, in effect, do more to help to pay the energy bills of those who could least afford them. The conventional wisdom was that this would be akin to using taxpayers' money to enable energy companies to continue to make much more money that they ought to. Instead, the conventional wisdom dictated, those companies should be penalised.

[104] Eluned Morgan became Baroness Morgan of Ely in November 2010

CERT and CESP came to a conclusion and in 2013 were replaced by the Energy Companies Obligation (ECO). Ofgem summed this up as follows[105]:

ECO places legal obligations on the larger energy suppliers to deliver energy efficiency measures to domestic energy users. It operates alongside the Green Deal which is designed to help people make energy efficiency improvements to buildings by allowing them to pay the costs through their energy bills rather than upfront.

ECO is intended to work alongside the Green Deal to provide additional support in the domestic sector, with a particular focus on vulnerable consumer groups and hard-to-treat homes.

It is noticeable that the rules of the game are changed from time to time – EESoP became EEC, which became CERT and CESP, which became ECO and the Green Deal. What is not apparent from this brief summary, however, is the huge administrative detail which is required to underpin the schemes and indeed, the changes to them. A few minutes spent on the Ofgem website will reveal the extent of consultations and responses, explanations, advice and guidance to cover the detail that has to be complied with. These things involve many hidden costs – for government, regulators and companies – which may well be huge, but are seldom exposed to the light of day.

Electricity generation

The assessment of the situation for electricity generating businesses is also 'good in parts'. The market became very open and as referred to above, producers have a level of access to the system that they could only have dreamed of when the Association of Independent Electricity Producers began lobbying in 1987.

---

[105] https://www.ofgem.gov.uk/environmental-programmes/energy-companies-obligation-eco

Government intervention in order to steer the choice of generating fuels and technologies, however, was huge. Governments professed fairly consistently their commitment to competitive energy markets and from time to time they stated that they were not in the business of picking winners. In the White Paper of 2003, for example, whilst making an exception for renewable energy, the government wrote:

We do not propose to set targets for the share of total energy or electricity supply to be met from different fuels. We do not believe Government is equipped to decide the composition of the fuel mix. We prefer to create a market framework, reinforced by long-term policy measures, which will give investors, business and consumers the right incentives to find the balance that will most effectively meet our overall goals.

But there has been an enormous difference between the rhetoric and the practice. An industry that was expected to make its own investment decisions in a competitive market – with customers enjoying the benefit of that – has been driven through twists and turns of policy changes that have been almost nausea-inducing.

Even changes in the wholesale trading arrangements – introduced with good intentions, of course – were not entirely helpful. The original mechanism, the Electricity Pool of England and Wales, was often the subject of grumbles from small producers, mostly for its apparent complexity. But at least it provided a reliable market for their power. When the Pool was threatened with abolition, the medium-sized producers were unhappy and even the small players seemed to appreciate the Pool more, because its replacement, NETA, was a less friendly trading environment. It explicitly rewarded reliability and was financially hostile to producers that were obliged to spill power on to the system with little regard for the supply/demand situation at the time. When NETA was proposed, the AEP and other associations warned the government – in consultation responses and face-to-face – that it would be particularly unhelpful to two technologies that the policy-makers said that they wanted to encourage, namely CHP and wind power. That was merely a small example of the muddle that can arise from having conflicting objectives for the industry and changing priorities from time to time.

CHP was often talked about as 'the technology whose time has come'. But it never did assume the importance that its supporters envisaged, even when government set for it a target of 10,000 MW of electricity by 2010. At one stage, rising gas prices were blamed for the sector's troubles, but regardless of the price of gas, CHP failed to grow as expected. The technology is, of course, supremely efficient when both heat and electricity are required at the same time and in situations where they are, the best sites must be well known, or, perhaps they have already been exploited. Where those two demands are out of balance, however, the efficiency of a CHP project will not look as impressive. A scheme which is driven by the demand for heat may find itself making and having to sell electricity when demand for that commodity is low and the price reflects that.

Wind power, of course, grew enormously and became the big success story for renewable energy - despite NETA's hostile trading arrangements. Not because of its ability to compete in a competitive market, but because of successive support schemes for renewable energy – the Non-Fossil Fuel Obligation (NFFO), the Renewables Obligation, the Feed-In Tariff and Electricity Market Reform proposals designed to support low carbon generating technologies. Public opinion about wind power – perhaps most often associated with the visual impact of wind turbines – has not always been helpful to it and under NFFO, with the support mechanism due to end in 1998 and pay-back for projects necessarily compressed into a short period, it attracted the first of numerous bouts of adverse publicity, for the 11p per kWh wholesale price that it received – a price that was far above the prevailing retail price of electricity for end users. The wind turbine, however, became the journalists' symbol for renewable energy – a status that owes much to the effective campaigning of the British Wind Energy Association and its successor organisation, Renewable UK. Other renewable energy technologies, such as hydro power, marine power, energy from waste and biomass schemes which can deliver power when it is wanted, rather than at the whim of the weather, were overshadowed by wind power. That had much to do with the UK having to meet a target under the EU Renewable Energy Directive – in order to get anywhere near having 15 per cent of our energy from renewables, huge amounts of renewable energy production had to be built in a short space of time and offshore wind power was the only technology that offered any prospect of that. Offshore wind turbines may not have been entirely out of sight, but by and large, they were out of mind. They also produce electricity more often than their onshore relatives – a rule of thumb seems to be that offshore wind power is available about 35 per cent of the time, whereas on land, the figure tends to be nearer 26 per cent[106].

One success story, however, was written without the help of subsidy. Although, in the early 1990s, the technology was new to the British electricity system, the Combined Cycle Gas-Fired Turbine (CCGT) found its way into the market with comparative ease and attracted backing from ex-state companies and newcomers. Manufacturers of CCGTs saw the prize and were competing hard to offer maximum efficiency in the conversion of

[106] Digest of United Kingdom Energy Statistics. Department of Energy and Climate Change. 28 November 2013.

gas to power. The very first in the UK – ABB technology, built by Lakeland Power, at Roosecote, near Barrow – was the initiative of private investors; many others followed and at the time of writing, it seemed likely that the next CCGT to be commissioned would be at Carrington, Manchester – a plant developed by the Irish state-owned electricity company, ESB.

Between those two projects a great many CCGTs were commissioned, by a range of different companies, ex-state and 'independent'. At one stage, there were so many that in a generating market over-provided with capacity, wholesale prices crashed and some companies went bust. In 2002, the Chief Executive of PowerGen, Dr Paul Golby, was quoted as saying 'The market is bust' – a statement that was among the most-quoted in the privatised industry's relatively short history and one that was said to have irritated Callum McCarthy when he was Chief Executive at Ofgem.

The biggest coal-fired power station in Europe, at Drax, in Yorkshire, was among the casualties of the collapse in wholesale prices. In August 2003 its then owner, AES, had to hand the keys to its creditors. For a while, banks actually owned power stations. We had often had banks in the membership of AIEP and later, AEP, but it had always been as 'non-generating' members, alongside consultants and equipment suppliers. It was never envisaged that they might be found in the 'generator' category. Those business failures were gruesome for the companies concerned and for their employees, but there was, for me, a silver lining. This was no comfort to those who had seen their investments fail, but for confronting those who doubted whether the generating market was competitive, I was gifted a compelling response – 'This market certainly is competitive; so much so that some of my members have gone bust.' But whereas I felt sorry for members that were in that predicament, Ofgem seemed to shed no regulatory tears about their plight – the distressed generating businesses would be sold and the new owners would enjoy the benefit of less expensive assets with which to compete, probably from a lower cost base, in the market. I suppose that when the dust of these financial disasters had settled, potential new investors in the industry would assess their risks with one eye on recent history. They would have been bound to conclude that competition in the market was real and that midway through the decade after the one in which the privatisation had taken place, the government still saw competition and lower prices as the main driver for the industry.

It was not just fossil-fuelled plant that went under. In 2002, the nuclear power company British Energy ran into financial difficulties and had to be given a loan by the government. Interviewed on the BBC *Today* programme, I acknowledged that the government had little option but to step in. The idea that a business producing perhaps 20 per cent of the nation's electricity – and which was also portrayed by the anti-nuclear lobby as dangerous – could be left to collapse would not have gone down well with the public. It was not long, however, before my phone rang. A member running a CCGT plant was unhappy with what I had said and argued that the market should have been allowed to do its worst and that a plant such as theirs would not have attracted government support. On the second point, she was right. On the first, I am not so sure.

But British Energy could not have known how thinking about nuclear power would change. Within a few years, the government's attitude to nuclear power would go from being embarrassed by the technology (almost hostile to it and preferring not to mention it) to wanting much more of it. This was an astonishing change of policy and one which summed up how political the energy business had become. It was events-led policy-making writ large. Anyone who doubts the significance of this bend in the road should compare the energy White Papers of 2003 with the Prime Minister's statements in 2006 and the debate in the news media at that time. The nuclear industry was delighted with the government's change of direction and 'opting back in' to nuclear may well have been the right thing to do. But consider also the impact on potential investors in other, non-nuclear, technologies – especially those that still fondly imagined that the government did not see its role as deciding which fuels and technologies should be used.

Having been, for years, in virtually an informal partnership with nuclear power, coal-fired electricity production suffered the opposite fate from that of its significant other. Protected for so long, it came to occupy the space on the politicians' popularity chart that had been vacated by nuclear power. Coal had and still has huge advantages as a fuel for electricity production. The fuel is plentiful, available from a wide range of countries (including the UK, although few pits remain open) and it can be stored – hugely important during the miners' strike. Coal-fired power stations are proven, reliable, flexible in their operations and long-lasting. New ones are also much cleaner and more efficient than their predecessors. But coal fell foul of the re-ordering of the agenda when the UK government decided, notably through the Climate Change Act 2008, that the most important of the three main energy policy objectives was the reduction of carbon emissions. It was not enough that coal-fired plant would have to operate within the constraints of the EU Emissions Trading Scheme. When energy companies announced that they wanted to build new coal-fired plant, to replace, with cleaner and more efficient plant, some of the capacity that would have to close to meet European air quality requirements, the government pulled a very disapproving face. Protesters, wishing to save the planet, had attacked the existing coal-fired power station at Kingsnorth, in Kent, and the most intrepid among them had even climbed the 220-metre-high chimney to draw attention to their cause. I could not help but admire their courage, but as closing Kingsnorth would make no noticeable difference to global emissions of carbon, I was more concerned with using fuels and technologies that would help to maintain electricity supply at reasonable cost.

As well as appearing on TV about this, I wrote an article for *The Guardian*, explaining why it was important that a new coal-fired power station should get planning consent. I was surprised to see in the online comments that followed the article that although, as I had expected, there were numerous vitriolic responses, many readers thought the arguments in the article had been sensible.

It was to no avail. Eventually, the plans had to be shelved. The government seemed to think it could not pursue its ambitions for world leadership on the climate change issues and give consent for a new coal-fired power station – even one which would have had to operate within the constraints of the EU Emissions Trading Scheme and would have been much cleaner and more efficient that the old coal-fired station it was to replace.

Officially, 'carbon capture and storage' technology (CCS) was coal's hope for the future. But a government website[107] reminded us how far off that technology – for coal- and gas-fired plant – might be. Nevertheless, under the UK government's CCS commercialisation programme, in 2013 and early 2014, two preferred bidders were announced, namely the White Rose Project (based on a new coal-fired generation project adjacent to Drax power station in Yorkshire) and the Peterhead Project (based on the gas-fired plant at Peterhead in Aberdeenshire). In 2014, the government had referred to £1 billion being available to support

---

[107] https://www.gov.uk/government/policies/increasing-the-use-of-low-carbon-technologies/supporting-pages/carbon-capture-and-storage-ccs

practical experience in the design, construction and operation of commercial-scale CCS.[108] In July 2014, the EU announced that it would be awarding up to 300 million euros to the White Rose project – the money apparently coming from the income from the auctioning of EUETS allowances. That may have been good news, but the process of funding the development of CCS was undeniably slow. I could not help but recall that there had already been a competition among companies for subsidy to bring forward the commercialisation of the technology. In the course of it, one by one, the competing companies dropped out of the race. Eventually, one competitor – a consortium led by Scottish Power – was left, but the project did not go ahead. I wondered if this might have been the first time that a competition prize of £1 billion had not been accepted by the winner.

CCS or no CCS, note that although the UK government could not bring itself to encourage new coal-fired electricity production (apart from pilot projects for CCS), Germany was about to build eight new coal-fired power stations.

Security of supply

Electricity production must be matched by consumption – electricity must have customers to make use of it. Supply and demand has to be balanced. To that extent, the customers have been served very well. But most do not understand that and those that do understand probably take a secure supply for granted. They can now choose not only between competing suppliers, but can, if they wish, choose a supplier that provides, for example, only renewable energy. Only a small minority do that, but when asked about it, voters express considerable support for renewable energy. More

---

[108] https://www.gov.uk/government/news/peterhead-carbon-capture-and-storage-project

obvious, though, is that they are plainly worried about their energy bills and they care, too, about security of supply.[109]

The industry can expect no thanks for the highly reliable supply it provides for its customers. But there is an issue – which interests engineers and economists – about how that reliability should be secured and maintained, and it has a clear relationship with the price of electricity. At least, it is clear to the insiders that there is such a relationship. The customers, however, are less likely to realise that they have to pay not only for the electricity that they use, but for the investment that makes just-in-time production available to respond when they change their demand. In an 'energy-only' market, the electricity production facilities that are little used, but have to be available when demand is high, were expected to enjoy much higher than usual wholesale prices when they were asked to generate electricity. That was an important part of the thinking behind the New Electricity Trading Arrangements (NETA) of 2001, but many in the industry were concerned that there was a risk that when those prices actually had to be paid, there would be a great fuss and the issue would become political and newsworthy. The Coalition Government's Electricity Market Reform programme put this issue on the industry's agenda through its proposal for a capacity mechanism. Its introduction was prompted not by economic theory, but by the distortion caused by subsidised renewable energy production – running to meet the mandatory target of the Renewable Energy Directive – which reduced the opportunities for conventional plant to earn its keep. The plant that was being displaced had to receive sufficient remuneration to keep it available so that power could still be delivered when the wind was not blowing. It was clear that to meet the EU target for 2020, 30 per cent of the UK's electricity would come from technologies such as wind and solar power. In that

---

[109] DECC Public Attitudes Tracker survey Wave 9. Summary of Headline Findings. Department of Energy & Climate Change. 29 April 2014.

trading environment, gas-fired power stations started to become unprofitable and decisions to build new ones became virtually impossible. The capacity mechanism was meant to overcome those problems. I used to think that it was odd, however, that the discussions that surrounded it seemed to take place without much debate about the level of security we were trying to achieve. It was rather like contemplating the payment of an insurance premium without having a clear idea of the cover that would be provided. Eventually, a 'Reliability Standard', based on a level of lost load, was introduced to the reform programme.

The customer, of course, is not asked what level of reliability he wants and I reflect that, at our house in France, EdF exercises control over our domestic demand through a limiter alongside the meter. If we exceed our limit, the entire power supply trips off immediately and cannot be restored until something has been switched off. In 2013, after we had 'self-disconnected' a few times, I signed a new agreement with EdF which allowed us to raise our limit from 9kW to 12kW – at a higher price, of course. A noticeable part of our peak demand in the summer, incidentally, is the 2.84 kW consumed by the heat pump, which is our energy-saving device for keeping the swimming pool warm at those times when the sun cannot be entirely relied upon. A trip-off in the summer is liable to be caused when the washing machine, the electric cooker, the electric kettle, the dishwasher and the heat pump happen to be running at the same time. It may be the coffee maker or the hair dryer that finally causes the trip. So, from time to time, it still happens, but we are now far better at managing our demand. I find it hard, however, to imagine British electricity customers tolerating demand management which is as brutal and inconvenient as the one EdF operates.

Higher energy bills – whose fault?

It is the bills that have caused customers most concern. In that respect, clearly, they feel let down. But by whom? Neither government nor the industry could do very much about, for example, rising international oil and gas prices that force up costs for many electricity producers. But governments were willing to impose costs on the energy industry that they knew would find their way to customers' bills, and they were not always open about that. Then there were the costs that they may not have realised they had contributed to – for example, pushing up the cost of capital when political uncertainty increased investors' risks, or preventing companies from pursuing an investment which they had decided was commercially attractive. If E.ON's proposal for a new coal-fired power station at Kingsnorth had gone ahead, I am sure that at least one other company would have pursued a similar project and the problem with the shrinking capacity margin would not have been as challenging.

But the industry cannot escape some blame. Not, as is popularly supposed, for making too much money on the backs of hard-pressed customers, but because it seldom seemed to tell government as plainly as it might have what the outcome of policies might be. There were, of course, reasons for that. First of all, companies try hard not to fall out with the government of the day. Broadly speaking, they benefit from operating in a democracy and at times it involves them in having to do things which they might not have chosen to do. Not only that, but in the case of the 'intermittent' technologies, they were given hefty inducements to build what the policy-makers wanted. Looking back, it was remarkable, however, how long it took the industry to point out to politicians and the news media that if, in future, the industry were to be using large amounts of electricity production that was dependent on the forces of nature, conventional plant would have to be retained or built. And that would have to be paid for.

Growth of intervention

Just as it had never been intended to make the privatised industry entirely free of government involvement, there was never a single decision to increase so significantly the amount of intervention in the industry and degrade the role of independent, market-led investment. By about 2010, however, it had reached a level that had certainly not been envisaged in 1990 and there were promises of much more to come. New norms were reached and were accepted virtually without question – the more measures that were implemented, the less of an issue the next one seemed to present.

Surely, someone needed to say something?

There are two important areas of the electricity agenda – engineering and investment – where government's experience and understanding is far from adequate and where, with customers in mind, the industry should probably have had more to say. But with government asking the industry to dance to its tune and having such a variety of tunes in its playlist, I believe that companies became corporately giddy and the importance of the customer went out of focus. From time to time, I have wondered how the state-owned electricity supply industry would have reacted to that kind of political direction. I suspect that it might have dealt with it more robustly. It reputation was far from perfect – those who have fond memories of state ownership of the industry should read some of the reports of select committee inquiries into the industry, from long before privatisation was contemplated – but it was expected to advise politicians and it was not accustomed to being pushed around. The privatised industry acquired a poor reputation and companies' willingness (and that of associations like AEP) to argue against some measures may have been lessened because of the politicians' lack of trust in the industry and its poor reputation in the eyes of the electorate. We would have heard 'They would say that, wouldn't they?' So all too often, the industry simply followed in the tyre tracks of the politics and when companies did raise questions, they tended to be about detail – how (sometimes 'how on earth') were they expected to implement a particular proposal and deal with its consequences – some of which had been apparent neither to the government nor to the lobbyists who had first put the idea in the minister's head. That is a state of affairs that cannot be improved upon rapidly, but nevertheless should be seen for what it is - unhealthy. The customers may never come to love their electricity supply industry, but that industry should at least seek to be respected. At least, in terms of its representation arrangements, the industry is now much better equipped to pursue that end.

CHAPTER TWENTY

TWISTS AND TURNS

In his foreword to the Energy White Paper of 2003[110], the Prime Minister, Tony Blair MP, wrote:

This white paper is a milestone in energy policy. It is based on the four pillars of the environment, energy reliability, affordable energy for the poorest, and competitive markets for our businesses, industries and households. This white paper sets out a strategy for the long term, to give industry the confidence to invest to help us deliver our goals - a truly sustainable energy policy.

The White Paper of 2003 had envisaged an energy future in which gas, renewable energy and energy efficiency would play the biggest part. It held out little hope for coal or nuclear power. But confidence in this extensively-researched and much-consulted-on policy fell away. The increasingly-in-vogue word 'sustainable' was being used, but subsequent events meant that the policy which followed that foreword would prove to be anything but lasting. In 2003 there were power cuts in various parts of the world, famously on the eastern seaboard of the United States, including New York. The one in central London on Thursday 28 August 2003, however, was more significant[111]. The following year, security of supply climbed higher up the agenda when a dispute led to Russia cutting

---

[110] Energy White Paper. Our energy future – creating a low carbon economy. CM 5761. February 2003.
[111] Chapter Ten.

off the gas supply to its neighbour, Ukraine. Also in 2004, on Wednesday 10 March, the BBC television broadcast the dramatised documentary 'IF the lights go out' – a fictional tale about the UK in December 2010, reliant by then on gas imports and plunged into darkness because of terrorist action against a gas pipeline in Russia.

In 2006, just three years after the government's review of energy policy and the publication of the White Paper *Our energy future - creating a low carbon economy*[112], Prime Minister Tony Blair was calling for new nuclear power and plenty of it. This new preference held firm beyond the governments of Tony Blair and Gordon Brown. In 2013, Coalition Prime Minister David Cameron announced the deal which, he hoped, would secure the construction of a new nuclear power station at Hinkley Point in Somerset. All this in a market where decisions about what to invest in, of course, were meant to have been left to a customer-driven industry.

The customer-driven industry, of course, had never been entirely free to choose. At privatisation, coal had been protected, and so was nuclear power. Renewable energy was supported fairly consistently, albeit not without having to cope with frustrating 'stop-start' programmes and several fundamental changes to the support mechanisms themselves. The UK had a long-standing target of achieving 10 per cent of its electricity production from renewables by 2010. It was never likely to achieve that, but in 2008, the EU put on the table the Renewable Energy Directive, which gave each Member State a mandatory renewable energy target for 2020 – the UK would have to deliver 15 per cent of its energy from renewables by 2020, which meant that over 30 per cent of its electricity must come from renewables by that time[113]. This would demand a massive increase in the rate of construction of renewable energy projects and it took little account of the impact on

---

[112] Our energy future - creating a low carbon economy. CM 5761. February 2003.
[113] Changes in energy sources for transport and for domestic heating are harder to achieve, so the onus is on electricity production to meet the target.

customers' bills, the consequences for the electricity market or of the ability of the networks to accommodate the new technologies – often located well away from the existing transmission system and in the case of wind and solar schemes, able to deliver power only when the wind blew, or when the sun shone, and not necessarily when customers wanted it.

The EU, of course, was as guilty as national governments of playing tunes with the three strands of energy policy. It attached a great deal of importance to the achievement of a single market for electricity and its main instrument for the reduction of carbon emissions, the Emissions Trading Scheme (EUETS) was meant to be compatible with that – a measure to encourage cost-effective compliance with emissions limits. Under EUETS, energy companies were charged for carbon emissions that exceeded agreed limits, but were left free to decide how to provide electricity within that constraint. They were not free for long. The EU's demand that a large part of the market should be powered by renewable energy was completely at odds with the intentions of the 'flagship' EUETS – a technology-neutral scheme designed to make emissions reduction compatible with a competitive electricity market.

In the UK, the Renewables Obligation had begun in 2002[114] as a technology-neutral, 'cheapest-first' support scheme, but in 2009 it was 'banded' – providing different rewards for different technologies and a role for government in choosing which ones deserved more, or less, support. The government, of course, argued that this was not a shift of policy in favour of 'picking winners'. It was, however, an important step towards helping the UK meet its 2020 renewable energy target, set by the EU. More expensive technologies such as offshore windpower looked likely to be able to deliver the capacity to meet the target, whereas one of the

114 In 2002 in England, Wales and Scotland and 2005 in Northern Ireland.

cheapest renewables, onshore wind, would be constrained by the controversy surrounding its visual impact. Remember, that EU target was legally binding and the UK tends to be a 'good European' where the rules are concerned.

If banding of renewable energy technologies was not considered to be 'picking winners', then neither were the electricity market reforms which flowed from the Energy Act of 2013. But they owed little or nothing to the principles which lay behind electricity privatisation, nor even to the thinking that under-pinned the Blair government's White Paper of 2003. Among other things, the reforms of 2013 sought to ensure that power companies built the generating technologies that the government wanted to meet its objective of reducing carbon emissions. So those companies were to be offered long-term contracts 'for difference', where, if the market price was not sufficient to remunerate the production, the necessary difference would be charged to customers and underwritten by a government agency. New nuclear power was expected to benefit from this and so would other low-carbon technologies. But as more and more electricity production is linked to contracts of this kind, the 'market' price against which they are pitched seems to be less meaningful. Yet the whole point of these contracts is that they should give energy companies and their investors the confidence to put vast sums of money into the technologies that are favoured by government, which may or may not be the technologies that would be built by companies competing to supply customers as cheaply as possible.

Some technologies do happen to be favoured by the energy companies – EdF's commitment to nuclear power and the company's vast experience of it, for example, cannot be taken lightly – but they simply would not go ahead without government support. Investors will now rely on future governments to keep to the bargain struck by their predecessors, but fortunately, they recognise that the UK has a decent reputation for keeping promises of that kind and over the years, that reputation has played a part in helping to secure huge amounts of investment. For its part, the government, of course, is placing a bet that its view of the future for electricity-producing fuels and technologies is the right one and that the customers will be able and willing to pay for it. If there were such a thing as an online betting site for energy policy, however, I have little doubt that it would offer long odds for bets that energy forecasts by government would prove accurate.

In what is still described as a market, there is now no generating technology that investors can put their money into without first ensuring that it meets government approval and that it will enjoy long-term support of some kind, enshrined, as far as possible, in law. For a while, the exception to this seemed to be gas-fired generation, but faced with so much plant on the system which, by its nature, has to run when the weather dictates – and when doing so, may displace other plant which is more competitive – gas-fired power stations now need assurance about being paid not just to produce electricity, but to stand and wait for when they are required to do that. Government has taken upon itself the role of providing that assurance, through a mechanism that pays for capacity simply to be available.

From time to time in the privatised industry, there were legitimate discussions about whether 'capacity payments' were necessary. I recall that the then Chairman of the AEP's Electricity Trading Committee, Tony Bramley, with Malcolm Taylor's support, held two 'awaydays' in Doncaster, dedicated to finding an agreed AEP position on that issue. Despite the immense brainpower in the room, members found it hard to reach agreement, except on a series of principles. One of these was that if there were to be a mechanism, it should be one which allowed for a competitive market in capacity. This AEP debate, of course, came long before the emergence of the situation where the commercial viability of reliable, 'despatchable' power capacity would be undermined by the subsidised, weather-dependent type.

In Britain, on its route through the Renewables Obligation, Feed-In Tariffs and the EMR reforms, the market for electricity production took on an entirely new meaning, and it is hard to define precisely what it now is. It was not central planning as that was understood in the days of the CEGB, but almost a system of government procurement. Whatever the definition, it was far removed from the expectations of the White Paper in 1988. An electricity market that led the world with its openness, provided a remarkably reliable supply and usually delivered prices that were among the most competitive in Europe was changed beyond recognition. Above all, it was the political response to environmental issues – leading to investment problems and doubts about security of supply – which drove the change.

The difficulty for the industry and its customers is that, even though politicians are usually aware of the need for stable policy, they are apt to shuffle their priorities to suit the political cycle and the short-term political agenda. It is as if they cannot help themselves and almost perversely, the political cycle makes it rather too easy to change emphasis – a government in office at the time of power shortages, for example, may have had little or no responsibility for the decisions – or lack of them – that led to the problem.

In 2013-2014, the Coalition Government appeared to be at risk of failing against all three of its main objectives at more or less the same time – surely an outcome to astonish those who fondly imagined that the three strands of policy were as comfortably compatible as prominent politicians were apt to assert that they were. The government faced dire warnings about future power shortages arising from the failure to replace soon enough the power stations required to close to meet EU air quality standards; there was incessant criticism of energy prices and they seemed to be making little or no impact on carbon emissions. The problem with energy bills, of course, had been festering for years. But in terms of policy, it came to a head in September 2013 when the leader of the Opposition, Ed Miliband MP, announced to his party's conference that an incoming Labour government in 2015 would freeze energy prices for 20 months whilst it reformed the market, to make it more competitive. He also declared his intention to break up the vertically-integrated energy companies, to replace Ofgem with a tougher regulatory body, create an Energy Security Board and introduce an 'open pool'[115]. With short-term politics in mind, this was an astute move. Out of the three drivers, it put prices first. Even though, at the time, electricity prices in London were well below the average for those of the European capital cities and gas prices were almost the lowest in Europe[116], the announcement won a great deal of approval.

It did nothing, however, to help with decisions to invest in new plant. In fact, quite the reverse. Companies found those decisions even harder to make and one of them, SSE, announced that it would be putting all investment decisions on hold until after the general election of 2015. In February 2014, the new Chairman of Centrica, Rick Haythornthwaite, complained of the damage being caused by the debate about energy prices between the major parties and argued that it could threaten investment, meaning that by 2015, 'the possibility of the lights going out in Britain will be looming much larger'.

---

[115] Note that the previous Labour Government had abolished the Electricity Pool and replaced it with NETA in 2001.
[116] BBC website http://www.bbc.co.uk/news/business-25200808 'Energy bills: who pays the most in Europe?'

Higher bills and power shortages are part of the staple diet of the news media. At AEP and Energy UK, when talking to journalists, I used to emphasise the need for stable energy policy and for energy companies to be allowed to be profitable in order for them to attract investment to secure the future of the industry. Some journalists understood. Many did not. Some may well have understood, but seemed almost to have their own agenda. But it was not simply that energy policy should be clear and stable. It also had to be credible. Maybe it was not just experience of the twists and turns of energy policy but the risk that the journey would eventually prove too expensive – with consequences for the industry and its customers – that tempered companies' willingness to invest. They had witnessed politicians saying openly that their low carbon agenda would mean that prices would have to go up and they had seen them later expressing concern when the bills reached customers' doormats and smartphone screens. They knew that, if prices went up to fund it all and customers objected, a future government would be expected to 'do something', with unpredictable consequences – unpredictable except that the return on companies' investments could be at risk.

But before a crisis point was reached, there was the risk of more bad news. If the margin between capacity and demand tightened in the way that had been predicted by Ofgem, wholesale prices should have risen – although National Grid contracting with companies to reduce demand at times of system stress and with smaller electricity producers to deliver power if things became critical may well have reduced the impact of that.[117] But it is the market – a rise in wholesale prices – that is meant to attract little-used or redundant power stations back on to the system; only plant that is fit to be operated, however. For some gas-fired stations which had become uneconomic and were mothballed, there was the issue

[117] Demand-side reduction and generation – Demand Side Balancing Reserve and Supplemental Balancing Reserve.

of whether their original engineering and their current condition allowed them to be used intermittently, rather than steadily producing power in the manner for which they were designed. Some were clearly beyond further use. The 1875 megawatt plant at Teesside, which the Pool Executive Committee visited when it was nearing completion in 1992 and where Graham Thomas told me of PowerGen's interest in joining the AIEP, was being dismantled as I wrote this. In little more than 20 years, that power station went from state-of-the-art technology to scrap metal.

In a period of time roughly similar to the rise and fall of the Teesside power project, much of what we associate with a competitive electricity market went from innovative, world-leading policy to scrap paper. It had begun with a commitment to an electricity supply industry where customer demand would drive the investment that also delivered security of supply. It started to unravel when the third objective – that of reducing carbon emissions – was added to the politicians' wish list. Not because a competitive market was unable to accommodate the third objective, but because of the way it was expected to do that. It lacked consistency and before long, it lacked credibility.

If one accepts the idea that by controlling the level of global carbon emissions, mankind can manage future changes to climates and weather, then accepting the EU's limit on emissions through the EUETS was not an unreasonable way to start. In fact, with greater belief in the problem and the solution, the EUETS could have formed the basis of a global mechanism to reduce carbon emissions. Even if one considered it naïve to expect a world-wide agreement of that kind, the EUETS was at least in harmony with the other objective, developing a European electricity market.

But politicians in various parts of Europe and in the UK in particular were frustrated by the lack of progress of the EUETS in steering investment towards low carbon technologies. A gradual transition was not enough for them. The EU introduced its ambitious and mandatory renewable energy targets. EUETS emissions allowances, which were initially allocated free of charge, became the subject of auctioning, pushing up costs. In Westminster, the UK government wanted to lead the world on the climate change issue. The EUETS was not enough for the UK's elected leaders. In 2008, with wide political support, the Labour government's Climate Change Act made the carbon reduction regime for the UK more stringent than the European target and legally binding on future governments. In 2013, the Conservative-led Coalition Government introduced a carbon price floor, imposing for UK power companies an additional tax on emissions when the carbon price failed to reach a certain level. The healing of political wounds had been having an influence, too. In advance of the general election of 2010, the Conservative Party wrapped itself in greenery, to try to win voters from among those whom it feared may not have been attracted to vote for it. They were serious. Finding himself Prime Minister of a coalition government, David Cameron wasted no time in telling government staff that this would be the 'greenest government ever'. In terms of the position of environmental issues on the political agenda and judged by the measures that were introduced, he may well have been able to claim that he had succeeded. Was he, in fact, too successful? In 2013, with accusing fingers pointed at the government for policies which helped to push up energy prices, he announced a rolling-back of some of the green measures, in order to reduce energy bills. There was concern that what was meant to attract votes in 2010 would contribute to losing them in 2015. Governments change their minds. Voters have mood changes.

All this led to predictable tension, exemplified when the

Chancellor of the Exchequer, George Osborne MP, told the Conservative Party conference in October 2011 of his concern about the impact of the UK trying to reduce its carbon emissions faster than the rest of Europe. At times, there were also clear signs of the Prime Minister's office being out of alignment with the Liberal Democrat members of the coalition and of the Secretary of State for Energy and Climate Change (Ed Davey MP, Liberal Democrat) being out of step with Conservatives, including the Energy Minister and the Secretary of State for the Environment. Not only that, but on this issue, there were clearly deep divisions among the Conservative Members of Parliament. There were even unsubstantiated reports that, concerned about the impact of environmental measures on energy bills, the Prime Minister had vented his frustration by referring to 'green crap'.

Some of these tensions were replicated in other European countries and in the machinery of the EU itself, where the issues of European competitiveness were made even more sensitive by the huge reduction of energy prices in the United States. We learned in 2013-2014 that in Germany, the policy of *Energiewende* – the energy transition (to low carbon technologies) was attracting increasing criticism, not least for its impact on commercial and domestic energy bills. In February 2014, it was reported that one German household in six found itself in a state of fuel poverty. At one time this problem had been thought to be a largely British phenomenon, so it came as a surprise to many who admired the way the German economy was managed.

There were also signs of energy-intensive industries moving investment to other parts of the world. A commission that advised the German government on research and innovation concluded that the country's renewable energy law should be abandoned, because it was neither helping with climate change nor promoting innovation. Green energy subsidies in Germany were running at 22 billion euros a year at that time. In April 2014, the German government approved reforms aimed at reducing subsidies to renewable energy and curbing increases in energy prices. 'The coalition is providing for a reboot of the *Energiewende'* said Economy and Energy Minister Sigmar Gabriel. For 2017, a competitive tendering process for renewable energy was planned and more immediately, exemptions for German industry from the cost of supporting renewables – a matter that attracted the attention of the European Commission because of its possible 'state aid' implications. The UK government's proposed support for new nuclear power had demanded similar consideration by the Commission, of course.

The tension arising from the cost of the environmental agenda was exhibited at EU level, too. The EU Energy Commissioner, Günther Oettinger, apparently criticising the EU's Energy and Climate package for 2030 (to which he had been a signatory), told a BusinessEurope conference in January 2014 that he doubted whether a planned reduction of 40 per cent in carbon emissions could be achieved and suggested that those who believed that it could 'save the world' were either 'arrogant' or 'stupid'. He also argued that a proposed 27 per cent target for member states' use of renewable energy should not be legally binding.

It was hardly surprising then to find that that energy companies were behaving cautiously as far as investment was concerned. They could be confident that their customers would continue to want plentiful and reliable electricity at a price which is as competitive as possible. But investing to deliver that was not enough. They were also expected to respond to the huge political commitment to reducing the carbon emissions from the power industry, which had a major and expensive influence on how they met customers' expectations. As they came to terms with that and embraced the policy-makers' expectations, they began to witness the effect on the electricity market and their customers and the consequent effect on political thinking.

Some 25 years after the privatisation of the British electricity supply industry, many journalists were still apt to report from time to time that the government was planning to 'invest' large sums in the industry or to 'build' wind farms or nuclear power stations. Some may not have understood where the investment now came from. Others may simply have been tempted to overlook the facts in their desire to keep things simple for their audience. As everyone in the energy industry knows, the UK government does not fund these things. Instead, it passes laws and regulations to induce other bodies to do that, leaving their customers eventually to foot the bill. Yet it already borrows some £2 billion every week because government spending exceeds revenue[118] and faces, when it cares to look, a national debt of well over £1 trillion, so it is not uninterested in the economic impact of investment in electricity supply. Most of the customers of the electricity supply industry are also voters and taxpayers and they feel the pressure as government tries to close the financial gap by increasing revenue or reducing its outgoings. So, as one government economist looks at the impact of jobs being created by private investment in electricity production or energy-saving measures and the favourable headlines that might follow, another will be looking at the impact on energy bills, the customers' ability to pay them and the less appealing headlines that might arise from that. Therefore, although it is not 'government money' that supports the low carbon generating technologies (although the cold callers trying to sell me a rooftop PV system invariably enthuse about what the government will 'give me'), there are limits on what may be levied to fund them.[119]

[118] Budget 2014. Out-turn 2012-2013. Office for National Statistics and Office for Budget Responsibility.
[119] Control Framework for DECC levy-funded spending. HM Treasury. March 2011.

I recall that after the privatisation of 1990, when I was invited to speak at conferences on the subject, I used to report that the industry had driven down its costs by, among other things, reducing substantially the number of people it employed and that it had even managed to do it without undue trauma for those affected personally. Efficiency of that kind helped to keep customers' energy bills down and in the 1990s this ticked the box. It was accepted with virtually no debate. 25 years later, such matters seem to be less clear-cut, but it is clear that we do not like high energy bills and for many of us, those bills are of huge concern.

CHAPTER TWENTY ONE

TAKING STOCK

More or less by chance, I was given the opportunity to play a small part in a major industry that was about to undergo immense change. In fact, the impact of that change was so great that it had an influence far beyond Great Britain. Many other countries followed Britain's lead and liberalised electricity supply. They may not have adopted the British approach in every detail, but the key principles were widely accepted. Perhaps most remarkable was the European Union's decision to create a single, internal market in electricity. But putting that into effect was harder than making the decision to do it. It was technically and financially challenging and weighed down with politics – not least the extent to which many key energy issues were, not unreasonably, devolved to the Member States – and also the emergence of other policies for the industry, which were sometimes at odds with the very reasons for having a market and the way that markets work. In 2014, the year which the European Commission finally said would be the year in which the single electricity market would come into effect, half of the member states of the EU still regulated electricity prices – hardly a signal of belief in the benefits of markets; more likely a fear of them.

When the state electricity industry in Britain[120] was privatised

---

[120] Although it might seem easier to refer to the 'UK' electricity industry, changes were neither uniform nor simultaneous. The lead was taken in England and Wales and there was no competitive market in Scotland until the British Electricity Trading and Transmission Arrangements (BETTA) were introduced in 2005, nor in Northern Ireland until it entered the single Irish market in 2007.

and liberalised, the task was also immensely challenging, but the expectations were fairly straightforward. The networks would remain monopolies with their charges controlled by regulation and the rest of the industry would be competitive and customer-driven, but with regulatory oversight. Access to the system – an area of particular difficulty for independent companies in the days when most of the industry was state-owned – would become open to all. Investment in power generation would be made by companies whose culture would enable them to compete with the ex-state businesses. Similarly, in the confusingly-named 'supply' side of the industry, as well as the ex-state incumbents, there would be newcomers that would buy power in a competitive wholesale market and become retailers to the end customers.[121] In the last analysis, it would be what customers wanted that would drive the industry.

In the 16-page White Paper of February 1988[122] which set out the Thatcher government's proposals for privatising the state electricity supply industry, the concluding paragraph read:

The benefits of privatisation

66. The proposals set out in this White Paper will secure a more efficient and economic supply of electricity, by building on what is best in the industry and ending what is wrong about the present structure.

■ *Decisions about investment in power stations will be driven by the distribution companies and so will reflect the needs of customers.[123]*

---

[121] The opening up of this market was phased, which meant that domestic customers were not able to choose between competing suppliers until 1999.

[122] 122 Privatising Electricity. The Government's proposals for the privatisation of the electric supply industry in England and Wales. February 1988. HMSO, Cm 322.

[123] Today, this may seem hard to understand, but I suspect that it may have been intended to reflect the early role of the distribution companies in 'sourcing' generation and supplying customers. In the House of Commons, when he brought forward the White Paper, Secretary of State for Energy, Cecil Parkinson MP actually said 'Decisions about the supply of electricity should be driven by the needs of customers.'

- *Greater competition will create downward pressures on costs and prices, and ensure that the customer, not the producer or distributor, comes first.*
- *Customers will be given new rights, not just safeguards.*
- *Management will have more freedom to use their initiative within a clear regulatory framework.*
- *The security and safety of electricity supply will be maintained.*
- *Investment plans will be subject to commercial tests, and the industry will have access to private sector finance.*
- *Employees will have the right to own shares in their industry, and customers will also have the opportunity.*
- *A modern competitive industry will be created, widely owned by the public, and more responsive to the needs of customers and employees. The industry will have a better chance of meeting electricity demand at minimum cost. There are real benefits in prospect for the customer, employee and the economy.*

This paints a picture of an electricity supply industry which is concerned about costs and prices and is essentially customer-driven. But a little over a quarter of a century later, the idea of an industry driven by its customers would have been deemed laughable by the very people who were expected to be in the driving seat. They were able to save money and make a point by switching suppliers and although they learnt to do that, many of them became disenchanted with the process and some appeared to doubt that it had anything but a short-term benefit. Those who chose not to switch, of course, must have lost out heavily. Switching or not, customers enjoyed a highly reliable electricity supply, but they took that for granted and it would not have occurred to them that not only did the energy they used have to be paid for, so did supply security – making it available whenever they wanted it. Nor did they understand that the investment that financed both the industry's expensive hardware and the systems that made it work so well had to provide a return to those who had put large sums of money into it. Nor was it any comfort to the customers that, in the UK, they usually enjoyed some of the lowest energy prices in Europe.

The industry might have concluded that it was doing what was, broadly speaking, a good job. Its customers, however, had begun to dislike it intensely. By April 2014, the reputation of the industry was confirmed as being as bad as that of banking. [124] Serious damage had been done to the supplier–customer relationship.

The press gorged on the plight of the industry, and its appetite seemed insatiable. If a billing system's computer sent a pensioner a bill for £15,000, instead of perhaps £150, the tabloid headlines were hardly a surprise. That kind of thing will happen from time to time in systems far better than those through which the energy companies issue hundreds of millions of bills every year. But the response of the company concerned – apart from saying it was sorry and stepping up its efforts to improve its sometimes clunky data handling – should always have been so sympathetic as to prompt a reaction on the lines of 'Wow, that was nice!' Sadly, that was rarely how those stories ended.

Of course, problems of that kind will never be eliminated completely and however distressing they may be to the pensioner in Acacia Grove, they are no more than the froth on the mixture of publicity. Below that froth, the mixture became toxic.

'Doorstep selling', which was a highly successful means of getting customers to switch supplier – usually to good effect and without problems – became a victim of its own success. Some sales people, albeit only a tiny minority, were tempted to depart from the script to get signatures from customers who were persuaded to switch supplier by the promise of an effortless saving that did not always materialise. The rule-breakers were exposed and companies

---

[124] British attitudes to the household energy market. YouGov. April 2014.

were sometimes fined, but the headlines served only to reinforce customers' growing suspicions. Even when companies had abandoned doorstep selling, there were still a few practices that prompted unfortunate headlines.

In 2013, using a price comparison site, I switched supplier with great ease and made a saving that proved useful to the budget of someone who had retired at a time when annuity rates were deeply depressed and interest rates on savings were insulting. A switch many years earlier had gone less smoothly, however. At home in Cornwall, my wife had taken a cold call from one of the vertically-integrated companies and had been offered a substantially lower tariff. We began the process of switching, only to find that when it came to the crunch, the tariff was no better than we were already paying. A disagreement ensued and our file on the issue began to fatten up.

Then came a stroke of luck. As Chief Executive of the AEP, I was invited to a company reception at which my electricity supplier was to announce a high-profile sponsorship decision. I was circulating, with a glass of wine in hand, when my host ushered me towards one of his colleagues. 'David, do you know (naming him), our Retail Director?' he said.

'No,' I replied, 'but I should be delighted to meet him.'

The matter was sorted out in two or three days. The tabloids would have loved that story. The company would have been pilloried and I would have been depicted not only as an apologist for the industry but privileged to boot.

It was not long after privatisation that the press realised that there were also stories to be written about how the bosses of the privatised industry were rewarded. The journalists' comparisons with the former state industry were not really justified – the task was different, the risks were different and the rewards were meant to be, too – but resentment was easy to whip up and the industry found it hard to respond convincingly. It was very busy making the new arrangements work, but it was also totally unprepared for criticism of that kind and unaware of how damaging it would become.

Years later, criticism was even harder to deal with when prices rose and profits were deemed to be too high. In fairness, the energy industry is hardly unique in Britain in having to cope with an unenthusiastic attitude to business. There appears to be a low level of understanding of how business functions and what it must achieve before government is able to take a share of its wealth and redeploy it. By way of contrast, the level of interest in how that wealth should then be deployed is intense. When an energy company announces its results, the latest bottom-line figure is usually quoted without any hint of whether it is reasonable in relation to the company's turnover, nor with any indication of what has been invested in the business. It is presented simply as a large number and one that is, of course, unreasonable. At times, even the industry's regulatory body seemed tempted to indulge in that kind of thing, perhaps drawing attention to gains from Pool prices over a brief period of time. Even in the post-Pool era, Ofgem would often publish its view of the current level of profit being made per customer – a snapshot assessment and one with which the companies sometimes disagreed strongly.

All this attention becomes a little more understandable when one is reminded how important electricity – and the cost of it – is to industry, commerce and the daily lives of the voters. The energy industry is fully aware of its important role, but like many other industries, it is sometimes guilty of being introspective. Too often, it is apt to see the electricity that is produced and distributed as the end product. In one sense, it is, so that is perfectly understandable.

But this is an end product that is different from so many others, not merely because, unlike most other commodities, it cannot be stored and has to be used immediately, but because it is so vital to the productive activity of other businesses. For some of them, it is more than that. It is a hugely significant factor in their ability to remain in business.

Those companies should be highly influential in the corridors of power. They are well represented by organisations like the Energy Intensive Users' Group (EIUG) and the Major Energy Users' Council (MEUC) and they can usually be relied upon to have grown-up views about the big energy issues that face them and affect the well-being of the country. On the occasions when I found myself in a public discussion with Jeremy Nicholson, the Director of the EIUG, I knew that, although we might not agree on every issue, there was a great deal we would agree on and the debate would be conducted around the facts.

Those companies have the ability to lobby, of course, and they usually do that well. One big difference between them and the millions of people who pay household electricity and gas bills, however, is that they have no voting power. It is the domestic energy bill payers who are more likely to command the attention of our politicians.

The biggest energy companies could be forgiven (well, almost) for losing sight of that and forgetting who keeps them in business. At times it must have seemed that the customer of those companies was, in practice, the government, because government had interposed itself between the companies and the people who pay their bills. Unfortunately, it did not do this in a very elegant way. That it wanted to influence the big picture was one thing, but time and again it succumbed to the temptation to micro-manage other things that are best left to a competitive market, the customers and the regulator. Popular thinking, of course, was that the market was not competitive and this was one of the excuses for intervening. But rather than telling companies how they should design customers' bills, or, that they should restrict the number of tariffs they offer, it would have been better to have had the effectiveness of the market tested by the competition authorities.[125]

In my last couple of years at AEP, with a full-scale competition inquiry being mooted, a number of the players in the industry protested on the grounds that an inquiry would have taken two years, during which time badly-needed investment would have ground to a halt. I added AEP's voice to that argument, but looking back, it was a mistake to have done so. We should have said 'Bring it on'.[126]

Eventually, it was brought on. Under pressure from the tactics of the Labour Opposition and from a critical press feasting on the industry's discomfort, in 2013, the Coalition Government asked the regulator, Ofgem (with the Office of Fair Trading and the Competition and Markets Authority involved), to conduct an investigation into whether the electricity and gas markets were working properly. Ofgem's report, published on 27 March 2014, highlighted what might be described as 'feelings' about the market, rather than any clear evidence of anything being wrong. It found no evidence of collusion, for example. But it referred to the possibility of 'tacit collusion'– something which seems hard to define and in any case, I believe, is not illegal. Ofgem pointed out correctly, however, that the Competition and Markets Authority (CMA) had more powers of investigation than it had as the energy regulator and it recommended that the market should be referred

---

[125] In October 2013, the Prime Minister, David Cameron MP announced that there would be an annual 'competition test', beginning in 2014 with a competition 'audit' by Ofgem and other competition authorities.

[126] In October 2013, the Chief Executive of E.ON UK, Dr Tony Cocker, called publicly for a Competition Commission inquiry to 'de-politicise' the debate.

to the CMA.[127] Bearing in mind the political pressure, the hostility of the news media and the opportunity of a fresh start presented by the recent appointment of a new Chief Executive[128] at Ofgem, it was hard to see how the regulator could ever have concluded that all was well – despite many previous investigations having found no evidence sufficient to prompt a referral to the Competition Commission.

With Ofgem's recommendation announced, there was a risk that plans for investment would gather dust. But many plans for new power plant had already been filed away because of the market distortion caused by the forced growth of renewables and uncertainties arising from that and from Electricity Market Reform. Furthermore, the Labour Party had pledged that if it were to be elected in 2015, it would freeze prices for 20 months and reform the market. The growing risk of power shortages in 2015 was well known, so all concerned were already braced for problems. I suppose there is rarely a good time for a two-year long investigation that would guarantee uncertainty and could lead to enormous upheaval in the market, but it might have been argued that this was as good a time as any.

On 26 June 2014, Ofgem announced that it had referred the six largest suppliers of energy for investigation by the CMA. It appeared that the CMA would decide for itself what aspects of the market to focus on – although Ofgem gave it some clues – and that it was expected to report by the end of 2015.

The role of the CMA (it became the successor to the Competition Commission in 2014) is to strengthen competition in British business and to cut out anti-competitive practices. All the major political parties in Britain say they want more competition in electricity and gas supply, in order to protect the interests of

---

[127] https://www.ofgem.gov.uk/publications-and-updates/state-market-assessment

[128] Dermot Nolan, from March 2014.

customers. But I wonder if the CMA will notice that, although the flame of competition does still burn in the energy sector, it is the decisions of policy-makers – in Westminster and in Brussels – that have starved it of so much of the oxygen that would have enabled it to have burned more brightly? If our politicians really did want customers, and what they pay for electricity and gas, to drive the decisions of the market participants, those policy-makers would have surely have been less willing to constrain the companies' commercial decisions – such as supporting coal-fired electricity, then virtually banning new coal-fired plant; putting a moratorium on new gas-fired plant; playing down the role of nuclear power, then enthusiastically supporting it; demanding that, by 2020, some 30 per cent of electricity should come from renewable energy, instead of letting those technologies find their place in the market; telling energy companies that they must not offer such a wide choice of tariffs; putting social obligations on some energy companies (but not others); unilaterally raising the price of carbon emissions when the European market price was considered too low for British political taste... the list is even longer than that, but the CMA will have the opportunity to scrutinise it carefully – if it has the time and inclination to do so.

By 2014, interventions in the market had been stacked upon each other so many times that it was becoming hard to remember what the base layer looked like. That problem was particularly acute in the field of officialdom, where institutional memory can be embarrassingly short and experience did not seem to be valued. It was reflected in the politics, too. In October 2011 the press reported, with a certain amount of approval, that the Labour Party energy team, in opposition, had announced a new policy for the electricity market. If elected, they would scrap the bilateral trading arrangements and introduce pooling of electricity. The *Financial*

Times kindly published a letter from me which, with un-disguised astonishment, pointed out that we had once had an electricity pool, but that it had been abolished by the predecessors of those modern-day politicians on the grounds that it was not sufficiently competitive and that the change had been implemented, as recently as 2001, at a cost of about £1 billion.

The impact on the energy industry of changes in political thinking – in sometimes quite a short space of time – should not be underestimated. One of the concerns about switching from a state-owned industry to a privately-owned one was that, although the privately-owned industry would certainly make more efficient use of resources, it would have the disadvantage of not being able to raise capital as cheaply as a state monopoly could. One way the privatised industry's cost of capital could be held down, of course, would be by governments having clear and stable policies and sticking to them. I do not have access to figures, but I feel sure that, because of the winding route that energy policy has followed, the cost of capital has been far higher than it needed to be. Customers, of course, are paying for that.

UK governments hold office for a fixed five-year term. But after no more than four years, they find themselves focused on the next general election. In terms of investment in the electricity supply industry, four years is short-term. Power station investments are for the long term – never less than two decades, sometimes double that time, or even longer. This mismatch with political timescales is an uncomfortable one and in fairness to the politicians, I have heard Energy Ministers and opposition spokesmen, privately, make it clear that they understand the problem only too well. It is something which, towards the end of its period in office, the Labour government (1997-2010) began to recognise with an Electricity Market Review. Its successor, the Coalition, with its Electricity

Market Reform[129], tried to address it with the assurance of long-term government-backed contracts. Note, however, that before EMR had been implemented fully by the Coalition Government, the Labour Party was publishing its own plans for reform of the market if it were to be elected in 2015 – creation of an electricity pool, breaking up of large companies, the formation of an Energy Security Board and the replacement of Ofgem with a tougher regulator. Not only that, but the CMA would also be reporting with its conclusions and recommendations about the market. So in 2014, investors in the industry faced the market reforms of 2014 (largely known, albeit with some important details to be agreed), further changes if a Labour government were to be elected in May 2015 and probably even more when the CMA reported at the end of 2015 – if it had managed to work within its ambitious timescale. The industry was never meant to be risk-free, but nor was it expected that so much of its risk would be of a political nature. The industry's 'textbook' business risks – choice of capital equipment, financing, fuels, staffing, competitors' actions, changing demand etc – are demanding enough, but largely manageable. Political risk is another matter.

After a glass of wine or two, I can easily reach the conclusion that, rather than being too important to be in private ownership (as many of the critics of privatisation had argued), electricity supply is far too important to be in the hands of politicians. Other people have considered the problem soberly. As long ago as 2001, Dr Dieter Helm suggested[130] that the major decisions should come from an 'Energy Agency' at arm's length from the government. Setting up such a body would undoubtedly constitute a clear signal of the need to maintain stable policy, one step removed from the capricious politicians. But it would be those very politicians who

[129] Energy Act 2013.

[130] Energy Policy and the Case for an Energy Agency. Dr DieterHelm. 26th August 2001

would have to approve the legislation to set up the Agency, agree its terms of reference and policy framework, appoint what would almost certainly have to be a 'balanced' group of people as the Agency's decision-making body and perhaps even reserve the right to over-rule the Agency's decisions. And if a major problem arose under the Agency's stewardship, would the press and public accept a response from the government of the day on the lines of 'It's not our fault'?

So I am not convinced that an Energy Agency is the answer, but I do realise how serious the question is. One way or another, lessons need to be learned, but I suspect that there will not be a step change in the way that we address this challenge unless we encounter serious power shortages or a major revolt about the level of energy bills.

There will, however, be changes in the way we produce and manage energy. Increasing amounts of renewable energy will feature on the system. The benefits of reliable, large amounts of renewable energy could be a huge prize, but we have tried to grab it in a rather clumsy and probably expensive way. I am far from convinced that using European and UK law to force high levels of renewable energy on to a system that was not ready for it was the right approach. Nor could it have been right to set up competitive markets and then expect the participants in those markets to compete with large amounts of subsidised power that would have to be used first, would sometimes trigger negative prices and would often deprive them of vital revenue. Some new technologies will get ahead of others, of course, and it could well be that micro-scale electricity production will find its way on to far more rooftops if the advances in photovoltaic panels continue at the present rate. If costs fall enough, perhaps we shall see panels being installed not as a status symbol for green consumers, nor as a subsidised alternative to the inadequate returns on savings and annuities,[131] but simply because they are cost-effective in reducing energy bills.

This could be nicely in tune with the development of smart meters, smart grids and smart cities, but note that for every producer and retailer of electricity, domestic-level production will also represent a reduction in overall demand for the commodity, with all that that implies for today's energy businesses. Note also that even if household or community-level electricity production increases as much as some people would wish it to, very few customers are likely to want to become detached from the wider network and the security it provides. The network may become smarter, but it will still have to be there and if the electricity flows over it are reduced, that network – smart or dumb – will still have to be paid for by the users. Those flows, of course, would increase dramatically if electric charging points began to replace our petrol stations. A switch to electric cars might alleviate energy companies' concerns about falling demand and revenue. But we should not underestimate the challenge of such a transition. It would be anything but smooth and there would be huge social and economic implications arising from the scaling-down of the old fuelling infrastructure and its replacement with the new; to say nothing of the problem individuals, families and companies would face in scrapping vehicles and acquiring new ones. The roll-out of high-speed broadband, or indeed smart meters, would look a trivial exercise in comparison. For good measure, we could add to the challenge the transition from gas-fired heating of homes to electric heating, which is often mooted as a climate change mitigation measure.

If changes of this kind do come about, it would be good to think that it was because rigorous cost-benefit analysis told energy companies, politicians and, most of all, customers that they were

---

[131] Solar panels better than a pension, says Minister. Daily Telegraph 3 February 2014.

worthwhile. But for government, any such analysis would also take account of the revenue implications – direct and indirect – for the Exchequer. For those trying to judge political risk in the sector, it would be unwise to overlook that. Before encouraging any serious switch to electric cars (or even hybrids), a government that had already begun to grapple with the problem of falling revenue from UK oil and gas production[132] would have to look hard at how it would replace an annual income of roughly £27 billion from fuel duty[133] that had already come under some threat from vehicles' improved fuel efficiency. Similar considerations would arise in relation to the sustainability of emissions-based subsidies for the purchase of electric cars and hybrids, exemptions from congestion charging and low, or zero, rates of road tax for favoured vehicles.

I have sometimes said on conference platforms and at industry meetings 'Electricity is for customers.' The statement sounds as though it might have come from *Forrest Gump*[134] and it was certainly not meant to be profound. It was intended simply to remind an audience of two basic facts about the electricity supply industry. First, in an integrated electricity system, what is produced must also be used - by the customers. The stability of the system depends on a carefully-managed balance being struck between supply and demand. If that is not maintained, the system fails, equipment may be damaged and customers lose the power that they depend on so much. But the relationship with the customer is about more than engineering and the laws of physics. Customers pay the bills. That is how, over time, the industry's huge investments are rewarded. The industry knows that perfectly well, but at times it has been guilty of not paying enough attention to that fundamental relationship. It has often talked of the need for a

---

[132] http://www.hmrc.gov.uk/statistics/prt/og-stats.pdf

[133] https://www.gov.uk/government/uploads/system/uploads/attachment_data/file/293759/37630_Budget_2014_Web_Accessible.pdf

[134] Winston Groom. Doubleday. 1986. Paramount Pictures 1994.

conversation with the customers. It tries harder to engage in that than it gets credit for. But most of its more serious conversations have been with the government. The fingerprints of government now seem to be all over the industry's work, from market reforms and approval or disapproval of fuels and technologies, to decisions about what customers' bills should look like. The industry cannot turn its back on the realities of politics, but somehow it should put its relationship with the policy-makers on a more equal footing. No less importantly, however, it must find more time for the customers – the people that keep it in business and who, in 1988, our policy-makers expected to be the driving force behind everything that it did.

The industry will continue to be busy making, transporting and selling electricity. But the engineering, economics and management of those tasks will become intensely complicated as 2020's mandatory target for using renewable energy is met and thousands of wind turbines try to deliver power - sometimes helpfully, but at other times when their production is out of kilter with demand. Of course, there will also be times – typically on cold, still days in the winter – when customer demand is at its peak and those same turbines are producing nothing. The impact of the growth of photovoltaic electricity from domestic roof-tops will add to the complication, albeit more modestly. Little wonder then that the system will have to be 'smarter'.

Today, 'smart' technology is expected to help us to address those difficulties – smart grids, smart meters, smart appliances, in fact, smart nearly everything. 'Smarter' is inevitable, but we must be careful to avoid being smart just because we can be. Chez Porter, we made the mistake of replacing our clapped-out washing machine with an excessively smart washer-dryer that is so particular about what it will wash and when that it sulks and practically pulls a face when we ask it politely to wash any load that it considers not to be deserving of its attention. So, it is with guarded enthusiasm that I contemplate the days when, in the supermarket, my smartphone will pick up a signal from our refrigerator to tell us whether we need to buy any milk, butter or salads. Of course, it may not be wise to rely entirely on that communication, because with sophisticated demand-side management, the electricity system might have decided to turn off our fridge as a smart 'demand-side' measure, just as we were expecting to take a virtual look inside it from Sainsbury's car park. If so, maybe a back-up battery would keep it in touch. If not, perhaps my smart tee shirt would be able to warn me that I was getting stressed.

Energy policy, of course, has been nowhere near as smart as it should have been – a winding road with different destinations and changes of direction. The 'clarity and stability' that energy companies and the AEP called for with monotonous regularity, was not forthcoming and although plant closures were clearly flagged up, investment in production capable of replacing them – able to respond to demand – was held back by uncertainty. Perhaps, calling for 'clarity and stability', we had been inviting, unwittingly, more intervention than actually we had in mind. The earlier message to government of 'Just set the high-level framework and leave the industry to get on with the job' was a far better one, but it was blown away by the winds of change in politics.

The Coalition Government's Electricity Market Reform was a genuine attempt to offer – notably through long-term contracts and a capacity mechanism – the stability that investors appeared to want. But in a country which, despite its financial and fiscal challenges, was still rated the fourth most attractive in the world by foreign investors[135], the need for special measures to attract investment in a sector as vital as electricity was a clear indication

[135] Foreign Direct Investment Confidence Index 2014. A T Kearney.

that something had gone badly wrong. I have heard the EMR measures being justified on the grounds of 'market failure' and we shall probably hear the sceptics of 1990 – who called the liberalisation of electricity supply the 'British experiment' – saying 'I told you so'. No doubt history will make a superficial judgement and declare them to be right. But if they are left to do what they do well, markets do not usually fail.

This one, of course, did not enjoy that kind of freedom; at least, not for very long. With the best of intentions, politicians in London and Brussels wanted it to deliver much more than a reliable supply at an affordable price. They wanted a reduction in carbon emissions, too, so they set up a mechanism to cap emissions and price carbon – compatible with their wish that customers should have the benefit of a competitive market, albeit a market in which, they admitted openly, electricity would become more expensive. Britain was expected to show the world how to develop a 'low carbon' economy. But policy-makers lost patience with their cap and trade scheme when carbon emissions fell and the carbon price fell, too; as much a result of the global financial crisis than because of any deficiency in the EU Emissions Trading Scheme.

The very same financial crisis introduced other complications. With government spending under pressure, family budgets were squeezed and rising energy bills became a huge political issue. It had always been taken for granted that customers, large and small, would pay for the transition to a low carbon electricity industry. Then it became obvious that, although surveys may have suggested that customers supported it, they also showed that they did not want to pay for it. The UK government wobbled. EU leaders wobbled too. Investors, who reportedly had plenty of money to invest, but had already become more cautious because of the financial crisis, could not fail to notice the policy conflicts and the way that many of Europe's dull and safe utility companies were taking a financial battering[136]. Uncertainty ruled and investors lost confidence in the sector.

In the UK, the way out – focused firmly on long-term, government-backed tariffs and 'contracts for difference' for low-carbon electricity production – was through measures that were totally different from the expectations of the White Paper of 1988. EMR may not have prescribed precisely the fuel mix, but by offering – to the policy-makers' approved technologies – long-term contracts with price guarantees, it came very close to that. They may have called it 'electricity market reform', but in fact it seemed to confirm the politicians' lack of belief in the market; certainly a lack of confidence in the market being able to deliver what they wanted. They may have intended that their reform should bring forward investment in low-carbon electricity production, but it was at least as much a huge insurance policy for security of supply – security which the pursuit by governments of an unstable mix of objectives had undermined. An insurance policy was sought. Government decided on the best buy. The customers would pay the premiums.

I have not disguised my enthusiasm for the competitive, customer-driven electricity market that had been envisaged in the White Paper of 1988, so it is a disappointment to me that the UK government's 'Electricity Market Reform' ever became necessary. I would have liked a government faced with public discontent about energy bills and staring at the real possibility of a capacity shortage to have reaffirmed the importance of independent investment decisions in a competitive market – influenced, if necessary, by the carbon price arising from the EUETS and driven by the fundamental requirement to satisfy customer demand. But

---

[136] See, for instance 'How to lose half a trillion euros: Europe's electricity providers face an existential threat.' The Economist. Oct 12th 2013.

once the Renewable Energy Directive had taken effect, that was no longer a possibility. So I accept that something had to be done in order to give the electricity industry the confidence to invest. It was essential to take some decisive steps and I hope and expect that they will be successful. But the outcome was something that is cumbersome, complicated, riddled with judgements by politicians, civil servants and regulators and an ongoing lobby-fest for technologies seeking support.

Quite apart from anything else, when the lobbying and monitoring efforts of the industry's companies and their various advisers are included the sheer number of people involved must be enormous. Of course, if this 'market' becomes too difficult to comprehend, or too expensive for the customers, there will be calls for more change, but that will be hard to deliver. Interestingly though, the Department of Energy and Climate Change appeared to see EMR's government-backed contracts only as a phase, at the end of which the competitive market would come back to life. I think they believed that. Very early in the EMR process, I had a meeting with couple of senior civil servants at DECC. They must have been expecting me to grumble about the way things were shaping up (in fact, I had intended to listen and comment constructively) and before the discussion began, I was told 'David, I just want to say that we still believe in the market.' I replied 'You will be hard put to convince people of that.'

There will be further twists and turns in the story of British electricity supply. But they are seldom anticipated by policy-makers, even when they prepare a 'road map' to a destination far off in time. It must be interesting and it may be helpful, but they should be careful not take their predictions too seriously.

At AEP, in discussions about the longer-term future, I sometimes used to say 'You are talking about how things are going to be in 25 years' time. So, first of all, take yourself back 25 years and tell me how you expected things to be today… '

INDEX

Printed in Poland
by Amazon Fulfillment
Poland Sp. z o.o., Wrocław